Grade 3

Scott Foresman

Reader's and Writer's Notebook
Teacher's Manual

 Glenview, Illinois • Boston, Massachusetts • Chandler, Arizona •
Upper Saddle River, New Jersey

ISBN-13: 978-0-328-48477-5
ISBN-10:   0-328-48477-6

7 8 9 10 V011 18 17 16 15 14 13 12

Unit 1: Living and Learning

Unit 2: Smart Solutions

Unit 3: People and Nature

Unit 4: One of a Kind

Unit 5: Cultures

Unit 6: Freedom

Name _____

Unit 1 Independent Reading Log

Reading Time	Title and Author	What is it about?	How would you rate it?	Explain your rating.
From ____ to ____			**Great** 5 4 3 2 1 **Awful**	
From ____ to ____			**Great** 5 4 3 2 1 **Awful**	
From ____ to ____			**Great** 5 4 3 2 1 **Awful**	
From ____ to ____			**Great** 5 4 3 2 1 **Awful**	
From ____ to ____			**Great** 5 4 3 2 1 **Awful**	

Name _____

Unit 2 Independent Reading Log

Reading Time	Title and Author	What is it about?	How would you rate it?	Explain your rating.
From ____ to ____			Great 5 4 3 Awful 2 1	
From ____ to ____			Great 5 4 3 Awful 2 1	
From ____ to ____			Great 5 4 3 Awful 2 1	
From ____ to ____			Great 5 4 3 Awful 2 1	
From ____ to ____			Great 5 4 3 Awful 2 1	

Name _____

Unit 3 Independent Reading Log

Reading Time	Title and Author	What is it about?	How would you rate it?	Explain your rating.
From ___ to ___			**Great** 5 4 3 2 1 **Awful**	
From ___ to ___			**Great** 5 4 3 2 1 **Awful**	
From ___ to ___			**Great** 5 4 3 2 1 **Awful**	
From ___ to ___			**Great** 5 4 3 2 1 **Awful**	
From ___ to ___			**Great** 5 4 3 2 1 **Awful**	

Name _____

Unit 4 Independent Reading Log

Reading Time	Title and Author	What is it about?	How would you rate it?	Explain your rating.
From ____ to ____			**Great** 5 4 3 2 1 **Awful**	
From ____ to ____			**Great** 5 4 3 2 1 **Awful**	
From ____ to ____			**Great** 5 4 3 2 1 **Awful**	
From ____ to ____			**Great** 5 4 3 2 1 **Awful**	
From ____ to ____			**Great** 5 4 3 2 1 **Awful**	

Name _____

Unit 5 Independent Reading Log

Reading Time	Title and Author	What is it about?	How would you rate it?	Explain your rating.
From ——— to ———			Great 5 4 3 2 1 Awful	
From ——— to ———			Great 5 4 3 2 1 Awful	
From ——— to ———			Great 5 4 3 2 1 Awful	
From ——— to ———			Great 5 4 3 2 1 Awful	
From ——— to ———			Great 5 4 3 2 1 Awful	

Name _____

Unit 6 Independent Reading Log

Reading Time	Title and Author	What is it about?	How would you rate it?	Explain your rating.
From ___ to ___			**Great** 5 4 3 2 1 **Awful**	
From ___ to ___			**Great** 5 4 3 2 1 **Awful**	
From ___ to ___			**Great** 5 4 3 2 1 **Awful**	
From ___ to ___			**Great** 5 4 3 2 1 **Awful**	
From ___ to ___			**Great** 5 4 3 2 1 **Awful**	

Selection Title _____ Author _____

Narrative poems tell a story. Like stories, narrative poems have plots, settings, characters, and a theme. Characteristics of narrative poems include the following.

• As with most poems, words are specially arranged in lines.

• The author chooses words and phrases carefully to create a particular rhyme and rhythm.

• The author often expresses his or her thoughts and feelings.

Directions As you read *When Charlie McButton Lost Power,* look for examples of how words are specially arranged in lines, the rhyme and rhythm of the words and phrases, and how the author expresses her thoughts and feelings. Write those examples below.

Arrangement of Lines _____

_____

_____

Rhythm and Rhyme _____

_____

_____

Author's Thoughts and Feelings _____

_____

_____

Explore the Genre

Think about the special arrangement of lines, rhythm and rhyme, and the thoughts and feelings of the author in another narrative poem that you've read. What similarities and differences do you find between that poem and *When Charlie McButton Lost Power*? Write about it. Use a separate sheet of paper if you need more space.

_____

_____

Name _____

Selection Title _____ Author _____

A **fable** is a very short story whose theme is a moral or a lesson. Characteristics of fables include the following.

- Characters in fables are very simple.
- Instead of names, characters are often named for the role they play in the story.
- Characters usually have one identifiable trait.

Directions As you read *What About Me?*, look for examples of character names and character traits and identify the theme or moral of the fable. Write the examples and moral below.

Character Names _____

_____

_____

Each Character's Trait _____

_____

_____

Theme or Moral _____

_____

_____

Explore the Genre

Think about the characters, character traits, and moral of another story you've read that is a fable. What similarities and differences do you find between that story and *What About Me?* Write about it. Use a separate sheet of paper if you need more space.

_____

_____

_____

Name _____

Selection Title _____ Author _____

A **tall tale** is a humorous story that uses realistic details to tell a story about characters and events that are impossible. Characteristics of a tall tale include the following.

- Many details are from everyday life.
- Characters are greatly exaggerated.
- The events described could not really happen.

Directions As you read *Kumak's Fish,* look for examples of realistic details, exaggerated characters, and impossible events that make the story a tall tale. Write those examples below.

Realistic Details _____

_____

_____

Exaggerated Characters _____

_____

_____

Impossible Events _____

_____

_____

Explore the Genre

Think about the realistic details, exaggerated characters, and impossible events in another story you've read that's a tall tale. What similarities and differences do you find between that story and *Kumak's Fish*? Write about it. Use a separate sheet of paper if you need more space.

_____

_____

Name _____

Selection Title _____ Author _____

Background knowledge is what we already know about a topic. Using background knowledge can help us better understand what we're reading. Activate your background knowledge by doing the following.

- Preview the selection to find out what it's about.
- Think about what you already know about the topic.
- Connect the selection to your own world—to people, places, and events you already know.

Directions Use the KWL chart below to chart your background knowledge about the selection. List what you already know in the K column. Then list what you want to learn in the W column. After reading, list what you learned in the L column. Write a brief summary of the selection on a separate sheet of paper.

What We **K**now	What We **W**ant to Know	What We **L**earned

© Pearson Education, Inc., 3

Name _____

Selection Title _____ Author _____

Story structure refers to the important parts of the story that happen at the beginning, middle, and end of a story. To identify story structure, strategic readers do the following.

- Look for the conflict, or problem, at the beginning of the story.
- Track the action as conflict builds.
- Recognize the climax when the characters face conflict.
- Identify how the conflict gets resolved.

Directions As you read the story, chart the story structure using the plot map below. When you are finished, briefly retell the story on a separate sheet of paper.

Characters

Setting

© Pearson Education, Inc., 3

Selection Title _____ **Author** _____

Strategic readers **monitor** their understanding of what they've read and use fix-up strategies to **clarify** understanding. Ways to monitor and clarify include the following.

- Ask questions during and after reading and summarize to check your understanding.
- Adjust your reading rate, read on, or reread the section that caused confusion.
- Visualize what you are reading.
- Use text features and illustrations to help clarify the text.

Directions As you read, write down the page numbers of places that you had trouble understanding. Then describe the fix-up strategy you used to clarify the meaning.

Where in the text I had trouble: _____ _____ _____

_____ _____ _____ _____ _____

Fix-Up Strategies I Used

_____

_____

_____

_____

Selection Summary

Write a two- or three-sentence summary of the selection. Use a separate sheet of paper if you need more space.

_____

_____

_____

_____

Name _____

Selection Title _____ Author _____

We **visualize** to create pictures in our minds as we read. Creating pictures can help us better understand what we're reading. To visualize, try the following.

- Combine what you already know with details from the text to make a mental image.
- Think about the events of the story or selection. Use your five senses to create pictures and to try to put yourself in the story or selection.

Directions As you read the selection, use your senses to help you visualize what's happening or the information the author provides. Write down what you can see, hear, taste, smell, and touch.

See _____

_____

_____

Hear _____

_____

_____

Taste _____

_____

_____

Smell _____

_____

_____

Touch _____

_____

_____

Name _____

Selection Title _____ Author _____

A **fantasy** tells a make-believe story and often includes illustrations. Characteristics of fantasies include the following.

- Characters and settings may not be real.
- Animals may do things that only people could do.
- Events happen that are not real.

Directions As you read *Prudy's Problem,* look for examples of characters and settings that are not real, animals that do things that only people do, and events that cannot really happen. Write those examples below.

Characters and Settings _____

_____

_____

Animals _____

_____

_____

Events _____

_____

_____

Explore the Genre

Think about characters and settings that are not real, animals that do things that only people do, and events that cannot really happen in another fantasy that you've read. What similarities and differences do you find between that story and *Prudy's Problem*? Write about it. Use a separate sheet of paper if you need more space.

_____

_____

Selection Title _____ **Author** _____

When we **predict,** we tell what we think might happen in a selection. Predictions are based on our preview or what we've already read. We **set a purpose** to guide our reading. We can do the following to predict and set a purpose.

- Read the title and the author's name. Look at the illustrations and other text features.
- Think about why you're reading and set a purpose.
- Use your prior knowledge—what you already know—to make a prediction.
- As you read, check and change your prediction based on new information.

Directions Preview the selection. Make a prediction and set a purpose for reading the selection. As you read, check your predictions and set a new purpose as necessary. When you finish reading, write a summary of the selection.

Before Reading

Make a Prediction _____

_____

Purpose for Reading _____

_____

During Reading

Check and Change Prediction _____

_____

Set a New Purpose _____

_____

After Reading

Write a Summary _____

_____

_____

Selection Title _____ Author _____

Expository nonfiction tells about real people and events. Expository text is a type of expository nonfiction. Characteristics of expository text include the following.

- The topic provides information about the real world and people.
- The information in the text is factual.
- Selections often include text features such as diagrams, maps, charts, and graphs.

Directions As you read *Amazing Bird Nests,* look for examples of expository text. Write those examples below.

Selection Topic _____

_____

_____

Facts _____

_____

_____

Text Features _____

_____

_____

Explore the Genre

Think about another selection you've read that is expository text. What similarities and differences do you find between that selection and *Amazing Bird Nests*? Write about it. Use a separate sheet of paper if you need more space.

_____

_____

_____

© Pearson Education, Inc., 3

Selection Title _____ **Author** _____

Important ideas in nonfiction texts are the main ideas and details about a topic that the author wants the reader to understand. You can do the following to help identify important ideas and details as you read.

- Preview the selection and read the title, headings, and captions.
- Look for words in special type such as italics, boldface, and bulleted lists.
- Watch for signal words and phrases such as *for example* and *most important.*
- Use text features including photographs and illustrations, diagrams, charts, and maps.

Directions As you read the selection, use the chart below to write down any important ideas and details that you find. List any text features or signal words you used to locate these ideas. Use the important ideas and details to write a short summary of the selection.

Important Ideas	Details

Write a Summary _____

_____

_____

_____

_____

Selection Title _____ Author _____

Dramas, or plays, are stories that are written to be acted out for an audience. Dramas have the same story elements as other types of fiction. Story elements of dramas include the following.

- Character and setting
- Plot
- Theme

Directions As you read *Pushing Up the Sky,* look for examples of the story elements of drama. Write those examples below.

Character and Setting _____

_____

_____

Plot _____

_____

_____

Theme _____

_____

_____

Explore the Genre

Think about character, setting, plot, and theme in another drama that you've read. What similarities and differences do you find between that drama and *Pushing Up the Sky*? Write about it. Use a separate sheet of paper if you need more space.

_____

_____

_____

Selection Title _____ Author _____

Text structure refers to the way an author organizes a text. Cause and effect and compare and contrast are two types of text structure. Knowing how a text is structured can improve our comprehension. Here are ways to identify text structure.

- Before you read, preview the text. Make predictions, ask questions, and use titles, headings, and illustrations to try to identify the structure.

- As you read, look for language that gives clues to the organization.

- After reading, recall the organization and summarize the text.

Directions As you preview and read the selection, write down features of the text that help you identify the text structure. Remember to ask questions, use text features, and look for language clues to identify the text structure. After reading, write the name of the text structure and a brief summary of the selection.

Before Reading _____

_____

_____

_____

During Reading _____

_____

_____

_____

Text Structure/Summary _____

_____

_____

_____

Selection Title _____ Author _____

Fiction is a made-up story, either serious or humorous, of imaginary people who generally behave as we expect people to behave. Fiction might include real places and events, but the story is created from the author's imagination. Characteristics of fiction include the following.

- Characters generally behave like real people.
- Settings may or may not be real.
- The plot, or events that happen in the story, may or may not seem real.

Directions As you read *A Symphony of Whales,* look for examples of character, setting, and plot that make this story fiction. Write those examples below.

Character _____

_____

_____

Setting _____

_____

_____

Plot _____

_____

_____

Explore the Genre

Think about another story you've read that is fiction. What similarities and differences do you find between that story and *A Symphony of Whales*? Write about it. Use a separate sheet of paper if you need more space.

_____

_____

Selection Title _____ Author _____

The content of **narrative nonfiction** consists of real people, things, or events. It can be told in different forms such as a story, a letter, a field guide, or a poem. Characteristics of narrative nonfiction include the following.

- The content is about real people or things.
- The setting is a real place.
- Events are based on fact.

Directions As you read *Around One Cactus: Owls, Bats and Leaping Rats,* look for examples of people and things, settings, and events that make this selection narrative nonfiction. Write those examples below.

People and Things _____

_____

_____

Settings _____

_____

_____

Events _____

_____

_____

Explore the Genre

Think about another selection you've read that is narrative nonfiction. What similarities and differences do you find between that selection and *Around One Cactus: Owls, Bats and Leaping Rats*? Write about it. Use a separate sheet of paper if you need more space.

_____

_____

Selection Title _____ **Author** _____

When we **summarize** and **paraphrase,** we capture the important ideas or events of a selection in a few sentences. Paraphrasing is putting what we've read into our own words. Good readers summarize and paraphrase what they've read to check understanding and improve comprehension. Keeping important ideas and events in a logical order also improves comprehension. To summarize or paraphrase, do the following.

- In fiction, look for the important events of the plot, including the climax.

- In nonfiction, look for the important ideas that the author presents.

- Jot notes as you read to help you summarize or paraphrase, keeping events in a logical order.

- Restate important pieces of information in your own words.

Directions As you read the selection, use the chart below to write down any important ideas or plot events. Remember to record events in a logical order. When you're finished reading, use your notes to summarize or paraphrase the selection.

Important Ideas or Events

_____

_____

_____

_____

_____

Summary

_____

_____

_____

_____

_____

© Pearson Education, Inc., 3

Selection Title _____ **Author** _____

Important ideas in nonfiction texts are the main ideas and details about a topic that the author wants the reader to understand. You can do the following to help identify important ideas and details as you read.

- Preview the selection and read the title, headings, and captions.
- Look for words in special type such as italics, boldface, and bulleted lists.
- Watch for signal words and phrases such as *for example* and *most important.*
- Use text features including photographs and illustrations, diagrams, charts, and maps.

Directions As you read the selection, use the chart below to write down any important ideas and details that you find. List any text features or signal words you used to locate these ideas. Use the important ideas and details to write a short summary of the selection.

Important Ideas	Details

Write a Summary _____

_____

_____

_____

Selection Title _____ Author _____

One type of literary nonfiction is a **biography**. Biographies tell the story of all or part of a real person's life. Events in the person's life are generally told in the order that they happen. Characteristics of a biography include the following.

- The subject is part or all of the life of a real person.
- The events in the person's life are told in the order that they happen.
- Events are told in a third-person narration using *he, she, him,* or *her* when referring to the person.

Directions As you read *Rocks in His Head,* look for examples of who the subject is, events in order, and third-person narration that make this selection a biography. Write those examples below.

Subject _____

_____

_____

Events _____

_____

_____

Third-person Narration _____

_____

_____

Explore the Genre

Think about another selection you've read that is a biography. What similarities and differences do you find between that biography and *Rocks in His Head*? Write about it. Use a separate sheet of paper if you need more space.

_____

_____

Name _____

Selection Title _____ **Author** _____

Good readers ask questions as they read. **Questioning** helps us monitor our comprehension and clarify anything that's confusing. Questioning also helps to make inferences, interpret the texts we read, and promote discussion. As you read, use the following questioning strategy.

- Preview the selection and think about any questions you have about the topic.
- Read with a question in mind and make notes when you find information that addresses the question.
- Write down other questions that come up as you read and look for answers in the text.
- Remember that not all questions are answered in the text. Sometimes we have to make inferences or interpretations based on the information the author provides.

Directions As you read the selection, use the chart below to write down any questions that you have about the text in the column on the left. Write down any answers you find or inferences you make in the right hand column.

Questions	Answers, Inferences, Interpretations

Selection Title _____ Author _____

Folk tales are stories that were created by an unknown storyteller and handed down orally from generation to generation until someone wrote them down. Characteristics of folk tales include the following.

- The subject matter often shows the customs or beliefs of a particular culture.
- Human and animal characters usually represent some human trait or aspect of human nature.
- Themes about human nature are expressed.

Directions As you read *Fly, Eagle, Fly!,* look for examples of subject matter, characters, and theme that make this story a folk tale. Write those examples below.

Subject Matter _____

_____

_____

Characters _____

_____

_____

Theme _____

_____

_____

Explore the Genre

Think about another story you've read that is a folk tale. What similarities and differences do you find between that story and *Fly, Eagle, Fly*!? Write about it. Use a separate sheet of paper if you need more space.

_____

_____

Selection Title _____ Author _____

Realistic fiction tells the story of imaginary people and events. Characteristics of realistic fiction include the following.

- The characters seem like real people that you might know.
- The setting is realistic, such as a city or town, a school, or other places you might know.
- The plot is possible and could happen in real life.

Directions As you read *Suki's Kimono,* look for examples of character, setting, and plot that make this story realistic fiction. Write those examples below.

Character _____

_____

_____

Setting _____

_____

_____

Plot _____

_____

_____

Explore the Genre

Think about the characters, setting, and plot in another story you've read that's realistic fiction. What similarities and differences do you find between that story and *Suki's Kimono*? Write about it. Use a separate sheet of paper if you need more space.

_____

_____

_____

Name _____

Selection Title _____ Author _____

When we **infer,** we use our background knowledge with information from the text to come up with our own ideas about what we're reading. To infer, or make inferences, try the following steps.

- Think about what you already know about the topics.
- Combine what you know with information from the text to make inferences.
- Based on your inferences, think about ideas, morals, lessons, or themes in the text.

Directions As you read the selection, use your background knowledge and clues from the text to make inferences. Use the chart below to show how you made your inferences. Then write a statement that summarizes the theme, moral, or lesson from the selection.

What I Know	Information from the Text	What I Infer

Statement that summarizes the theme, moral, or lesson _____

_____

_____

_____

© Pearson Education, Inc., 3

Name _____

Selection Title _____ **Author** _____

Strategic readers **monitor** their understanding of what they've read and use fix-up strategies to **clarify** understanding. Ways to monitor and clarify include the following.

• Ask questions during and after reading and summarize to check your understanding.

• Adjust your reading rate, read on, or reread the section that caused confusion.

• Visualize what you are reading.

• Use text features and illustrations to help clarify the text.

Directions As you read, write down the page numbers of places where you had trouble understanding. Then describe the fix-up strategy you used to clarify the meaning.

Where in the text I had trouble: _____ _____ _____

Fix-Up Strategies I Used

_____

_____

_____

_____

_____

Selection Summary

Write a two- or three-sentence summary of the selection. Use a separate sheet of paper if you need more space.

_____

_____

_____

_____

Selection Title _____ **Author** _____

When we **summarize** and **paraphrase,** we capture the important ideas or events of a selection in a few sentences. Paraphrasing is putting what we've read into our own words. Good readers summarize and paraphrase what they've read to check understanding and improve comprehension. Keeping important ideas and events in a logical order also improves comprehension. To summarize or paraphrase, do the following.

- In fiction, look for the important events of the plot, including the climax.
- In nonfiction, look for the important ideas that the author presents.
- Jot notes as you read to help you summarize or paraphrase, keeping events in a logical order.
- Restate important pieces of information in your own words.

Directions As you read the selection, use the chart below to write down any important ideas or plot events. Remember to record events in a logical order. When you're finished reading, use your notes to summarize or paraphrase the selection.

Important Ideas or Events

_____

_____

_____

_____

_____

Summary

_____

_____

_____

_____

_____

Name _____

Selection Title _____ **Author** _____

Historical fiction, like realistic fiction, is a made-up story which may include both real and imaginary characters and events. Characteristics of historical fiction include the following.

- The story takes place in the past.
- The setting is a place that still exists or existed in the past.
- Authentic details about the characters and setting help the reader understand what it was like to live in that place at that time.

Directions As you read *Me and Uncle Romie,* look for examples of the time and place in which the story is set and the authentic details that make this story historical fiction. Write those examples below.

Time _____

_____

_____

Place _____

_____

_____

Authentic Details _____

_____

_____

Explore the Genre

Think about the time, place, and authentic details in another story you've read that's historical fiction. What similarities and differences do you find between that story and *Me and Uncle Romie*? Write about it. Use a separate sheet of paper if you need more space.

_____

_____

Selection Title _____ **Author** _____

Good readers ask questions as they read. **Questioning** helps us monitor our comprehension and clarify anything that's confusing. Questioning also helps to make inferences, interpret the texts we read, and promote discussion. As you read, use the following questioning strategy.

- Preview the selection and think about any questions you have about the topic.

- Read with a question in mind and make notes when you find information that addresses the question.

- Write down other questions that come up as you read and look for answers in the text.

- Remember that not all questions are answered in the text. Sometimes we have to make inferences or interpretations based on the information the author provides.

Directions As you read the selection, use the chart below to write down any questions that you have about the text in the column on the left. Write down any answers you find or inferences you make in the right hand column.

Questions	Answers, Inferences, Interpretations

Selection Title _____ **Author** _____

When we **infer,** we use our background knowledge with information from the text to come up with our own ideas about what we're reading. To infer, or make inferences, try the following steps.

- Think about what you already know about the topics.
- Combine what you know with information from the text to make inferences.
- Based on your inferences, think about ideas, morals, lessons, or themes in the text.

Directions As you read the selection, use your background knowledge and clues from the text to make inferences. Use the chart below to show how you made your inferences. Then write a statement that summarizes the theme, moral, or lesson from the selection.

What I Know	Information from the Text	What I Infer

Statement that summarizes the theme, moral, or lesson _____

_____

_____

Selection Title _____ **Author** _____

A **photo essay** is a collection of photographs that share a common topic or theme. Characteristics of a photo essay include the following.

- An introduction often explains the topic of the essay.
- Text is included that explains the people, animals, or events in the photographs.
- Each photograph usually has a caption that gives specific information about it.

Directions As you read *Talking Walls: Art for the People,* look for examples in the introduction, text, and captions that make this selection a photo essay. Write those examples below.

Introduction _____

_____

_____

Text _____

_____

_____

_____

Captions _____

_____

_____

Explore the Genre

Think about another selection you've read that is a photo essay. What similarities and differences do you find between that selection and *Talking Walls: Art for the People*? Write about it. Use a separate sheet of paper if you need more space.

_____

_____

_____

Name _____

Selection Title _____ Author _____

An **animal fantasy** is a made-up story that uses animal characters instead of people. Characteristics of an animal fantasy include the following.

- The animal characters talk and live as humans do.
- The animal characters show human feelings.
- Illustrations help the reader understand the story and identify with the characters.

Directions As you read *Two Bad Ants,* look for examples of animals behaving like humans, showing feelings like humans, and illustrations of animals that make this story an animal fantasy. Write those examples below.

Animals with Human Behavior _____

_____

_____

Animals with Human Feelings _____

_____

_____

Illustrations _____

_____

_____

Explore the Genre

Think about another story you've read that is an animal fantasy. What similarities and differences do you find between that story and *Two Bad Ants*? Write about it. Use a separate sheet of paper if you need more space.

_____

_____

Selection Title _____ **Author** _____

Like a folk tale, a **legend** is an old story passed down by word of mouth. Characteristics of a legend include the following.

- The story is usually about the great deeds of a hero.
- The events in many legends are impossible.
- Legends are often based on some historical facts.

Directions As you read *Atlantis,* look for examples of a hero's great deeds, impossible events, and historical facts that make this story a legend. Write those examples below.

Great Deeds _____

_____

_____

Impossible Events _____

_____

_____

Historical Facts _____

_____

_____

Explore the Genre

Think about another story you've read that is a legend. What similarities and differences do you find between that story and *Atlantis*? Write about it. Use a separate sheet of paper if you need more space.

_____

_____

Name _____

Book Talk Tips

Book Talk Tips

- Speak clearly.
- Make eye contact.
- Talk about a book YOU liked reading.
- Don't give away the ending.
- Talk for 2–4 minutes, sharing amusing or important information from the book.

Directions Use the talking points below to help organize your book talk.

1. What is the title of the book?

2. Who is the author?

3. What is the genre?

4. What other book has the author written?

If your book is fiction...

5. What is the most exciting part of this book? The plot, characters, theme? Explain why.

6. Briefly describe a setting, scene, or character from this book.

If your book is nonfiction...

7. What important information did you learn from this book?

8. Briefly describe an interesting part of the book.

9. Do you have a personal connection with the story or topic? Explain.

10. Explain why your listeners should read this book.

Peer Conferencing Tips

Before writing

- Help your partner brainstorm ideas for writing.
- Discuss the writing topic with your partner. Does he or she need to narrow the topic or expand it?

After the first draft

- Before you exchange papers, tell your partner what you would like him or her to look for when reading your writing.
- Using sticky notes or a piece of notebook paper, note any questions or comments you have about your partner's writing.
- Point out the information or ideas that are well written.
- Discuss any information that seems unneeded or confusing, but make sure your comments are helpful and considerate.

Revision

- Read your partner's paper out loud to listen for strengths as well as places for improvement.
- Always tell your partner what you think works well in his or her paper.
- Start with a compliment, or strength, and then offer suggestions for improvement. For example, "I liked how you _____. What if you also _____?"
- Remember also to look for correct spelling and grammar.

Other areas you might comment on:

- Title
- Introduction
- Conclusion
- Descriptions
- Examples
- Use of verbs, nouns, adjectives or adverbs

Name _____

Writing Self-Evaluation Guide

Name of Writing Product _____

Directions Review your final draft. Then rate yourself on a scale from 4 to 1 (4 is the highest) on each writing trait. After you fill out the chart, answer the questions.

Writing Traits	4	3	2	1
Focus/Ideas				
Organization/Paragraphs				
Voice				
Word Choice				
Sentences				
Conventions				

1. What is the best part of this piece of writing? Why do you think so?

    _____

    _____

    _____

2. Write one thing you would change about this piece of writing if you had the chance to write it again.

    _____

    _____

    _____

© Pearson Education, Inc., 3

Short Vowels: Syllables VC/CV

Directions Choose the word with the **short vowel** sound in the **first syllable** to complete each sentence. Write the word on the line.

__hospital__   1. My mom works in a big (hotel/hospital).

__winter__   2. She got the job last (April/winter).

__doctor__   3. She works for a (doctor/painter).

__messages__   4. Mom writes (poems/messages).

__pencil__   5. She uses a (pencil/notepad).

Directions Circle the word with the **short vowel** sound in the **first syllable**. Then underline the letter that stands for that short vowel sound.

6. (happen)	higher	hoses
7. miner	(problem)	music
8. paper	private	(puppet)
9. lately	(lettuce)	likely
10. trial	toaster	(tunnel)
11. (napkin)	native	notebook
12. spoken	spider	(signal)
13. baby	(basket)	biker
14. (sister)	safety	season
15. tasteful	timer	(tennis)

Home Activity Your child identified words with a short vowel sound in the first syllable, such as *happen*, *lettuce*, and *tennis*. Have your child make a collage of magazine pictures showing items that have a short vowel sound in the first syllable of each item's name. Help your child label each picture.

© Pearson Education, Inc., 3

Literary Elements: Character, Setting, and Theme

- A **character** is a person or an animal in a story.
- The **setting** is when and where a story takes place.
- The **theme** is the lesson or meaning of a story.

Directions Read the story. Then fill in the chart to describe in your own words details about the characters, setting, and theme.

Annie rushed into the family room. Her older sister Marsha was using the computer.

Annie held up her yellow pad. "May I use the computer now?" she asked. "I need to type the final draft of my story. It's due tomorrow."

"No," said Marsha. "I'm busy chatting with Paula and Roy. So get lost!"

"That's not fair!" said Annie. "You've been using the computer for more than an hour."

Just then Dad poked his head in the door. "What's all this noise about?" he growled.

The girls looked at each other. They knew Dad would make them turn off the computer if they could not find a way to share it.

"We're sorry," Annie said. "We'll work together to make a fair schedule for using the computer."

"Good for you," Dad smiled. "Solving problems on your own shows that you're grown up enough to use a computer."

Characters	Setting	Theme
Annie seems more responsible because she does her homework and suggests a way to share the computer. **Possible response: Marsha is older and more selfish, but she will work together with her little sister. Dad is patient and wants the girls to solve their own problems.**	**Possible response: family room that has a computer**	**Possible response: Working together to solve problems shows maturity.**

 Home Activity Your child restated the characters, setting, and theme, or lesson, of a story. Read a story together. Discuss the characters, setting, and theme with your child and ask which story details helped with his or her ideas.

Writing • Narrative Poem

Key Features of a Narrative Poem

• tells a story

• has rhythm or a repeated accent

• often has lines that rhyme and use meter

• has a setting, characters, plot, and theme

• may be humorous or dramatic

Supper in the Storm

One afternoon last week at the park,
Blue sky quite suddenly grew very dark.
I raced home, and as I reached the door
heavy rain started falling, more and more.

Flickering lights killed my hope of a meal.
Thunderstorms make my mother feel
the kitchen is not the best place to be,
so good-bye to dinner for Dad and me.

Suddenly there stood Dad at the door,
and I could hope for some food once more!
"I knew that we could use some supper,"
and he handed me a sack—things looked up and upper!

After we ate, all the lights came back on,
Now Mom's fears of the kitchen were gone.
"I think," she said, "this is the night to make
our very favorite chocolate cake!"

1. Read the poem. Who are the characters in this poem?

The characters are the narrator, his mother, and his father.

2. What problem does the narrator have? How is the problem solved?

The narrator doesn't think there will be any supper because the

power is out. His dad brings home a carry-out meal, though, and

his mom plans to bake a cake when the power returns.

Vocabulary

Directions Choose the word from the box that best matches each definition. Write the word on the line.

__fuel__   1. anything that you can burn that gives heat or power

__term__   2. the length of time that something lasts

__vision__   3. the power of using your imagination to see what the future may bring

__bat__   4. a flying mammal with very good hearing

__battery__   5. an energy source

Directions Choose the word from the box that best matches each clue. Write the word on the line.

__battery__   6. Some toys need this to run.

__blew__   7. This is something the wind did.

__plug__   8. An electrical cord has this on the end.

__bat__   9. It flies at night.

__fuel__   10. A car burns this.

Write a Diary Entry

On a separate sheet of paper, write a diary entry. Pretend the power went out at your house, and tell what happened. Tell what you did and what your family did for dinner. Use as many vocabulary words as possible.

Students' writing should include lesson vocabulary.

Home Activity Your child identified and used vocabulary words from *When Charlie McButton Lost Power*. With your child discuss what it would have been like to live before houses had electricity. Encourage your child to use vocabulary words in your conversation.

© Pearson Education, Inc., 3

Sentences

> A **sentence** tells a complete thought. It begins with a capital letter and ends with a punctuation mark. An incomplete sentence is called a **fragment.**
>
> **Sentence**   The lights go out.
> **Fragment**   Suddenly blink on and off.

Directions Write the group of words that is a sentence.

1. The boys make a fort.   Can't play computer games.

The boys make a fort.

2. Played checkers and board games.   Mom tells stories.

Mom tells stories.

Directions Decide whether each group of words is a sentence or a fragment.
If it is a sentence, write the sentence with correct capitalization and punctuation.
If it is a fragment, write *F.*

3. the doll walks and talks

The doll walks and talks.

4. has a battery

F

5. we play card games

We play card games.

6. with our friends next door

F

© Pearson Education, Inc., 3

Home Activity Your child learned about sentences. Have your child write two or three sentences about an event at school.

Short Vowels; Syllables VC/CV

Classifying Write the list word that belongs in each group.

1. lunch, breakfast, __**supper**__
2. toy, animal, __**puppet**__
3. cabbage, spinach, __**lettuce**__
4. box, container, __**basket**__
5. reading, math, __**spelling**__
6. placemat, tablecloth, __**napkin**__

Rhymes Finish each sentence. Use a list word that rhymes with the underlined word.

7. Franco got a <u>splinter</u> when he built the shelves last __**winter**__.
8. My __**sister**__ uses a <u>mister</u> to spray the plants.
9. I __**suggest**__ that you get some <u>rest</u>.
10. She will charge a <u>dollar</u> to sew your __**collar**__.

Making Connections Draw a line to connect the first syllable with the second syllable to make a list word. Write each word you make.

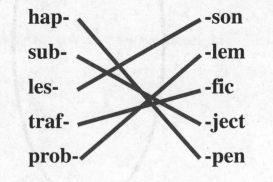

First Syllable	Second Syllable
hap-	-son
sub-	-lem
les-	-fic
traf-	-ject
prob-	-pen

11. __**happen**__
12. __**subject**__
13. __**lesson**__
14. __**traffic**__
15. __**problem**__

School + Home **Home Activity** Your child wrote words with short vowel sounds. Have your child circle the VC/CV (vowel-consonant-consonant-vowel) pattern in each list word.

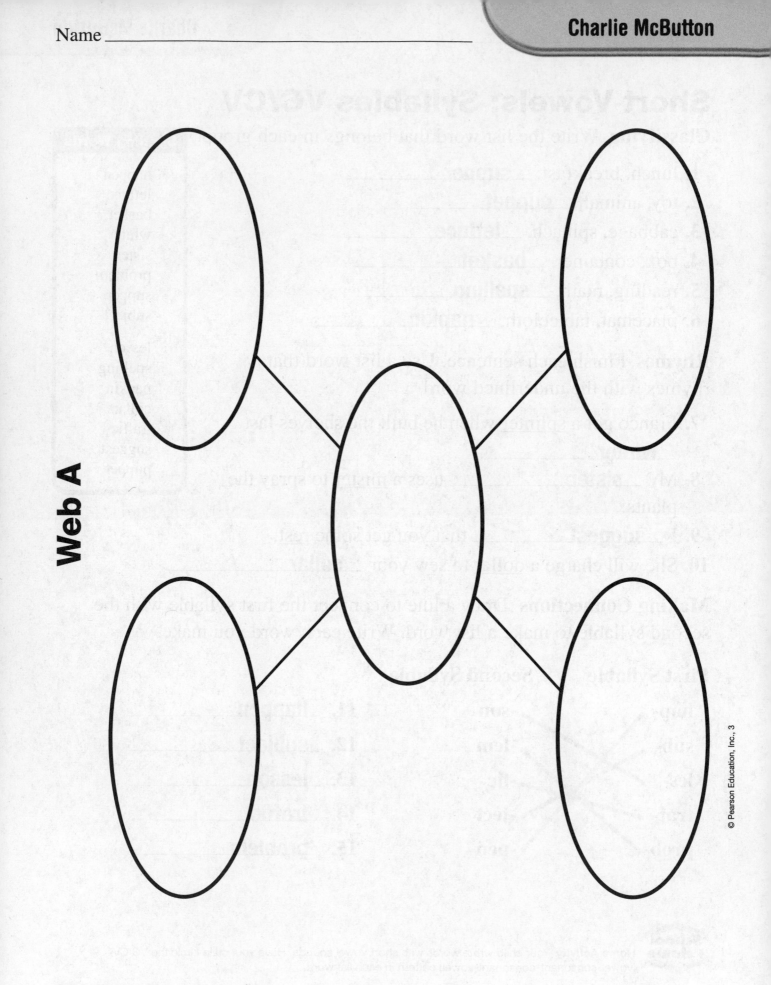

Web A

Vocabulary • Context Clues

- **Homonyms** are words that are spelled and pronounced the same way but have different meanings.
- **Homographs** are words that are spelled the same way but have different pronunciations and meanings.
- Use **context clues,** or the words around a homonym or homograph, to figure out what the word means.

Directions Read the following passage. Then answer the questions below. Look for context clues that show the meanings of homonyms and homographs as you read.

> When the power went out, I was bored. Then my friends and I decided to play baseball. My team had a great game. We couldn't do anything wrong. Every fly ball came right down into our mitts. When we dove for the ball, we got it. As I walked home, I saw a bat flying around a lamppost. It was too dark to play baseball, so I went inside to read a good sports book.

1. In this passage, does *down* mean "a bird's soft feathers" or "from above"?

"from above"

2. The word *dove* has two pronunciations and two meanings. What clues tell readers the word's pronunciation and meaning in this passage?

The words *for the ball* tell readers that *dove* is pronounced with a long *o* sound and means "moved suddenly."

3. What does *bat* mean in this passage? How does the context help you?

Bat means "a flying mammal." The context mentions the word flying.

4. How do you pronounce the word *read* in the last line?

with a long *e* sound

Home Activity Your child used context clues to understand homonyms and homographs. Provide sentences with homonyms such as *ball* (a round object/a dance) or *row* (to move a boat with oars/a line of people or objects) and homographs such as *bow* (to bend down) and *bow* (a loop made with ribbon). Ask your child to use context clues to determine the meaning of each word.

Reference Texts

Books have different features that help you find the information you need. At the front, a **table of contents** lists chapters, articles, or stories and their page numbers. An **index** lists subjects that the book covers and tells the page on which the information can be found. An index is usually in the back of the book.

Directions Use the table of contents and the index to answer the questions.

Table of Contents The Wonder of Electricity	Index

Chapter 1
What Is Electricity? 3
 	
Chapter 2
Ben Franklin and His Famous Kite ... 11
 	
Chapter 3
Inventing the Light Bulb 17
	atoms, 4
	
	current, 5
	
	electrons, 4
	
	inventors
	    Edison, Thomas, 19
	    Faraday, Michael, 18
	    Franklin, Ben, 11–16

1. In which chapter will you look to read about the invention of the light bulb?

Chapter 3

2. On which page will you look to find information about Thomas Edison?

page 19

3. Which chapter has information about Ben Franklin?

Chapter 2

4. On what page does Chapter 2 start?

page 11

5. On what page would you find information about atoms?

page 4

© Pearson Education, Inc., 3

Home Activity Your child used a table of contents and an index to answer questions about reference texts. Ask your child to locate information using a table of contents and an index in a favorite book.

Short Vowels; Syllables VC/CV

Proofread a Sign The Rodriguez family stopped at a farmers market. Circle four spelling mistakes on the sign. Write the words correctly. Then find the punctuation error. Write the sentence correctly.

Spelling Words

happen
lettuce
basket
winter
sister
problem
supper
subject

lesson
spelling
napkin
collar
traffic
suggest
puppet

FRESH CORN
We suggest grilled corn for supper?

berries	$3 a baskit	letuce	$1 a head
sweet peas	$2 a bunch	summer an wintar	
melon	$4 each	squash	2 for $3

1. __basket__   2. __lettuce__
3. __and__   4. __winter__
5. __We suggest grilled corn for supper.__

Proofread Words Circle the word that is spelled correctly. Write it.

6. (happen)   hapen   6. __happen__
7. prablem   (problem)   7. __problem__
8. spulling (spelling)   8. __spelling__
9. (subject) subjeck   9. __subject__
10. traffick (traffic)   10. __traffic__
11. (supper) super   11. __supper__
12. seggest (suggest)   12. __suggest__

Frequently Misspelled Words

then
and
with
was

School + Home **Home Activity** Your child identified and corrected misspelled words with short vowel sounds. Have your child sketch a sign that contains several spelling words and frequently misspelled words.

Sentences

Directions Read the selection. Then read each question that follows the selection. Decide which is the best answer to each question. Mark the space for the answer you have chosen.

Using Computers

(1) Computer games can be a lot of fun (2) You can use a computer for other things, too. (3) Keep track of your money. (4) A computer can help you with your math work. (5) A computer to talk to your friends. (6) You can use it to learn about almost anything in the world. (7) What do you use computers for.

1 What change, if any, should be made to sentence 1?

- ⬭ Change *Computer* to **computer**
- ⬭ Change *fun* to **fun?**
- ⬮ Change *fun* to **fun.**
- ⬭ Make no change

2 What change, if any, should be made to sentence 3?

- ⬭ Change *money.* to **money?**
- ⬮ Change *Keep track* to **You can keep track**
- ⬭ Change *Keep* to **keep**
- ⬭ Make no change

3 What change, if any, should be made to sentence 4?

- ⬭ Change *A computer* to **A Computer**
- ⬭ Change *work.* to **work,**
- ⬭ Change *math work.* to **math work and sometimes.**
- ⬮ Make no change

4 What change, if any, should be made to sentence 5?

- ⬭ Change *friends.* to **friends?**
- ⬮ Change *A computer* to **You can use a computer**
- ⬭ Change *A* to **a**
- ⬭ Make no change

5 What change, if any, should be made to sentence 7?

- ⬮ Change *for.* to **for?**
- ⬭ Change *for.* to **for!**
- ⬭ Change *for.* to **for,**
- ⬭ Make no change

Home Activity Your child prepared for taking tests on sentences. Ask your child to explain the difference between a sentence and a fragment.

© Pearson Education, Inc., 3

Plurals -s, -es, -ies

Directions Use the plural form of each word in ( ) to complete each sentence. Write the word on the line.

pockets   **1.** Tanya put her hands into her (pocket).

pennies   **2.** She pulled out a handful of (penny).

pencils   **3.** She also found two (pencil).

paints   **4.** She traded each pencil for two boxes of (paint).

brushes   **5.** She used the money to buy two new (brush).

glasses   **6.** She filled (glass) with water for cleaning her brushes.

bushes   **7.** She painted a forest filled with trees and (bush).

beaches   **8.** She made pictures of (beach) and waves.

families   **9.** She showed (family) having fun together.

copies   **10.** Tanya gave away many (copy) of her pictures.

Directions Write the plural form of each word below.

11. lady   **ladies**   **16.** supply   **supplies**

12. dish   **dishes**   **17.** fox   **foxes**

13. class   **classes**   **18.** boss   **bosses**

14. peach   **peaches**   **19.** list   **lists**

15. kiss   **kisses**   **20.** book   **books**

© Pearson Education, Inc., 3

Home Activity Your child wrote plurals—words naming more than one person, place, or thing. Ask your child to look around a room in your home and tell what he or she sees. Work with your child to write a list of twenty things in the room. Ask your child to write the plural form of each word.

Sequence

- The **sequence** is the order in which things happen in a story—what happens first, next, and last.
- Sometimes a writer uses **clue words** such as *first, so, then,* and *at last.*

Directions Read the following passage.

First, Cisco raked leaves for Mrs. Rey. He put the leaves into four piles on the lawn.

Cisco could not put the leaves in plastic bags by himself. So Cisco asked his brother Rico to help.

Rico held the bags open, and then Cisco dumped leaves inside. When a bag was full, Cicso tied it at the top.

At last they were done, and Mrs. Rey gave Cisco twenty dollars. Cisco gave Rico five dollars for helping.

Directions Write these sentences in the correct place on the organizer.

- Cisco put leaves in a bag.
- Cisco asked Rico to help.
- Mrs. Rey paid Cisco $20.
- Cisco raked the leaves.

1. First
Cisco raked the leaves.

↓

2. Next
Cisco asked Rico to help.

↓

3. Then
Cisco put leaves in a bag.

↓

4. Last
Mrs. Rey paid Cisco $20.

5. On another piece of paper, use the sentences to write a summary of the story.
Cisco raked leaves. He asked Rico to help. Cisco put the leaves in a bag. Mrs. Rey paid Cisco $20.

© Pearson Education, Inc., 3

Home Activity Your child put events from a story in the order they happened. Read a simple story to your child. Name events from the story by asking, "What are some things that happened in the story?" Then ask your child to retell the story putting the events in the order they happened.

Writing • Fable

Key Features of a Fable

- often has animals that talk and act like humans
- is usually very short and tells a simple story
- usually has a moral at the end

Mia Cleans House

Mia Mouse had a messy house. "How can you ever find anything?" asked her friend Gus Mouse.

"I can find what I need," Mia said.

That night Mia could not find any cheese.

"I know I have some," she said to herself. She could not find it and went to bed hungry.

The next day, Gus was surprised to see Mia cleaning.

"What are you doing?" he asked.

"Cleaning never hurt anyone," Mia replied. "Would you like some cheese?"

Moral: There are good reasons to be clean and organized.

1. Read the fable. Who and what are the characters?

The characters are Mia and Gus. They are mice.

2. Why can't Mia find her cheese? How does she solve her problem?

Her house is messy, and her cheese got lost somewhere in the

mess. She solves her problem by cleaning, like Gus said she

should do.

© Pearson Education, Inc., 3

Name _____

Vocabulary

Directions Write the word from the box that best completes each sentence.

> **Check the Words You Know**
>
> ___carpenter   ___merchant
> ___carpetmaker   ___plenty
> ___knowledge   ___straying
> ___marketplace   ___thread

plenty   **1.** Sara had _____ of clothes to mend.

thread   **2.** She needed to buy _____ for sewing.

marketplace   **3.** She walked to the _____ to go shopping.

merchant   **4.** She found a _____ who sold what she wanted.

carpetmaker   **5.** Later she talked to the _____ about a new rug.

Directions Write the word from the box that best matches each clue.

carpenter   **6.** a person who builds with wood

plenty   **7.** a lot

straying   **8.** wandering or roaming

knowledge   **9.** facts and ideas

carpetmaker   **10.** someone who makes rugs

Write an Interview

On a separate paper, write five questions you could ask a carpenter, merchant, or a carpetmaker. Answer each question. Use as many vocabulary words as possible.

Students' interviews should use lesson vocabulary in five questions and answers.

 Home Activity Your child identified and used vocabulary words from *What About Me?* With your child, act out a conversation that might have taken place in an old-time village marketplace. Use vocabulary words as you and your child discuss what you are buying or selling.

Subjects and Predicates

A sentence has a **subject** and **predicate**. The subject is the sentence part that tells whom or what the sentence is about. All the words in the subject are called the complete subject. The predicate is the sentence part that tells what the subject is or does. It includes a verb. All the words in the predicate are called the complete predicate.

In the following sentence, the complete subject is underlined once. The complete predicate is underlined twice. The verb is circled.

The market (has) many interesting things.

Directions Underline the complete subject of each sentence.

1. Many people buy beautiful carpets at the market.

2. Farmers bring goats to the market too.

3. The vegetables in the stalls look delicious.

4. Children run around the town square.

5. Everything happens at the town market!

Directions Underline the complete predicate of each sentence. Circle the verb.

6. A young boy (asks) for help.

7. The old man (is) wiser than the boy.

8. The students in a classroom (learn) lessons all the time.

9. Animals (learn) differently from people.

10. My parents (teach) me many lessons.

 Home Activity Your child learned about subjects and predicates. Say a sentence. Have your child identify its complete subject and predicate.

© Pearson Education, Inc., 3

Plurals -s, -es, -ies

Categories Write the word that names each category.

1. Colored and sharpened are types of ___.

2. Paper and pens are types of school ___.

3. Birthday and graduation are types of ___.

4. Drinking and eye are types of ___.

5. Bushes and flowers are types of ___.

6. Grocery and Christmas are types of ___.

1. **pencils**   2. **supplies**

3. **parties**   4. **glasses**

5. **plants**   6. **lists**

Writing Plurals Write the plural of the underlined word in each sentence.

7. Three <u>family</u> went on the camping trip.   7. **families**

8. The snake was thirty <u>inch</u> long.   8. **inches**

9. Big <u>bunch</u> of balloons were tied to her bike.   9. **bunches**

10. Our <u>body</u> need good food, exercise, and rest.   10. **bodies**

11. My jeans have lots of <u>pocket</u>.   11. **pockets**

12. I found some <u>penny</u> on the curb.   12. **pennies**

13. She made three <u>wish</u> on her birthday.   13. **wishes**

14. There were many <u>crash</u> during the ice storm.   14. **crashes**

15. Let's make some <u>copy</u> of the map.   15. **copies**

School + Home **Home Activity** Your child spelled plurals that end with -s, -es, and -ies. Ask your child to explain how he or she knows which ending to use when making a word plural.

Story Sequence B

Title _____

Beginning

Middle

End

Vocabulary • Compound Words

- Sometimes you may come across a word you don't know. The word may be a long **compound word** made up of two small words.

- If you know the meaning of the small words, it will help you figure out the meaning of the long compound word.

Directions Read the riddle. Then circle the compound word that solves the riddle.

1. I take care of goats. I watch them during the day. I watch them at night. Who am I?
(goatkeeper)   goaltender

2. I sit and weave all day. I make wonderful patterns of many colors. I make things you put on your floor and walk on. Who am I?
coverup   (carpetmaker)

3. I raise goats. When they are big, I sell them to people. Who am I?
cowboy   (goatseller)

4. I help people get married. I help men meet women. I help women meet men. Who am I?
(matchmaker)   firefighter

5. I am a place where people go to buy things. There are many people selling things here. There are many people buying things here. What am I?
doorknob   (marketplace)

6. I am a place for children. I have swings and monkey bars. I have many things that children can play on. What am I?
(playground)   outline

7. Birds live inside me. I have a perch for them to sit on. I have cups for food and water. What am I?
cardboard   (birdcage)

8. I own a store. I help my customers. I stand behind the counter. People who buy things in my shop pay me. Who am I?
(shopkeeper)   airport

 Home Activity Your child used word structure to figure out the meaning of unfamiliar compound words. Read a newspaper article or store advertisement with your child. Encourage your child to identify unfamiliar compound words by defining the small words that make up each compound word.

Alphabetical Order

Entries or subjects in encyclopedias, dictionaries, and indexes are listed in **alphabetical order,** so you can find information quickly and easily. When two entries or subjects have the same first letter, alphabetize by the second letter. If the second letters are also the same, alphabetize by the third letter, and so on. See how these occupation entries have been alphabetized in an index.

Accountant, 12	Butcher, 35	Counselor, 14
Actor, 22	Carpenter, 18	Dancer, 23
Auto Mechanic, 32	Carpet Installer, 20	Dentist, 29
Bank Teller, 34	Cashier, 9	Designer, 24
Barber, 8	Chef, 7	Educator, 26
Bus Driver, 10	Computer Operator, 6	Engineer, 19

Directions Put these words from *What About Me?* in alphabetical order. Use the index example above to help you.

master   carpet   work
thread   spun

moral   wise   weave
spinner   merchant

1. carpet

2. master

3. spun

4. thread

5. work

6. merchant

7. moral

8. spinner

9. weave

10. wise

Home Activity Your child put words in alphabetical order. Give your child a list of 5 names of family members and/or friends. Ask him or her to put the names in alphabetical order.

Plurals -s, -es, -ies

Proofread a List Circle four spelling mistakes in Ben's school supply list. Write the words correctly. Write the last sentence, using correct grammar and punctuation.

> **School** ⟨supplys⟩ **I need**
> colored pencils
> folders with ⟨pocketes⟩
> ruler with centimeters and ⟨inchs⟩
> snacks—extras for ⟨friens⟩
> lined paper
> Remember to turn in them copies of doctor records

1. __supplies__   2. __pockets__

3. __inches__   4. __friends__

5. __Remember to turn in those copies__
   __of doctor records.__

Proofread Words Fill in the circle to show the correctly spelled word. Write each word.

6. ○ familys   ● families   ○ familes   6. __families__

7. ○ crashs   ● crashes   ○ crashies   7. __crashes__

8. ● lists   ○ listes   ○ listies   8. __lists__

9. ○ bunchs   ○ bunchies   ● bunches   9. __bunches__

10. ○ glassies ● glasses   ○ glasss   10. __glasses__

11. ○ wishs'   ○ wishs   ● wishes   11. __wishes__

12. ○ plantes   ● plants   ○ plantts   12. __plants__

© Pearson Education, Inc., 3

Home Activity Your child identified and corrected misspelled plural nouns. Have your child help you make a shopping list. Include some list words.

Subjects and Predicates

Directions Read the selection. Then read each question that follows the selection. Decide which is the best answer to each question. Mark the space for the answer you have chosen.

The Market

(1) The market is a busy place. (2) Many people buy beautiful carpets at the market. (3) Farmers bring goats to the market, too. (4) People in the stalls sell fresh vegetables. (5) A woman yells out for her family. (6) _____ run around the market square. (7) You can have a lot of fun at the market!

1 What is the complete subject in sentence 1?
- ⬭ is
- ⬭ place
- ⬬ The market
- ⬭ exciting

2 What is the verb in sentence 2?
- ⬬ buy
- ⬭ people
- ⬭ carpets
- ⬭ the market

3 What is the complete subject in sentence 4?
- ⬭ People
- ⬭ the stalls
- ⬭ fresh vegetables
- ⬬ People in the stalls

4 What is the complete predicate in sentence 5?
- ⬭ A woman
- ⬭ family
- ⬬ yells out for her family
- ⬭ A woman yells

5 What subject makes the most sense in sentence 6?
- ⬭ Carpets
- ⬬ Children
- ⬭ Stalls
- ⬭ Picnic baskets

© Pearson Education, Inc., 3

School + Home **Home Activity** Your child prepared for taking tests on subjects and predicates. Say a sentence about your family. Ask your child to identify the complete subject and predicate of the sentence. Continue with other sentences.

Base Words and Endings

Directions Add **-ed** and **-ing** to each word on the left. Remember that you may have to double the last consonant, drop the final **e**, or change **y** to **i**.

Word	-ed	-ing
plan	planned	planning
1. please	**pleased**	**pleasing**
2. use	**used**	**using**
3. shop	**shopped**	**shopping**
4. worry	**worried**	**worrying**
5. tug	**tugged**	**tugging**

Directions Add **-er** and **-est** to each word on the left. Remember that you may have to double the last consonant, drop the final **e**, or change **y** to **i**.

Word	-er	-est
heavy	heavier	heaviest
6. great	**greater**	**greatest**
7. easy	**easier**	**easiest**
8. thin	**thinner**	**thinnest**
9. angry	**angrier**	**angriest**
10. big	**bigger**	**biggest**

© Pearson Education, Inc., 3

Home Activity Your child wrote words that end with *-ed, -ing, -er,* and *-est*. Work with your child to write a story using the words on the page above. Before the writing begins, ask your child to review the words he or she wrote and think about ways to use the words.

Name _____

Sequence

- **Sequence** is the order in which things happen in a story.
- **Clue words,** such as *first, second, then, next, finally,* and *last,* can tell you when something happens.

Directions Read the following passage. Draw a line under the words or phrases that help you follow the sequence of story events. Then answer the questions below.

> Tina's mother liked to watch rainbows. Tina decided to make her mother a rainbow. First, she found a large piece of white fabric. She sewed a row of red buttons to the fabric. Next, she sewed a row of orange buttons under the red buttons.
>
> Then Tina found some yellow and green glitter. She used glue and made a row of yellow glitter and then a row of green glitter under the buttons.
>
> Next, Tina found some blue fabric scraps. She sewed the blue fabric under the green glitter.
>
> Then Tina found some violet buttons. She sewed a row of violet buttons under the blue fabric.
>
> Finally, Tina made fabric loops to hang her rainbow. Now her mother can see a rainbow any time.

1. When did Tina sew orange buttons to her fabric?

   after she sewed the red buttons

2. What did Tina glue on the fabric after she sewed the red and orange buttons?

   yellow and green glitter

3. When did Tina sew the violet buttons?

   after she sewed on the blue fabric

4. What did Tina do last?

   made fabric loops to hang her rainbow

5. Write the colors Tina used in the sequence she used them. Why do you think she did things in this order? **red, orange, yellow, green, blue, violet;**

   She was following the order of the colors in a rainbow.

© Pearson Education, Inc., 3

Home Activity Your child answered questions about the order of events in a story. Write the events from a story on cards or pieces of paper. Mix them up. Then have your child put the cards in the correct order.

Writing • Thank-You Note

Key Features of a Thank-You Note

- uses the format of a friendly letter
- has a friendly tone
- explains why the writer is grateful

2218 Magnolia Street
San Antonio, TX 78201
October 14, 2011

Dear Aunt Teresa,

   Not a day has gone by that I haven't played the guitar you left with me. Thank you for trusting me to take care of your guitar while you are away. I practice every day, and I can already play a few songs.

   Naturally, my goal is to learn that gorgeous song you played for us during your last visit. Do you remember it? I'm talking about the Spanish lullaby, of course! If I haven't learned the song by the time you get back, you will have to teach me.

   Until then, I will miss you terribly. I hope you are having a great time on your trip! I am counting the days to your return.

With love,
Carmen

---

1. Identify the format features of a thank-you note by underlining the date, drawing a box around the greeting, and circling the name of the person who has written the note.

2. Why is Carmen writing this friendly thank-you note?

Carmen wants to thank her Aunt Teresa for trusting her to take care of a guitar while her aunt is away.

© Pearson Education, Inc., 3

Name _____

Vocabulary

Check the Words You Know

___gear   ___twitch
___parka   ___willow
___splendid   ___yanked

Directions Draw a line to match each word with its definition.

1. gear — pulled with a sudden motion

2. parka — to move with a quick jerk

3. splendid — a heavy, waterproof coat or jacket with a hood

4. yanked — the equipment needed for some purpose

5. twitch — very good; excellent

Directions Write the word from the box that best completes each sentence.

parka   6. I put on my boots and _____ to go out in the snow.

gear   7. Tim put all his fishing _____ into his dad's truck.

willow   8. We sat by the pond under the huge _____ trees.

yanked   9. Jassy _____ the weeds out of the garden by hand.

splendid   10. It was a _____ day for a hike in the woods.

Write a Story

On a separate sheet of paper, write a story about a boy or girl who goes fishing. Use as many vocabulary words as possible.

Students' stories should be about fishing and include vocabulary words.

Home Activity Your child identified and used vocabulary words from *Kumak's Fish*. Play a game with your child in which you take turns pantomiming and guessing an action involving a vocabulary word, such as putting on a parka.

Declarative and Interrogative Sentences

A sentence that tells something is a **statement.** It is also called a **declarative sentence.** A sentence that asks something is a **question.** It is also called an **interrogative sentence.**

 Statement   The lake has many fish.   **Question**   Did you catch a fish?

A statement begins with a capital letter and ends with a period. A question begins with a capital letter and ends with a question mark.

Directions Write each sentence. Add the correct end punctuation. Write *S* if the sentence is a statement, or declarative sentence. Write *Q* if the sentence is a question, or interrogative sentence.

1. Are the winters long in the Arctic

Are the winters long in the Arctic? Q

2. Spring is a good season for fishing

Spring is a good season for fishing. S

3. We have a good fishing pole

We have a good fishing pole. S

Directions Add one word from the box to make each statement into a question. Write the new sentence. Use correct capitalization and punctuation. **Possible answers:**

> can   will   should   do

4. The people catch fish in the frozen lake.

Can the people catch fish in the frozen lake?

5. They take them home for a feast.

Will they take them home for a feast?

 Home Activity Your child learned about statements and questions. Have your child make up one statement and one question about an animal he or she likes.

© Pearson Education, Inc., 3

Name _____

Base Words and Endings

Rhymes Write a list word that rhymes with each underlined word.

Spelling Words

using
getting
easiest
swimming
heavier
greatest
pleased
emptied

leaving
worried
strangest
freezing
funniest
angrier
shopped

1. Our <u>latest</u> invention is the ___.

2. Nobody is ___ to be <u>teased</u>.

3. Everyone who had been <u>weaving</u> was ___.

4. We <u>hopped</u> out of the car and ___.

5. He is <u>sneezing</u> because it is ___ outside.

6. The ___ cartoon was about the <u>sunniest</u> day.

1. __greatest__   2. __pleased__

3. __leaving__   4. __shopped__

5. __freezing__   6. __funniest__

Word Endings Add an ending to each word in parentheses to form a list word that completes the sentence.

7. (heavy)   This box is __heavier__ than that one.

8. (swim)   I take __swimming__ lessons twice a week.

9. (get)   He is __getting__ a watch for his birthday.

10. (strange) That is the __strangest__ bug I have ever seen.

11. (easy)   That is the __easiest__ way to solve the puzzle.

12. (use)   I am __using__ three different colors on my poster.

13. (worry)   He __worried__ that he would be late.

14. (empty)   She __emptied__ the wastebasket in her classroom.

15. (angry)   She was __angrier__ than I thought.

Home Activity: Your child wrote words that end in *-ed*, *-ing*, *-er*, and *-est*. Ask your child to find list words in which a consonant is doubled or an *e* is dropped before adding *-ing* (consonant doubled in *getting*, *e* dropped in *using*, *leaving*, *freezing*).

Outline Form A

Title _____

A. _____

　　1. _____

　　2 _____

　　3. _____

B. _____

　　1. _____

　　2. _____

　　3. _____

C. _____

　　1. _____

　　2. _____

　　3. _____

Name _____

Vocabulary • Reference Sources

- You can use a **glossary** or a **dictionary** to find the meanings of unknown words.
- Entries in glossaries and dictionaries are in **alphabetical order.** When two words have the same first and second letter, alphabetize by the third letter.

blizzard *NOUN.* a blinding snowstorm with very strong, cold winds

blow *VERB.* **1.** to make air come out of your mouth. **2.** to move in the wind

parka *NOUN.* a warm, heavy jacket with a hood

pattern *NOUN.* an arrangement or design

Directions Put these words in alphabetical order. Use the glossary example above to help you. Then answer the questions.

| wander   wake   waist |
| walrus   wade |

| waves   water   wax |
| warm   was |

1. _____ **wade** _____

2. _____ **waist** _____

3. _____ **wake** _____

4. _____ **walrus** _____

5. _____ **wander** _____

6. _____ **warm** _____

7. _____ **was** _____

8. _____ **water** _____

9. _____ **waves** _____

10. _____ **wax** _____

11. Which word comes just before *warm* in the glossary?

wander

12. Which word comes just after *water* in the glossary?

waves

Home Activity Your child put words whose first two letters are the same in alphabetical order. Give your child a list of three names that begin with the same two letters, such as *Sam, Sandy,* and *Sally.* Have your child put the names in alphabetical order.

Glossary

- Sometimes you come across a word you don't know. You can use a **glossary** to find the meaning of the unfamiliar word.
- A **glossary** has the meanings of important words in a book. It is usually found in the back of a book. The words are listed in alphabetical order.

Directions Study the sample from a glossary page below. Then use it to answer the questions.

> **spell • yanked**
>
> **spell** *v.* to write or say the letters of a word in order
> **splendid** *adj.* very good; excellent
> **twitch** *v.* to move with a quick jerk
> **vision** *n.* the power of using the imagination to see what the future might bring
> **willow** *n.* the wood of the willow tree

1. What are the guide words on this page? **spell, yanked**

2. Would the word *space* be on this page? How do you know?

   no; it comes before *spell* in alphabetical order.

3. The abbreviation *n.* stands for *noun*. Which words shown are nouns?

   vision, willow

4. Where in a book is a glossary usually found? **in the back**

5. Do you think this section of the glossary is at the beginning of the glossary or near the end? Why?

   near the end, because the words begin with letters at the end of the alphabet

6. Write the meaning of the word *vision*: **the power of using the imagination to see what the future might bring**

Home Activity Your child learned how to use a glossary. Ask your child to name the word on the sample glossary page above that is a verb and explain his or her answer.

Name _____

Base Words and Endings

Proofread a Thank-You Note Circle four misspelled words in Joe's thank-you note. Circle the word with the capitalization error. Write the words correctly.

> (dear) Uncle Jim,
>
> Thanks for (geting) me the (swiming) gear. I planned on (useing) my savings so I had (emptyed) my piggy bank. However, there wasn't enough. That's why I was so pleased with your gift. You're the greatest!
>
> Love,
> Joe

Spelling Words

using
getting
easiest
swimming
heavier
greatest
pleased
emptied

leaving
worried
strangest
freezing
funniest
angrier
shopped

1. __getting__   2. __swimming__
3. __using__   4. __emptied__
5. __Dear__

Frequently Misspelled Words

started
getting
swimming

Complete the Sentence Circle the word that is spelled correctly. Then write the word.

6. I picked out the (easiest) easyest puzzle.   6. __easiest__
7. Have you shoped (shopped) for a new bike?   7. __shopped__
8. The box was heavyier (heavier) than I thought.   8. __heavier__
9. Are you (leaving) leaveing before lunch?   9. __leaving__
10. I'm (freezing) freezeing!   10. __freezing__
11. Are you worry (worried) about the test?   11. __worried__
12. She was pulesed (pleased) with my report.   12. __pleased__

© Pearson Education, Inc., 3

Home Activity Your child identified misspelled words that end in *-ed*, *-ing*, *-er*, and *-est*. Name a base word and have your child explain how to add the ending.

Declarative and Interrogative Sentences

Directions Read the selection. Then read each question that follows the selection. Decide which is the best answer to each question. Mark the space for the answer you have chosen.

Fishing at the Lake

(1) What is your favorite lake for fishing? (2) My favorite lake is Mirror Lake. (3) I fish in the summer (4) how big are the fish you catch? (5) The fish smell good when they are cooked. (6) My family eats a lot of fish. (7) Does your lake freeze in the winter

1 What change, if any, should be made to sentence 1?

⬭ Change *What* to **what**

⬭ Change *fishing?* to **fishing.**

⬭ Change *fishing?* to **fishing**

⬛ Make no change

2 What change, if any, should be made to sentence 3?

⬭ Change *I* to **i**

⬛ Change *summer* to **summer.**

⬭ Change *summer* to **summer?**

⬭ Make no change

3 What change, if any, should be made to sentence 4?

⬭ Change *catch?* to **catch.**

⬭ Change *catch?* to **catch,**

⬛ Change *how big* to **How big**

⬭ Make no change

4 What type of sentence is sentence 5?

⬛ It is a statement.

⬭ It is a question.

⬭ It is an interrogative sentence.

⬭ It is an incomplete sentence.

5 What change, if any, should be made to sentence 7?

⬛ Change *winter* to **winter?**

⬭ Change *winter* to **winter!**

⬭ Change *winter* to **winter.**

⬭ Make no change

© Pearson Education, Inc., 3

Home Activity Your child prepared for taking tests on statements and questions. Read a story together. Have your child identify statements and questions in the story.

Long Vowel Digraphs

Directions Choose the word with the **long a**, **long e**, or **long o** sound that best matches each definition. Write the word on the line.

okay   **1.** all right   glad   okay   well

groan   **2.** a sound of pain   groan   sob   whimper

clean   **3.** free from dirt   clean   fresh   spotless

throw   **4.** toss   fling   pitch   throw

agree   **5.** go along with   accept   admit   agree

gain   **6.** reach or get   gain   gather   win

toast   **7.** heat until brown   cook   toast   broil

Directions Circle the word that has the **long a**, **long e**, or **long o** sound. Then underline the letters in the word that stand for that vowel sound.

8. chock   chop   (ch**ee**p)

9. best   (bl**ow**n)   bought

10. flash   (fl**oa**t)   flock

11. (br**ai**d)   brick   build

12. school   sorry   (st**ay**)

13. (f**ea**st)   flash   friend

14. dish   (dr**ea**m)   droop

15. sand   (scr**ee**n)   shoe

16. (pl**ai**n)   plant   print

Home Activity Your child wrote words in which the long *a* sound is spelled *ay* and *ai*, the long *e* is spelled *ee* and *ea*, and the long *o* is spelled *oa* and *ow*. Ask your child to list words that rhyme with the long *a*, *e*, and *o* words on the page above. Write the rhyming words and have your child read them noting different spellings for the same sound.

Compare and Contrast

- **Compare** by telling how two or more things are alike.
- **Contrast** by telling only how two or more things are different.

Directions Read the following article.

Dan, Tim, and Anna grocery shop for their family. Dan always heads for the supermarket. He likes lots of choices. Dan buys what he wants and leaves in a hurry. He thinks small stores are boring.

Tim prefers the small corner grocery. The store doesn't have much, but it has what Tim needs. Tim likes the store's owner, Mrs. Garza. When the store isn't busy, Tim stays and talks awhile. Tim likes cozy little stores. He thinks big stores are too noisy and crowded.

Anna likes both stores. She dashes to the corner when she needs basic supplies. She goes to the supermarket to find special foods.

Directions Fill in the chart to compare and contrast Dan's, Tim's, and Anna's shopping habits.

	Big Supermarket	**Corner Store**
Dan	Possible response: prefers it; likes choices	Possible response: thinks it's boring
Tim	Possible response: thinks it's noisy and crowded	Possible response: prefers it; thinks it is cozy
Anna	Possible response: prefers it for big selection	Possible response: prefers it for basic foods

Home Activity Your child compared and contrasted three shoppers. Talk with your child about shopping likes and dislikes. Discuss how your child's attitudes about shopping are like and unlike your own attitudes.

Writing • Description

Key Features of a Description

- uses sensory language
- includes important details
- creates a picture in the reader's mind

My Favorite Place to Shop

Our local thrift shop makes money for Children's Hospital. People bring in things they no longer need or want and the thrift shop sells them for a fair price. It's made for me!

Sometimes I see a game I've been wanting but don't want to pay $15 for. Other times there's a great looking pair of jeans that have hardly been worn. Mom always finds something to brighten up the house. Once she found a sparkly, red painting. Another time she found a tall, rectangular lamp. "Leave your wallets at home," Dad says as we head to the shop.

The woman who owns the shop likes to burn candles. The whole store smells like vanilla. It smells delicious! I hear the sound of the cash register and people talking about items to buy. The thrift shop is a great place to spend my money.

I wonder if every town has a thrift shop. I am so glad our town does!

---

1. List three sensory words or phrases from the selection.

   ___*sparkly, tall, rectangular*_____

2. How many exclamatory sentences are included in the selection? How do you know?

   ___**Three; They end with exclamation points.**_____

Vocabulary

Directions Match the word with its meaning. Draw a line from the word to its definition.

1. store   clothes that have been washed or need to be washed

2. laundry   thin flat pieces of wood or other material fastened to a wall or frame to hold things

3. shelves

4. spoiled   exchanged, bartered

5. traded   a place where things are sold

            became bad, not good to eat

Directions Choose a word from the list that best fits the meaning of the sentence and write it on the line.

6. The milk **spoiled** quickly in the warm weather.

7. My favorite part of the supermarket is the bakery **section**.

8. You can find a huge **variety** of fruit in a supermarket.

9. It seemed like there were **thousands** of cars in the parking lot.

10. It's fun to shop in the grocery **store**.

Write a Grocery List

On a separate sheet of paper, write a description of a trip to the supermarket and list what you bought. Include items from different sections of the supermarket. Use as many vocabulary words as you can. **Students should include a variety of items from different store sections in their writing.**

© Pearson Education, Inc., 3

Home Activity Your child identified and used vocabulary words from *Supermarket*. With your child discuss your local supermarket and what things you buy there. Encourage your child to use vocabulary words in your conversation.

Name _____

Imperative and Exclamatory Sentences

A sentence that tells someone to do something is a **command.** It is also called an **imperative sentence.** A sentence that shows strong feelings is an **exclamation.** It is also called an **exclamatory sentence.**

Command   Buy some apples.
Exclamation What juicy peaches these are!

Some commands begin with *Please.* Commands usually end with periods. The subject of a command is *you.* The word *you* is not written or said, but it is understood. Exclamations can express feelings such as surprise, anger, or excitement. Exclamations begin with a capital letter and end with an exclamation mark.

Directions Write the sentences. Add the correct end punctuation. Write *C* if the sentence is a command, or imperative sentence. Write *E* if the sentence is an exclamation, or exclamatory sentence.

1. Please get a loaf of bread

Please get a loaf of bread. C
_____

2. Wow! This supermarket is huge

Wow! This supermarket is huge! E
_____

Directions Use a word from the box to complete each command or exclamation. Write the new sentence. Use correct capitalization and punctuation.

What   Look   Talk   How

3. _____ on that shelf for cereal.

Look on that shelf for cereal.
_____

4. _____ busy the workers are!

How busy the workers are!
_____

Home Activity Your child learned about commands and exclamations. Have your child make up one command and one exclamation about saving money.

Vowel Digraphs

Rhymes Write the list word that rhymes with the underlined word.

clean
agree
teeth
dream
grain
coach
display
window
shadow
cheese
peach
braid
Sunday
float
thrown

1. Did you ever meet a <u>goat</u> that knew how

   to __**float**__ ?

2. Did you ever <u>approach</u> the other

   team's __**coach**__ ?

3. Did you ever <u>reach</u> for a big fuzzy __**peach**__ ?

4. Did you ever get a <u>pain</u> from eating

   green __**grain**__ ?

5. Did you ever <u>scream</u> when you had a

   bad __**dream**__ ?

6. Did you ever help <u>Jean</u> keep her room __**clean**__ ?

7. Did you ever get <u>paid</u> to wear your hair in a __**braid**__ ?

Context Clues Write the missing list word.

8. I like grilled __**cheese**__ sandwiches.

9. Floss your __**teeth**__ every day.

10. The first day of the week is __**Sunday**__ .

11. The tree cast a long __**shadow**__ .

12. Let's open the __**window**__ to get some fresh air.

13. Mom will __**agree**__ to drive us to the game.

14. I've __**thrown**__ out all my old papers.

15. Let's make a __**display**__ of our seashells.

© Pearson Education, Inc., 3

School + Home **Home Activity** Your child wrote words with long vowel digraphs (letter combinations that stand for long vowel sounds). Ask your child to circle the digraphs *ai, ay, ee, ea, oa,* and *ow.*

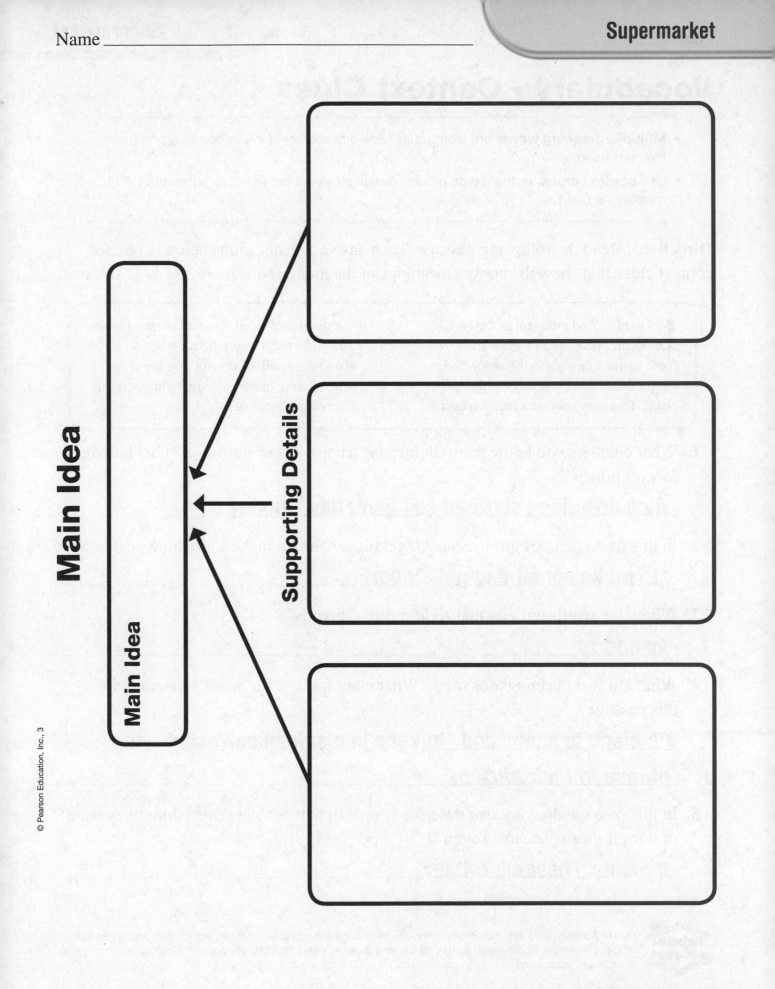

Main Idea

Main Idea

Supporting Details

Vocabulary • Context Clues

- **Multiple-meaning words** are words that have different meanings depending on how they are used.
- Use **context clues,** or the words around a multiple-meaning word, to figure out which meaning is used.

Directions Read the following passage. Then answer the questions below. Look for context clues that show the correct meanings of the multiple-meaning words as you read.

It's hard to find **rich** soil in the city, so most city people can't **grow** their own food. Instead they go to the supermarket. Each kind of food is always in the same place. That way shoppers can go **right** to the items they need. Then they rush home and **store** the food in their kitchen so it won't get **spoiled.** It's not good to shop when you're hungry. Hungry shoppers buy everything they see!

1. What clue lets you know that *rich* means "having lots of nutrition," not "having lots of money"?

   Rich describes *soil*, and soil can't have money.

2. In this passage, does *grow* mean "to get bigger" or "to make something get bigger"?

   "to make something get bigger"

3. What clue words tell you that *right* means "directly"?

   go and *to*

4. What are two meanings for *store*? What clues tell you the word's meaning in this passage?

   "a place to shop" and "to keep in a safe place"; clue—the phrase *in their kitchen*

5. In this passage does *spoiled* describe people or pets who get everything they want or does it mean "became rotten"?

   It means "became rotten."

Home Activity Your child used context clues to understand multiple-meaning words. Say sentences with multiple-meaning words, such as *run, place,* and *blue.* Ask your child to use context clues to determine the meaning of each word.

Pictographs

Graphs help you compare information. **Pictographs** use pictures or symbols.

Directions Mrs. Lee runs a fruit and vegetable store. The pictograph below shows how many pounds of each fruit she sold in one day last week. Use the pictograph to answer the questions.

bananas	🍌🍌🍌🍌🍌🍌🍌🍌
apples	🍎🍎🍎🍎🍎🍎
oranges	🍊🍊🍊🍊🍊
strawberries	🍓🍓🍓🍓🍓🍓🍓🍓🍓🍓
grapes	🍇🍇🍇🍇🍇
pears	🍐🍐🍐🍐

Each symbol stands for 1 pound of fruit.

1. How many pounds of fruit does each symbol stand for? __**1 pound**__

2. How many pounds of apples did Mrs. Lee sell? __**6 pounds**__

3. Which kind of fruit did Mrs. Lee sell the most of? __**strawberries**__

4. Did Mrs. Lee sell more pounds of grapes or of apples? __**apples**__

5. How many pounds of oranges did Mrs. Lee sell? __**5 pounds**__

Home Activity Your child answered questions by interpreting data in a pictograph. For one week, have your child keep track of how many hours he or she spends playing outside. Then have your child make a pictograph to show the results.

Vowel Digraphs

Proofread a Description Circle five misspelled words in Amy's description. Circle the word with a capitalization error. Write the words correctly.

> I can see a troll from my window. He has (realy) big (teath) and a long braid down his back. At night, I watch him (dreem) under the tree or (flote) in the moonlight. (mom) says he's just a (shado) but I don't always agree.

Spelling Words

clean
agree
teeth
dream
grain
coach
display
window

shadow
cheese
peach
braid
Sunday
float
thrown

1. **really**   2. **teeth**

3. **dream**   4. **float**

5. **shadow**   6. **Mom**

Frequently Misspelled Words

Halloween
really

Proofread Words Fill in the circle to show the correctly spelled word.

7. The model train was on _____ .

   ○ displaiy   ● display   ○ dissplay   ○ displaye

8. We are going to the lake on _____ .

   ○ sunday   ○ Sundaye   ○ Sundai   ● Sunday

9. Our _____ bought treats after the game.

   ● coach   ○ coche   ○ coash   ○ cowch

10. Everyone helped _____ the garage.

   ○ kleen   ○ cleen   ● clean   ○ klean

School + Home **Home Activity** Your child spelled words with long vowel digraphs (letter combinations that make long vowel sounds). Take turns with your child spelling a list word and using it in a sentence.

© Pearson Education, Inc., 3

Imperative and Exclamatory Sentences

Directions Read the selection. Then read each question that follows the selection. Decide which is the best answer to each question. Mark the space for the answer you have chosen.

Shopping Trip

(1) There are so many kinds of foods here! (2) Please get a box of crackers. (3) Check the price of tomatoes (4) Please look for the grapes (5) What a good price that is (6) The bread smells so good! (7) _____ put the bags in the car.

1 What type of sentence is sentence 1?
- ⬭ a command
- ⬭ an imperative sentence
- ⬬ an exclamatory sentence
- ⬭ an interrogative sentence

2 What type of sentence is sentence 2?
- ⬭ an exclamation
- ⬭ an exclamatory sentence
- ⬭ a declarative sentence
- ⬬ an imperative sentence

3 What change, if any, should be made to sentence 4?
- ⬬ Change *grapes* to **grapes.**
- ⬭ Change *grapes* to **grapes!**
- ⬭ Change *Please* to **Please!**
- ⬭ Make no change

4 What change, if any, should be made to sentence 5?
- ⬭ Change *is* to **is.**
- ⬬ Change *is* to **is!**
- ⬭ Change *What* to **what**
- ⬭ Make no change

5 Which word makes the most sense in sentence 7?
- ⬬ Please
- ⬭ Please!
- ⬭ What
- ⬭ Shopping

© Pearson Education, Inc., 3

Home Activity Your child prepared for taking tests on commands and exclamations. Have your child write a note about a chore to a family member, including a command and an exclamation. Ask your child to identify each kind of sentence.

Name _____

Vowel Diphthongs

Directions Circle each word with **ou** or **ow** that has the same vowel sound as **out**. Then write the word on the line.

___**counted**___   **1.** Jen slowly (counted) her money.

___**amount**___   **2.** She had the (amount) she needed.

___**proud**___   **3.** Jen was (proud) that she didn't have to borrow money.

___**powder**___   **4.** She could buy her mother some bath (powder.)

___**flowers**___   **5.** Jen would also buy some yellow (flowers.)

Directions Circle each word with **oi** or **oy** that has the same vowel sound as **toy**. Then write the word on the line.

___**choice**___   **6.** It was time for Al to make a (choice.)

___**employer**___   **7.** Should he find a new (employer?)

___**avoid**___   **8.** Al wanted to (avoid) a long ride to work.

___**enjoy**___   **9.** He wanted to (enjoy) his job.

___**noisy**___   **10.** He also hoped to work in an office that was not (noisy.)

Directions Circle each word with the same vowel sound as the first word. Then underline the letters in the circled word that stand for that vowel sound.

11. town	loyal	(pr<u>ou</u>d)	snow
12. boy	sound	know	(br<u>oi</u>l)
13. choice	coat	plow	(sp<u>oi</u>l)
14. hour	(cr<u>ow</u>n)	float	show
15. join	bay	(ann<u>oy</u>)	brown

Home Activity Your child wrote words with the vowel sound in *out*, spelled *ou* as in *proud* and *ow* as in *shower*, and the vowel sound in *toy*, spelled *oi* as in *choice* and *oy* as in *voyage*. Have your child list other words that have the vowel sounds in *out* and *toy*. Tell your child to underline the letters that stand for the vowel sound in each word.

© Pearson Education, Inc., 3

Author's Purpose

An **author's purpose** is the author's reason for writing. An author may write to inform or teach, to entertain, to persuade, or to express thoughts and feelings. Authors choose either a first-person narrator who is often one of the story's characters or a third-person narrator who tells the story without taking part in the events. First-person narrators use language such as "I" and "me." Third-person narrators use language such as "he" and "she."

Directions Read the story. Then complete the web. Finish the sentences. Write the author's purpose in the middle circle.

Jamal wanted to go to soccer camp, so he asked his dad to pay for it. "Let's make a deal," his dad said. "If you save half the cost, I'll pay the rest." Jamal thought that was fair, so he agreed.

Right away, Jamal started to save, but sometimes it was hard. He put almost all of his allowance into the bank. He did jobs for the neighbors. He didn't spend one cent of his birthday money! Whenever Jamal wanted to buy something, he thought about his goal.

When it was time to pay for camp, Jamal had saved more than half the cost. He was proud that he had worked hard to reach his goal. You should save for something special too. You will feel great when you reach your goal!

The main character of this story is **Jamal.**

When Jamal got birthday money, **he saved all of it.**

Author's Purpose: **to persuade readers to work hard to reach a goal**

When Jamal wanted to spend, he remembered his **goal.**

This story has a __third__-person narrator.

School + Home **Home Activity** Your child read a story and identified the author's purpose and the narrator. Read a story together. Discuss the author's purpose for writing and ask your child to tell whether the narrator is first person or third person.

© Pearson Education, Inc., 3

Writing • Writing for Tests

Aiming for the Moon

1 Every morning my mom gives me money to buy lunch at school. She gives me more money than I need, and she knows it. I usually buy something yummy to eat after school. I spend all the money I have.

2 Yesterday I saw a remote control moon, and I want one for my bedroom. My mom said, "Save your money to buy it." No more extra snacks for me! Instead I will put the money that I used to spend on treats in my bank. I can also use the money Grandpa gave me for my birthday. He told me to pick out something I really wanted.

3 This moon looks like lots of fun, and I will give up extra treats for it.

1. Find the characters in the model. Draw a box around each one. How are the characters related?

The characters are a family.

2. Describe the story's sequence of events.

Beginning: **Mom gives the narrator money each morning to buy lunch at school. The narrator spends any extra money on treats.**

Middle: **The mom tells the narrator to save money to buy the remote control moon that the narrator wants.**

End: **The narrator decides to give up extra treats in order to save money and buy the remote control moon.**

3. Write a number 1 next to the beginning of the story, a number 2 next to the middle, and a number 3 next to the end.

© Pearson Education, Inc., 3

Vocabulary

Directions Fill in the blank with the word that fits the meaning of the sentence.

1. Hold the ladder **steady** _____ so I can climb up.

2. I **wobbled** _____ often when I first learned to ride a bike.

3. He **unwrapped** _____ his birthday presents after the party.

4. She did a few **errands** _____ to help her grandmother.

5. We tied our clothes in _____ **bundles** _____ and went to the laundry.

Directions Draw a line from the word to its definition.

6. dangerously   put in order

7. arranged   shook from side to side

8. excitedly   uncovered

9. unwrapped   in an unsafe way

10. wobbled   with strong, lively feelings

Write an Advertisement

On a separate sheet of paper, write an advertisement for a job. Write about someone who is looking for a student to work after school. Describe the job and how much it pays. Use as many vocabulary words as possible. **Students' writing should use lesson vocabulary in a description of a job suited for a student.**

© Pearson Education, Inc., 3

Home Activity Your child identified and used words from *My Rows and Piles of Coins*. Read a story about a student who gets a job. Discuss the story with your child using this lesson's vocabulary words.

Name _____

Compound Sentences

A **simple sentence** has one subject and one predicate. A **compound sentence** contains two simple sentences joined by a comma and a word such as *and, but,* or *or.*

Simple Sentence	I rode my bike to Dan's house.
Simple Sentence	We rode to the park.
Compound Sentence	I rode my bike to Dan's house, and we rode to the park.

Directions Write *S* if the sentence is a simple sentence. Write *C* if the sentence is a compound sentence.

1. Bicycles are important to people in some countries. ___**S**___

2. People in some places do not have cars. ___**S**___

3. They ride bicycles to work, and they ride them to the store. ___**C**___

4. Bicycles cost less than cars, but they are not cheap. ___**C**___

5. Bicycles do not make the air dirty, but cars do. ___**C**___

Directions Choose one of the words in ( ) to combine each pair of simple sentences. Write the compound sentences on the lines.

6. Chris rode a bicycle up the hill. It was not easy. (but, or)

Chris rode a bicycle up the hill, but it was not easy.

7. Chris skinned his knee. He bumped his head. (but, and)

Chris skinned his knee, and he bumped his head.

8. Now Chris can ride to school. He can ride to the park. (or, but)

Now Chris can ride to school, or he can ride to the park.

© Pearson Education, Inc., 3

Home Activity Your child learned about compound sentences. Say two short, related sentences describing your child. Have him or her combine the sentences to make a compound sentence.

Vowel Diphthongs

Classifying Write the list word that belongs with each group.

1. second, minute, ___

2. fry, grill, ___

3. rain, sprinkle, ___

4. journey, trip, ___

5. million, hundred, ___

6. jump, spring, ___

1. **hour**	2. **broil**
3. **shower**	4. **voyage**
5. **thousand**	6. **bounce**

Spelling Words

proud
shower
hour
amount
voyage
choice
avoid
thousand

prowl
employ
bounce
poison
annoy
appoint
broil

Word Meanings Write the list word that means almost the same thing as the underlined word or phrase.

7. Don't <u>bother</u> me.

8. The winners were too <u>boastful</u>.

9. The bill was a large <u>sum</u>.

10. Some spiders use <u>venom</u> to kill their prey.

11. Will you <u>choose</u> an assistant?

12. My cat likes to <u>roam</u> around at night.

13. Summer camps <u>hire</u> many young people.

14. My grandparents <u>keep away from</u> crowds.

15. He was careful in his <u>selection</u> of players.

7. **annoy**

8. **proud**

9. **amount**

10. **poison**

11. **appoint**

12. **prowl**

13. **employ**

14. **avoid**

15. **choice**

© Pearson Education, Inc., 3

School + Home **Home Activity** Your child wrote words with the vowel sounds heard in *out* and *toy*. Ask your child to circle and pronounce *ou, ow, oi,* and *oy* in the list words.

Scoring Rubric: Writing for Tests: Realistic Fiction

	4	3	2	1
Focus/Ideas	Vivid narrative; well-developed characters and setting; realistic	Good narrative; adequate characterization and setting	Narrative lacking focus on characters or setting; somewhat unrealistic	Narrative with no focus on characters or setting; unrealistic
Organization	Clear series of events	Able to follow series of events	Unclear series of events	No series of events
Voice	Voice always matches word choice	Voice mostly matches word choice	Voice rarely matches word choice	Voice never matches word choice
Word Choice	Strong use of precise words	Some use of precise words	Weak use of precise words	No use of precise words; story lifeless
Sentences	Clear sentences of various lengths and types	Sentences of a few lengths and types	Sentences of similar length and type	No attempt at sentences of various lengths and types
Conventions	Few, if any, errors; correct use of compound sentences	Several small errors; correct use of compound sentences	Many errors; weak use of compound sentences	Many serious errors; incorrect or no use of compound sentences

Vocabulary • Prefixes and Suffixes

- Sometimes you may come across words you do not know. You can look to see if the base word has a **prefix** at the beginning or a **suffix** at the end that helps you figure out the meaning.

- The **prefix** un- makes a word mean "not" or "the opposite of." For example, *unhappy* means "not happy."

- The **suffix** -ly makes a word mean "in a ___ way." For example, *slowly* means "in a slow way."

Directions Read each sentence. One word is underlined in each sentence. Circle the prefix *un-* or suffix *-ly* in the underlined word. Then circle the correct meaning of the word.

1. When I (un)loaded the heavy things from the bike, it was easy to ride.
   (took off)   put on

2. I was dee(ply) pleased when I won the prize.
   (a strongly felt way)   very low

3. The boy stood dangerous(ly) close to the edge of the cliff.
   (in an unsafe way)   in an angry way

4. She (un)wrapped the gift and found ice skates inside.
   (took off the cover)   did not open

5. He laughed gleefu(lly) when he won the spelling bee.
   in a silly way   (in a happy way)

6. After the hike, we returned wear(ily) to our tents and went to sleep.
   very quickly   (in a tired way)

7. My father proud(ly) gave me a hug when he saw my report card.
   in a loud way   (in a pleased way)

8. I (un)tied the bundle of coins and gave my sister a dime.
   (opened)   spilled

Home Activity Your child used prefixes and suffixes to figure out the meaning of words. With your child, read a story about a person who gets a part-time job to earn money. Encourage your child to find words that have prefixes and suffixes and to use them to figure out the meaning of unfamiliar words.

Keyboarding

A **computer** can be used as a tool to help you learn. You can use it for research, to visit Web sites, or to send e-mail. Some people use it to keep an online journal, or blog, that others can read. You can use it to type and print a report or story.

You type on the computer, using the **keyboard.** You look at the computer screen, or **monitor.**

A **mouse** helps you move around on the computer screen.

A **cursor** shows you where you are on the screen.

You can put a **CD** or **DVD** into the data disk drive. You can use it to play a game or listen to music.

You may use a computer to access the **Internet.** The Internet is an extremely large network of computers. Using the Internet, people can exchange messages and information all over the world.

monitor

cursor

disk drive

keyboard

mouse

Oliver visited Eugene, Oregon.

Directions Read the information above and study the diagram. Then answer the questions.

1. Which computer part helps you move around on the computer?

   the mouse

2. Which computer part do you use to type?

   the keyboard

3. What does the cursor do?

   It shows you where you are on the screen.

4. What is the disk drive for?

   It is where you put a CD or DVD.

5. What are three things you can use a computer for?

   to do research, to play a game, to listen to music, to send e-mail,

   to visit a Web site, to keep a journal, to access the Internet, to

   print a report or story

© Pearson Education, Inc., 3

School + Home **Home Activity** Your child studied a diagram of a computer and answered questions. Either at home or at the library, explore with your child some of the things a computer is used for, how to use the keyboard and mouse, and some children's Web sites.

Name _____

Vowel Diphthongs

Proofread a Book Report Circle four spelling mistakes in Tom's book report. Write the words correctly. Then write the last sentence, adding the missing word.

> **Book Report**
> My book is about a boy who makes a voyage of two (thosand) miles. He has to (avood) a thief on the (proul) (posion) and other dangers. Finally, he is _____ by a kind man.

1. **thousand**   2. **avoid**
3. **prowl**   4. **poison**
5. **Finally, he is found by a kind man.**

_____

Proofread Words Draw a line through the word that is **not** spelled correctly. Write the word correctly.

6. I'm so **proud prowd** of you!   6. **proud**
7. Shall we **briol broil** the meat?   7. **broil**
8. I have to practice for an **howr hour.**   8. **hour**
9. Let's **bounce bownce** on the trampoline.   9. **bounce**
10. Do **appoint appoynt** three people.   10. **appoint**
11. The **choice choise** was correct.   11. **choice**
12. The pup doesn't mean to **annoy anoiy** you.   12. **annoy**

School + Home **Home Activity** Your child spelled words with the vowel sounds heard in *out* and *toy*. Read a sentence on this page, and have your child spell the list word.

Name _____

Compound Sentences

Directions Read the selection. Then read each question that follows the selection. Decide which is the best answer to each question. Mark the space for the answer you have chosen.

Bicycles in Other Countries

(1) Bicycles are important to people in some countries. (2) People in many places do not have cars. (3) People ride their bicycles to work, and they ride them to the store. (4) Bicycles cost less than cars, but they are not cheap. (5) There are advantages to bicycles, too. (6) Bicycles do not hurt the environment, and they do not cause traffic jams.

1 What is the subject in sentence 1?
- ⬤ Bicycles
- ◯ people
- ◯ countries
- ◯ important

2 What word joins the simple sentences in sentence 3?
- ◯ but
- ◯ or
- ⬤ and
- ◯ too

3 What are the subjects in sentence 4?
- ◯ Bicycles, cars
- ⬤ Bicycles, they
- ◯ cars, cheap
- ◯ hurt, cause

4 Which sentences in the paragraph are compound?
- ◯ 3, 4
- ◯ 3, 4, 5, 6
- ◯ 3, 6
- ⬤ 3, 4, 6

5 What is the predicate in sentence 5?
- ◯ There are advantages
- ⬤ are advantages to bicycles
- ◯ bicycles
- ◯ too

© Pearson Education, Inc., 3

Home Activity Your child prepared for taking tests on compound sentences. Have your child find compound sentences in a magazine and identify the two simple sentences that make up each compound sentence and the word that joins the two sentences.

Name _____

Short Vowels; Syllables VC/CV

Spelling Words				
happen	lettuce	basket	winter	sister
problem	supper	subject	lesson	spelling
napkin	collar	traffic	suggest	puppet

Syllable Match Cross out the extra syllable. Write the list word.

1. bas ~~kin~~ ket
2. les ~~low~~ son
3. hap pen ~~per~~
4. ~~sis~~ col lar
5. sug ~~ject~~ gest
6. ~~let~~ pup pet
7. mon ster ~~ter~~
8. sub ~~per~~ ject
9. ~~hap~~ nap kin
10. traf ~~per~~ fic

1. **basket** _____
2. **lesson** _____
3. **happen** _____
4. **collar** _____
5. **suggest** _____
6. **puppet** _____
7. **monster** _____
8. **subject** _____
9. **napkin** _____
10. **traffic** _____

Opposites Write the list word that completes each phrase.

11. not a **brother,** but a ___
12. not **summer,** but ___
13. not **breakfast,** but ___
14. not **cabbage,** but ___
15. not **math,** but ___

11. **sister** _____
12. **winter** _____
13. **supper** _____
14. **lettuce** _____
15. **spelling** _____

© Pearson Education, Inc., 3

Home Activity Your child is learning to spell words with short vowel sounds with the spelling pattern VC/CV. Choose a word. Write it, but leave out two letters, putting a blank in their places. Have your child write the missing letters and then write the whole word.

Sentences

Directions Read the groups of words. Write the group of words that is a sentence.

1. We play many computer games.
   Other kinds of games, too.
   We play many computer games.

2. High winds and heavy rain.
   A big storm blows power lines down.
   A big storm blows power lines down.

3. We don't need power for board games.
   Played checkers all day.
   We don't need power for board games.

4. Some kids got bored.
   No power to play video games.
   Some kids got bored.

5. Finished an art project.
   My friends painted a mural.
   My friends painted a mural.

Directions Decide whether each group of words is a sentence or a fragment.
If it is a sentence, write the sentence with correct capitalization and punctuation.
If it is a fragment, write *F*.

6. we can play tag and soccer outdoors
   We can play tag and soccer outdoors.

7. people on the baseball field
   F

8. looked everywhere for a battery
   F

9. they discovered new games during the storm
   They discovered new games during the storm.

Name _____

Plural -s, -es, -ies

Spelling Words				
pennies	inches	plants	families	bodies
glasses	wishes	pockets	lists	copies
parties	bunches	crashes	supplies	pencils

Word Changes Change the clue word. Write the new word. Then write the plural of the new word to make a list word.

	Clue	**Change**	**New Word**	**Plural**
1.	dish	**d** to **w**	wish	wishes
2.	rocket	**r** to **p**	pocket	pockets
3.	lunch	**l** to **b**	bunch	bunches
4.	mist	**m** to **l**	list	lists
5.	pass	**p** to **gl**	glass	glasses
6.	trash	**tr** to **cr**	crash	crashes
7.	ink	**k** to **ch**	inch	inches
8.	stencil	**st** to **p**	pencil	pencils
9.	grant	**gr** to **pl**	plant	plants

Ending Equations Use each word equation. Write the list word.

$$library - y + ies = libraries$$

10. $penny - y + ies =$ __pennies__

11. $family - y + ies =$ __families__

12. $body - y + ies =$ __bodies__

13. $party - y + ies =$ __parties__

14. $copy - y + ies =$ __copies__

15. $supply - y + ies =$ __supplies__

Home Activity Your child is learning to spell plurals. To practice together, write the base word of a list word. Ask your child to write the plural and to circle the letters that spell the plural form.

Subjects and Predicates

Directions Underline the complete subject of each sentence.

1. <u>Mom</u> needs help around the house.

2. <u>My little brother</u> needs attention.

3. <u>Everyone in the family</u> needs something.

4. <u>Each person</u> helps the others.

5. <u>All of us</u> think of the needs of others.

Directions Write the complete predicate of each sentence.

6. Julie cooks soup for dinner.

cooks soup for dinner

7. I wash the car with Dad.

wash the car with Dad

8. My brother picks up his toys.

picks up his toys

9. Each family member has a special job.

has a special job

10. Life at my house goes more smoothly this way.

goes more smoothly this way

© Pearson Education, Inc., 3

Base Words and Endings

Spelling Words				
using	getting	easiest	swimming	heavier
greatest	pleased	emptied	leaving	worried
strangest	freezing	funniest	angrier	shopped

Word Pairs Write the missing list word. Use the underlined word as a clue.

1. Sara's joke is <u>funny</u>, but Diego's is the ___ I've heard. **funniest**

2. A hippo is <u>heavy</u>, but an elephant is ___. **heavier**

3. That picture is <u>strange</u>, but this one is the ___ of all. **strangest**

4. Brent is <u>angry</u>, but David is ___. **angrier**

5. Math is <u>easy</u>, but Spelling is the ___ of all. **easiest**

6. Many movies are <u>great</u>, but this movie is the ___ ever. **greatest**

Analogies Write the list word that completes each phrase.

7. **Sit** is to **sitting** as **get** is to **getting**

8. **Ship** is to **shipped** as **shop** is to **shopped**

9. **Run** is to **running** as **swim** is to **swimming**

10. **Try** is to **tried** as **empty** is to **emptied**

11. **Hurry** is to **hurried** as **worry** is to **worried**

12. **Sneeze** is to **sneezing** as **freeze** is to **freezing**

13. **Come** is to **coming** as **leave** is to **leaving**

14. **Save** is to **saving** as **use** is to **using**

15. **Amuse** is to **amused** as **please** is to **pleased**

© Pearson Education, Inc., 3

Home Activity Your child is spelling words that end in *-ed, -ing, -er*, and *-est*. To practice at home, spell each word together. Have your child say which ending is used at the end of the word.

Declarative and Interrogative Sentences

Directions Write *statement* if the sentence is a statement. Write *question* if the sentence is a question.

1. Fish is a tasty, healthful food.   **statement**
2. What is your favorite kind of fish?   **question**
3. Fish tastes good with all kinds of spices.   **statement**
4. How shall we cook this big trout?   **question**
5. We can make tacos or soup with it.   **statement**

Directions Write the sentences. Add the correct end punctuation. Write *S* if the sentence is a statement and *Q* if the sentence is a question.

6. Can we fish in this pond

    Can we fish in this pond? Q

7. Has anyone caught anything

    Has anyone caught anything? Q

8. The fish leap out of the water

    The fish leap out of the water. S

9. There are big fish and little fish

    There are big fish and little fish. S

10. Did you see that colorful fish

    Did you see that colorful fish? Q

11. It is tugging on my line

    It is tugging on my line. S

12. How much does it weigh

    How much does it weigh? Q

Vowel Digraphs

Spelling Words				
clean	agree	teeth	dream	grain
coach	display	window	shadow	cheese
peach	braid	Sunday	float	thrown

Word Search Circle the list word hidden in each puzzle. Write the word.

1. b g f l o a t m p   **float**

2. h c l e a n d w n   **clean**

3. d j r s h a d o w t   **shadow**

4. g t h r o w n k s   **thrown**

5. g r a i n m h s   **grain**

6. y r a g r e e m v t   **agree**

7. c w i n d o w g n s   **window**

8. f n p c o a c h t z   **coach**

Word Clues Write the list word that means the same as the phrase.

9. A fuzzy fruit   **peach**

10. The day before Monday   **Sunday**

11. What is needed to chew   **teeth**

12. A food made from milk   **cheese**

13. To show something   **display**

14. Something you may do asleep   **dream**

15. A way to fix the hair   **braid**

© Pearson Education, Inc., 3

Home Activity Your child is learning to spell words with long vowel digraphs (letter combinations that stand for long vowel sounds). Have your child write each word. Together, circle the vowel pairs in each word that make up the vowel digraph.

Imperative and Exclamatory Sentences

Directions Write *command* if the sentence is a command, or imperative sentence. Write *exclamation* if the sentence is an exclamation, or exclamatory sentence.

1. Please buy some fruit. **command**

2. What big strawberries those are! **exclamation**

3. Try some grapefruit. **command**

4. The peaches are delicious! **exclamation**

Directions Write the sentences. Add the correct end punctuation. Write *C* if the sentence is a command and *E* if the sentence is an exclamation.

5. Go to the supermarket

Go to the supermarket. C

6. Get food for lunch, and buy some apples

Get food for lunch, and buy some apples. C

7. What a big choice there is

What a big choice there is! E

8. Don't forget the lettuce

Don't forget the lettuce. C

9. This turkey tastes too spicy

This turkey tastes too spicy! E

10. Find some American cheese

Find some American cheese. C

11. I like sandwiches, and I can make my own

I like sandwiches, and I can make my own! E

12. My lunch will be great

My lunch will be great! E

Vowel Diphthongs

Spelling Words				
proud	shower	hour	amount	voyage
choice	avoid	thousand	prowl	employ
bounce	poison	annoy	appoint	broil

Words in Context Write the missing list word.

1. During the sea **voyage** the ship was in a storm.

2. The play lasted about one **hour** .

3. One way to cook meat is to **broil** it.

4. The cat liked to **prowl** for mice.

5. I took a bath, not a **shower** .

6. Try to **avoid** that busy street.

Alphabetizing Write each group of words in ABC order.

choice   amount   bounce

7. **amount**

8. **bounce**

9. **choice**

employ   poison   appoint

10. **appoint**

11. **employ**

12. **poison**

thousand   annoy   proud

13. **annoy**

14. **proud**

15. **thousand**

© Pearson Education, Inc., 3

Home Activity Your child has been learning to spell words with the vowel sounds in *out* and *toy*. Divide a sheet of paper into two columns. Have your child write words with the vowel sound in *out* in one column and words with the vowel sound in *toy* in the other column.

Compound Sentences

Directions Write *S* if the sentence is a simple sentence. Write *C* if the sentence is a compound sentence.

1. Many people use bicycles for their jobs. **S**

2. Some people deliver messages on their bikes. **S**

3. James carries flowers on his bike, and Dave carries groceries. **C**

4. Dave prefers heavy loads, but it is hard work. **C**

5. Bicycles are fun, and they are also useful. **C**

Directions Use the word *and, but,* or *or* to combine each pair of sentences. Write the compound sentence.

6. Kevin worked hard. He saved money for a skateboard.
   Kevin worked hard, and he saved money for a skateboard.

7. The store had many skateboards. Kevin wanted a special one.
   The store had many skateboards, but Kevin wanted a special one.

8. You buy a skateboard from the store. You order one from a catalog.
   You buy a skateboard from the store, or you order one from a catalog.

9. Kevin found the perfect skateboard in a catalog. He ordered it right away.
   Kevin found the perfect skateboard in a catalog, and he ordered it right away.

10. Kevin waited a long time for his skateboard. It was worth the wait.
    Kevin waited a long time for his skateboard, but it was worth the wait.

Name _____

Notes for a Personal Narrative

Directions Fill in the graphic organizer with information about the event or experience that you plan to write about.

Summary

What happened?	**Answers should include details about each part of the student's personal narrative.**
When?	
Where?	
Who was there?	

Details

Beginning

Middle

End

Words That Tell About *You*

Directions How did you feel about your experience at the beginning, middle, and end? Choose one or two words from the word bank to describe each part of your experience. Then add details that *show* readers each feeling.

worried	excited	proud	sad
disappointed	embarrassed	satisfied	curious
puzzled	anxious	delighted	upset

Beginning **Answers should be based on adjectives from the word bank and elaborated with details that show feelings the adjectives suggest.**

Middle _____

_____

_____

_____

End _____

_____

_____

_____

© Pearson Education, Inc., 3

Combining Sentences

When you write, you can combine short, choppy simple sentences to make compound sentences. The two sentences you combine must make sense together. You can combine the sentences using the words *and, but,* or *or.*

Directions Use the word in ( ) to combine the two sentences. Remember to capitalize the first word of the new sentence and to replace the first period with a comma.

1. (but) Many huge weeds grew in the garden. I pulled each weed out.

Many huge weeds grew in the garden, but I pulled each weed out.

2. (and) The job was hard. It took me all afternoon.

The job was hard, and it took me all afternoon.

3. (or) Pull out the weed's root. The weed will grow back.

Pull out the weed's root, or the weed will grow back.

4. (and) I earned five dollars. I felt good about my hard work.

I earned five dollars, and I felt good about my hard work.

5. (but) I was tired. The garden looked great.

I was tired, but the garden looked great.

Editing 1

Directions Edit these sentences. Look for errors in spelling, grammar, and mechanics. Use proofreading marks to show the corrections.

Proofreading Marks	
Delete (Take out)	⟋͡ɔ
Add	∧
Spelling	⬭
Uppercase letter	≡
Lowercase letter	/

1. My mom and ~~me~~ decided to adopt a dog from the granville Animal Shelter.
   I (added) / **G** ≡

2. I was so excited I ~~has~~ wanted a dog forever.
   ! / **have**

3. But Mom said, "Youll have to help pay for the dog's (supplys)."
   ' / **supplies**

4. So i started a dog walking business in ~~their~~ neighborhood.
   ≡ / **our**

5. The neighbors listened to me as I ~~explains~~ my plan and my (gole).
   explained / **goal**

6. Soon little dogs, big dogs, and medium-sized dogs ~~was~~ pulling me around the
   block (evry) day after school.
   were / **every**

7. I made enough money, to buy (too) bowls, some dog food, a bed, a leash, and a
   collar, for my new dog.
   two

8. When we brought ranger home for the first time, I wanted to jump for joy!
   R ≡

Now you'll edit the draft of your personal narrative. Then you'll use your revised and edited draft to make a final copy of your narrative. Finally, you'll share your written work with your audience.

© Pearson Education, Inc., 3

Syllables V/CV, VC/V

Directions Circle each word in the box with the **long vowel** sound in the **first syllable**.
Underline each word in the box with the **short vowel** sound in the **first syllable**. Then
write each word in the correct column.

> (lady)   lemon   finish   (baby)   (robot)
>
> panel   (spider)   polish   (moment)   credit

long vowel

1. _____ **lady** _____

2. _____ **baby** _____

3. _____ **robot** _____

4. _____ **spider** _____

5. _____ **moment** _____

short vowel

6. _____ **lemon** _____

7. _____ **finish** _____

8. _____ **panel** _____

9. _____ **polish** _____

10. _____ **credit** _____

Directions Circle each word in the box with the **long vowel** sound in the **first syllable**.
Underline each word in the box with the **short vowel** sound in the **first syllable**.
Then use the words to complete the sentences. Write each word on the line.

> menu   (female)   (motor)   seven   (zebra)

_____ **female** _____   11. A _____ horse is called a mare.

_____ **zebra** _____   12. A _____ has black and white stripes.

_____ **menu** _____   13. A _____ is a list of food.

_____ **seven** _____   14. There are _____ little chicks.

_____ **motor** _____   15. A _____ is an engine.

Home Activity Your child identified words that have a long or short vowel sound in the first syllable.
Ask your child to read the long and short vowel words he or she circled or underlined on the page above.
Help your child use some of these words to write a story.

© Pearson Education, Inc., 3

Main Idea and Details

- The **topic** is what a piece of writing is about. The **main idea** is the most important idea about the **topic**. **Supporting details** are small pieces of information about the **main idea**.

Directions Read the following passage. Complete the graphic organizer below.

What if you wanted to cross Antarctica? What would you need to take along?

You would need warm clothes, such as a parka and fur-lined boots. You'd also need bulky socks, thick pants, and the warmest mittens you could find!

Don't forget to bring your own food. You could warm frozen casseroles over a fire and eat nuts and snack bars during the day.

At night you'll need a sleeping bag. Take the warmest one you can find so you are sure to keep warm all night long!

1. Topic

Crossing Antarctica

2. Main Idea

You need to take the right things with you.

3. Detail warm clothes

4. Detail food

5. Detail sleeping bag

© Pearson Education, Inc., 3

School + Home

Home Activity Your child found the topic, main idea, and details in a passage. Read a nonfiction book to your child. To find the topic, ask, "In one or two words, what is the book all about?" To find the main idea, help your child make a sentence that tells the most important part about the topic. Then ask your child to list several details that tell more about the main idea.

Writing • Cinquains

Key Features of Cinquains

- five-line poems that begin and end with a single word
- usually commas in the second and third line, separating the words

Play

Puppy
Silly, happy
Running, jumping, playing
Now it's time for
Sleep

1. Name one key feature that you see that makes this poem a cinquain.

   It begins and ends with one word.

2. What images of puppies do you see in your mind when you read "Play"?

   Responses will vary but might include: cute little puppy romping

   and playing with toys and sleeping.

Vocabulary

> ## Check the Words You Know
>
> ___hatch   ___pecks
> ___snuggles   ___preen
> ___flippers   ___frozen
> ___cuddles

Directions Choose the vocabulary word from the box and write it next to its meaning.

pecks   1. taps at

frozen   2. turned into solid ice

flippers   3. limbs used for swimming

preen   4. to make yourself clean and neat

cuddles or snuggles   5. curls up comfortably

Directions Write the word on the line that fits the meaning of the sentence.

6. Mother **cuddles or snuggles** the little baby penguin.

7. The chick is about to **hatch** out of its egg.

8. Penguins use their **flippers** to help them swim.

9. The penguins **preen** their young until their feathers are clean.

10. It was so cold that we could ice skate on the **frozen** lake.

Write a News Report

On a separate sheet of paper, tell what happens when a penguin chick hatches. Describe the setting and the sequence of events using as many vocabulary words as possible.
Students should use vocabulary describing an Antarctic setting and sequence of events as a penguin chick hatches.

Home Activity Your child identified and used vocabulary words from *Penguin Chick*. Read a story or a nonfiction article about penguins with your child. Discuss the story using this week's vocabulary words.

© Pearson Education, Inc., 3

Common and Proper Nouns

A **common noun** names any person, place, or thing. A **proper noun** names a particular person, place, or thing. Proper nouns begin with capital letters. The names of days, months, places, and holidays are proper nouns. Historical periods and special events are also proper nouns.

Common Nouns	You can see <u>penguins</u> at some <u>zoos</u>.
Proper Nouns	On <u>Labor Day</u>, a penguin from <u>Africa</u> was displayed at the <u>New York State Fair</u>.

Capitalize each important word in a proper noun: Fourth of July, Civil War.

Directions Write *C* if the underlined noun is a common noun. Write *P* if the underlined noun is a proper noun.

1. There are not many emperor penguins in our <u>country</u>. **C**

2. A sea park in <u>San Diego</u> has an emperor penguin. **P**

3. Jon went to the zoo on <u>Independence Day</u>. **P**

4. He saw penguins and other unusual <u>animals</u>. **C**

5. <u>Whales</u> and penguins are popular sea park attractions. **C**

Directions Underline the common nouns and circle the proper nouns in the sentences.

6. (Alaska) became a <u>state</u> on (January) 3, 1959.

7. <u>Penguins</u> do not come from the (United States.)

8. <u>Seals</u> and <u>polar bears</u> like the cold <u>weather</u>.

9. The (Millers) will visit (Juneau) at (Thanksgiving.)

10. The (Iditarod) (Trail Sled Dog Race) is held in (March.)

Home Activity Your child learned about common and proper nouns. Have your child write the names of friends and family members and explain why the names are proper nouns.

Syllables V/CV, VC/V

Missing Words Write the missing list word.

Spelling Words

finish
pilot
even
wagon
music
silent
rapid
female

lemon
pupil
focus
robot
tulip
camel
salad

1. It is easy to __focus__ this camera.

2. The __pilot__ of the plane has white hair.

3. My flute teacher has a new __pupil__ .

4. The mother cat had two male kittens and one __female__ kitten.

5. This type of __camel__ has two humps on its back.

6. You will be able to swim __even__ better after a little rest.

7. The song had a __rapid__ beat.

8. I pulled the children in a __wagon__ .

Syllables Find the list word that fits each word. Write the first syllable, the second syllable, and the complete word.

	First Syllable	Second Syllable	Base Word
9. song	mu	sic	music
10. flower	tu	lip	tulip
11. fruit	lem	on	lemon
12. end	fin	ish	finish
13. vegetables	sal	ad	salad
14. quiet	si	lent	silent
15. machine	ro	bot	robot

© Pearson Education, Inc., 3

Home Activity Your child divided long vowel and short vowel words into syllables and wrote them. Say a list word. Spell the first syllable, and have your child spell the second.

Writing • Diamante Poems

Key Features of Diamante Poems

- seven lines
- first and last lines have one noun, usually with opposite meanings
- second and sixth lines have adjectives
- third and fifth lines have verbs (*-ed* or *-ing*)
- fourth line has four nouns

Plants and Animals

Plants
Leafy, healthy
Watering, feeding, growing
Gardens, yards, forests, jungles
Running, hunting, surviving
Brave, wild
Animals

1. Name one key feature that you see that makes this poem a diamante.

It begins and ends with one noun; second and sixth lines have two adjectives each.

2. What images of animals do you see in your mind when you read "Plants and Animals"?

Responses will vary but might include: deer or raccoons in a forest; monkeys in trees.

© Pearson Education, Inc., 3

Vocabulary • Synonyms

- Sometimes you come across a word you don't know. The author may give you a clue about its meaning. The clue may be a **synonym**, a word that means the same thing.
- Look for **synonyms** to figure out the meaning of unfamiliar words.

Directions Read the sentences. One word is underlined. Circle the synonym of the underlined word. Write the meaning of the underlined word on the line.

1. The chick pecks at the inside of the egg. After the chick taps a hole in the egg, the chick can leave the egg.

   to strike at something with a beak

2. She made an error in her spelling, so she fixed the mistake.

   something that is done wrong

3. Penguins use their flippers or their fins to swim quickly.

   broad, flat body parts used for swimming

4. Penguins preen their chicks by cleaning and brushing them with their beaks.

   to smooth with a beak; to dress or groom carefully

5. The penguin chick must stay on its mother's feet to remain warm.

   continue to be

6. Penguins hunt creatures of the sea, such as the tiny animals called krill.

   any living person or animal

7. The newborn chick was very fluffy, with soft and fuzzy feathers all over it.

   covered with soft feathers or hair

8. Like human children who love hugs, penguin chicks love to cuddle.

   to lie close and comfortably

Home Activity Your child used context clues such as synonyms to figure out the meaning of new words. Read a story together and encourage your child to find synonyms in the text that help to figure out the meaning of unfamiliar words.

© Pearson Education, Inc., 3

Dictionary/Glossary

A **dictionary** is a book of words and their meanings. A **glossary** is a section of a book with a list of difficult words and their meanings from the book. A glossary is usually found at the end of a book. In both a dictionary and a glossary, words are listed in alphabetical order. **Guide words** are printed in large dark type at the top of each dictionary or glossary page. They show the first and last entry words on the page.

Directions Use the dictionary page to answer the questions.

romp • roost

rook, *n.*
  1 a large black European bird related to a crow, that lives in large flocks
  2 a cheat
  3 *v.* to cheat or trick someone

rookery, *n.* a breeding place for certain animals or birds, such as seals or penguins
rookie, *n.* a beginner, as on a police force or in a sport

1. Which word can be used to describe a baseball player during his or her first year on the team?

rookie

2. Which entry word or words can be used as a verb?

rook

3. Find the entry word *rook.* Which meaning of *rook* is used in this sentence? *The rook flew into the tree.*

a large black European bird related to a crow, that lives in large flocks

4. What are the guide words on this page?

romp and roost

5. Which of these words could also be found on this dictionary page: *round, roll, roof, rock?*

roof

Home Activity Your child read entries in a dictionary and used them to answer questions. Have your child practice looking up words in a dictionary or a glossary with you.

Syllables V/CV, VC/V

Spelling Words				
finish	pilot	even	wagon	music
silent	rapid	female	lemon	pupil
focus	robot	tulip	camel	salad

Proofread an Announcement Circle five misspelled words in this announcement about a special concert. Write the words correctly. Then write the word with a capitalization error.

Don't miss Friday's concert! The (musik) will focus on early america. You will (evin) hear a jug band. The (femail) group will sing (favorit) songs about (wagen) trains, the Gold Rush, and California.

Frequently Misspelled Words
favorite
before
pretty

1. **music**   2. **even**   3. **female**

4. **favorite**   5. **wagon**   6. **America**

Proofread Words Fill in the circle to show the correctly spelled word. Write the word.

7. ○ saled   ● salad   ○ salade   7. **salad**
8. ○ kamel   ● camel   ○ camal   8. **camel**
9. ● silent   ○ silant   ○ sylent   9. **silent**
10. ○ leman   ○ lemen   ● lemon   10. **lemon**
11. ○ finash   ● finish   ○ fenish   11. **finish**
12. ○ rowbot   ○ robat   ● robot   12. **robot**

© Pearson Education, Inc., 3

Home Activity Your child identified misspelled multi-syllable words with long and short vowels. Ask your child to explain how to divide a multi-syllable word (immediately after a long vowel; after the consonant that follows a short vowel).

Common and Proper Nouns

Directions Read the selection. Then read each question that follows the selection. Decide which is the best answer to each question. Mark the space for the answer you have chosen.

Penguins in America

(1) There are not many penguins in our country. (2) Penguins do not come from the United States. (3) They like colder weather. (4) A sea park in San Diego has penguins. (5) John went to the sea park on Independence Day. (6) He saw penguins and other strange animals. (7) Penguins remain a very popular attraction at sea parks and zoos.

1 What is the common noun in sentence 2?

- ⬭ the United States
- ⬭ come
- ⬭ from
- ⬬ Penguins

2 What is the proper noun in sentence 4?

- ⬭ He
- ⬭ penguins
- ⬬ San Diego
- ⬭ has

3 Which group names the proper noun(s) in sentence 5?

- ⬭ Independence Day
- ⬬ John, Independence Day
- ⬭ John, sea park, Independence Day
- ⬭ John

4 What are the proper nouns in sentence 6?

- ⬭ penguins
- ⬭ strange animals
- ⬭ He
- ⬬ There are no proper nouns.

5 What proper noun could replace *sea park* in sentence 7?

- ⬭ wildlife areas
- ⬬ Ocean World
- ⬭ nature preserves
- ⬭ tourist destinations

Home Activity Your child prepared for taking tests on common and proper nouns. On a drive, say the names of things you pass, such as *a street* and *Spring Creek*. Have your child identify which are common nouns and which are proper nouns.

Final Syllable -*le*

Directions Write the two syllables that make up each word on the lines.

1. __gig__ + __gle__ = giggle

2. __mid__ + __dle__ = middle

3. __ti__ + __tle__ = title

4. __nee__ + __dle__ = needle

5. __mar__ + __ble__ = marble

6. __ea__ + __gle__ = eagle

7. __bub__ + __ble__ = bubble

8. __sad__ + __dle__ = saddle

9. __can__ + __dle__ = candle

10. __tur__ + __tle__ = turtle

Directions Choose the word in the box that matches each picture. Write the word on the line. Then draw a line to divide it into its syllables.

| table   poodle   puzzle   rattle   cattle |

11. ___cat/tle___

12. ___poo/dle___

13. ___ta/ble___

14. ___rat/tle___

15. ___puz/zle___

© Pearson Education, Inc., 3

Home Activity Your child wrote words that end with the final syllable sound heard in *handle*. Help your child make a list of ten more words that end with -*le* (such as *little, juggle,* and *nibble*). Work with your child to write a silly poem using some of the -*le* words from your child's list and from the page above.

Compare and Contrast

- **Compare** by telling how two or more things are alike or different.
- **Contrast** by telling only how two or more things are different.

Directions Read the following story.

Ron and Blake wanted a puppy, but Dad always said, "A dog is hard work." One day Dad surprised them. He said, "If you two can find a solution to the puppy care problem, we'll visit a breeder tomorrow."

Ron and Blake thought fast.

"Dogs need exercise," said Ron. "I'll take our puppy for walks."

"Dogs need love," said Blake. "I'll pet our puppy."

"Dogs make a mess," said Ron, "but I won't mind cleaning up after our puppy."

"Good!" smiled Blake. "And I'll feed it and keep its water dish filled."

"You boys have a good plan," Dad agreed. "Tomorrow we'll get our new pup."

Directions Fill in the chart to compare and contrast Ron and Blake.

Compare and Contrast	
Ron	**Blake**
wants a puppy will help care for a puppy will walk the puppy will clean up after the puppy	wants a puppy will help care for a puppy will pet the puppy will feed and water the puppy

Home Activity Your child compared and contrasted two story characters. Read a story together. Discuss the characters with your child by comparing and contrasting them.

Writing • Fairy Tale

Key Features of a Fairy Tale

- imaginary story that may include heroic acts
- often begins "Once upon a time … "
- often ends " … and they lived happily ever after"
- characters are usually all good or all bad

The Skunk and the Mice

Once upon a time, in a quiet neighborhood, there lived a skunk. He was lonely. Each day, Skunk rested in a hole dug under the porch steps. Each evening, Skunk crept out to search for food.

There were others living under the porch steps. A group of mice lived there. All day long, they chattered and scurried about. At night they went out all together to find food. Skunk thought they looked very happy. One night, he asked if he could join them.

"No way," said the leader of the mice. "We are mice. You would make a funny looking mouse. You cannot come with us."

It so happened that cool weather was coming, and food was getting harder to find. The mice still went out at night, but they didn't find much to eat. Skunk became hungry, too. Once again he asked the mice if he could join them.

"No," said the leader of the mice. "We've told you before, and we'll tell you again. No! No! No!"

That night came a terrible storm. Snow and freezing rain came down in buckets. The mice huddled together, terrified of the sounds of the whipping wind. "How will we get food now!" they cried.

Skunk, without waiting a moment, went out in the storm to search for food for the mice. The cold wind almost blew him over, but he stayed close to the ground as best he could. Skunk finally found some morsels of food, and he rushed back to the porch.

When Skunk returned, the mice were so grateful for the food that they made him a special member of their family.

And they all lived happily ever after.

© Pearson Education, Inc., 3

1. What problems does the Skunk have?

He is lonely. The mice won't let him be part of their group. He is hungry.

2. What happens that solves these problems?

Skunk braves the storm to find food. The mice become his friends.

Vocabulary

> ### Check the Words You Know
>
> ___adorable   ___mature
> ___compassionate   ___mention
> ___exactly   ___trophies
> ___iguana

Directions Fill in the blank with the word from the box that fits the meaning of the sentence.

1. Look at this _____**adorable**_____ little kitten.

2. It is _____**exactly**_____ the kind of pet I want.

3. My brother would rather have a spiky _____**iguana**_____.

4. But a _____**mature**_____ cat is much smaller than a grown-up lizard.

5. I'll be sure to _____**mention**_____ that to Mom when I ask for the kitten.

Directions Draw a line from the word to its meaning.

6. compassionate   to talk briefly about someone or something

7. trophies   precisely

8. mature   with sympathy; wanting to help

9. exactly   fully grown; adult

10. mention   awards

Write a Speech

Imagine that you work in an animal shelter. Choose an animal that might be in the shelter and write a speech you could use to convince someone to adopt the animal. Use as many vocabulary words from this week as you can.

Speech should be about a shelter animal and include vocabulary words.

Home Activity Your child identified and used vocabulary words from *I Wanna Iguana*. Talk about pets you and your child have known. Use the vocabulary words on this page.

© Pearson Education, Inc., 3

Singular and Plural Nouns

A **singular noun** names only one person, place, or thing. A **plural noun** names more than one person, place, or thing.

Singular Nouns   The <u>boy</u> wanted a pet.

Plural Nouns   <u>Iguanas</u> and other <u>lizards</u> live in <u>deserts</u>.

Most nouns add *-s* to form the plural. Add *-es* to a noun that ends in *ch, sh, s, ss,* or *x: lunches, dishes, buses, dresses, boxes*. When a noun ends in a consonant and *y*, change the *y* to *i* and add *-es: bodies*.

Directions Write *S* if the underlined noun is a singular noun. Write *P* if the underlined noun is a plural noun.

1. Many <u>animals</u> live in the desert. ___**P**___

2. The desert is a very dry <u>place</u>. ___**S**___

3. People often keep <u>pets</u>. ___**P**___

4. Dogs and <u>cats</u> are popular. ___**P**___

5. A pet <u>store</u> sells food and supplies. ___**S**___

Directions Write the plural nouns in each sentence.

6. Many lizards eat bugs and vegetables.

lizards, bugs, vegetables

7. Snakes and buzzards live in the desert.

Snakes, buzzards

8. The boy and his mother write notes.

notes

9. He thinks iguanas are cuter than hamsters.

iguanas, hamsters

Final Syllable -*le*

Spelling Words				
handle	trouble	simple	people	middle
table	little	gentle	poodle	pickle
noodle	saddle	juggle	uncle	riddle

Missing Words Write the missing list word.

1. If you tease the dog, you will get in __**trouble**__ .

2. My uncle bought a new leather __**saddle**__ for his horse.

3. Would you like a dill __**pickle**__ on your sandwich?

4. Please set the vase in the __**middle**__ of the table.

5. She bought some dog shampoo for her __**poodle**__ .

6. Mom makes chicken __**noodle**__ soup for me when I am sick.

7. Have you heard the __**riddle**__ about a chicken crossing the road?

8. The __**handle**__ on Billy's lunchbox was broken.

9. The clown could __**juggle**__ five balls at a time.

10. I visited my aunt and __**uncle**__ last summer.

11. One of my jobs at home is setting the __**table**__ before dinner.

12. How many __**people**__ came to the soccer game?

Antonyms Write the list word that means the opposite.

13. big __**little**__

14. difficult __**simple**__

15. rough __**gentle**__

Home Activity Your child wrote words that end in -*le*. If your child is confident with the list words, have him or her try to use two rhyming list words in a sentence.

Scoring Rubric: Fairy Tale

	4	3	2	1
Focus/Ideas	Exciting story with interesting characters; amazing or heroic events	Good story with developed characters; somewhat amazing or heroic events	Story has some focus on characters; events are not very amazing or heroic	Story has no focus on characters; events are not amazing or heroic
Organization	Clear order of events	Can follow order of events	Unclear order of events	No order of events
Voice	Writer shows interest in the story and the characters	Writer shows some interest in the story and the characters	Writer is not interested in the story or characters	Writer makes no effort to show interest in the story or characters
Word Choice	Strong use of vivid verbs to bring the story to life	Good try at using vivid verbs	Poor use of vivid verbs; story is dull	No effort made to use vivid verbs
Sentences	Clear sentences of different lengths and types	Sentences of a few lengths and types	Sentences of similar length and type	No variety of sentence length and type
Conventions	Few, if any, errors; correct use of singular and plural nouns	Several small errors; use of singular and plural nouns	Many errors; weak use of singular and plural nouns	Many serious errors; incorrect or no use of singular and plural nouns

© Pearson Education, Inc., 3

Vocabulary • Unfamiliar Words

- Sometimes you can figure out the meaning of a word by looking at the words and sentences around it.
- Context clues are words around an **unfamiliar word** that help you figure out its meaning.

Directions Read the following passage about a girl starting a new school. Then answer the questions. Look for context clues as you read.

Cassie hesitated. Then she smoothed her dark red hair, took a deep breath and opened the door to her new classroom.

"You must be Cassie," the teacher said, smiling. "I'm Ms. Roberts. Welcome to South Street School."

Ms. Roberts showed Cassie where to hang her jacket. Then she introduced her to a girl with short black hair.

"Cassie," said Ms. Roberts, "this is Becky. She will help you today."

Becky grinned. "Hi," she said, grinning.

"Wow, your hair is pretty. I always wanted auburn hair."

Cassie smiled. She was shy about having red hair, but Becky seemed nice.

Just then a girl and boy at the computer began arguing. "No," the girl said in an angry voice. "I won't let you. It's still my turn."

"Marsha, what did I say to you about being obstinate?" Ms. Roberts said firmly.

Becky whispered to Cassie. "Don't mind Marsha. When she doesn't want to do something, she can be very stubborn."

1. What word does Becky use to describe Cassie's hair? **auburn**

2. What do you think the word means? What clues tell you? **dark red; clues—**

describes her hair as dark red; says she is shy about having red hair

3. What does *introduced* mean? What clues tell you?

made two people known to each other; clues—"Cassie, this is Becky."

4. What does *argued* mean in this passage? What clues help you know?

had a difference of opinion; clues—"No, I won't let you"; angry voice

5. What do you think *obstinate* means? What does Becky say that helps you know?

stubborn; Becky says Marsha can be very stubborn.

Home Activity Your child used context clues to figure out the meanings of new words. Work with your child to identify unfamiliar words in an article and to find context clues to help with the understanding of new words. Confirm the meanings with your child.

Maps

- **Maps** are drawings of places such as cities, states, and countries.
- A map key tells you what the symbols on the map stand for.

Directions Study the map of Texas below. Use it to answer the questions.

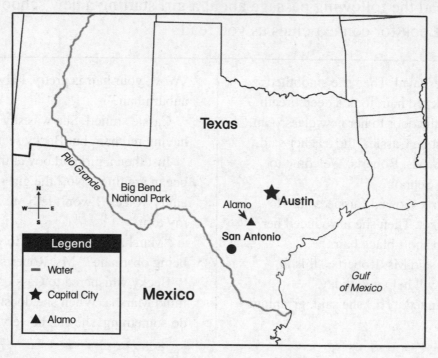

1. What natural landform is the boundary between Texas and Mexico?

Rio Grande

2. What is the capital city of Texas?

Austin

3. What body of water is just east of southern Texas?

Gulf of Mexico

4. In what city can you find the Alamo?

San Antonio

5. How do you think Big Bend National Park got its name?

It is right beside a big bend in the Rio Grande.

Home Activity Your child identified important landmarks on a map of Texas. Study a map of Texas with your child. Work together to locate places you may have visited.

© Pearson Education, Inc., 3

Final Syllable *-le*

Proofread a Biography Circle four spelling mistakes in the biography Ned wrote about his uncle. Write the words correctly. Add a comma to the compound sentence.

When my (unkle) came to America, he had very little money. He had to (juggel) two jobs to keep food on the table. Some kind (peeple) helped him⌄and he never complained about having more trouble than he could (handel).

1. __uncle__	2. __juggle__
3. __people__	4. __handle__

Proofread Words Circle the word that is spelled correctly. Write the word.

5. (simple)	simpel	5. __simple__	
6. (middle)	midle	6. __middle__	
7. gentol	(gentle)	7. __gentle__	
8. (poodle)	poodel	8. __poodle__	
9. (riddle)	ridle	9. __riddle__	
10. noodel	(noodle)	10. __noodle__	
11. pikle	(pickle)	11. __pickle__	
12. (saddle)	saddel	12. __saddle__	

Spelling Words

handle
trouble
simple
people
middle
table
little
gentle

poodle
pickle
noodle
saddle
juggle
uncle
riddle

Frequently Misspelled Words

little
people

School + Home   **Home Activity** Your child identified misspelled words that end in *-le*. Say a word that means almost the same thing as one of the list words and have your child name and spell the list word.

Singular and Plural Nouns

Directions Read the selection. Then read each question that follows the selection. Decide which is the best answer to each question. Mark the space for the answer you have chosen.

Alex and His Pet

(1) Alex and his mom write many letteres. (2) Alex wrote that iguanas are quiet animals. (3) They are common pets. (4) He has won soccer trophyes.

(5) Alex's mom wrote that a pet owner has many _____ . (6) Some _____ grow very large. (7) Puppyes are my favorite pet.

1 What change, if any, should be made to sentence 1?

- ⬭ Change *letteres* to **letteries**
- ⬬ Change *letteres* to **letters**
- ⬭ Change *letteres* to **letterses**
- ⬭ Make no change.

2 What change, if any, should be made to sentence 2?

- ⬭ Change *animals* to **animales**
- ⬭ Change *animals* to **animalies**
- ⬭ Change *animals* to **animal**
- ⬬ Make no change.

3 What change, if any, should be made to sentence 4?

- ⬬ Change *trophyes* to **trophies**
- ⬭ Change *trophyes* to **trophys**
- ⬭ Change *trophyes* to **trophyess**
- ⬭ Make no change.

4 Which word makes the most sense in sentence 5?

- ⬭ dutys
- ⬭ dutyes
- ⬬ duties
- ⬭ dutyies

5 What change, if any, should be made to sentence 7?

- ⬬ Change *Puppyes* to **Puppies**
- ⬭ Change *Puppyes* to **Puppys**
- ⬭ Change *Puppyes* to **Puppyies**
- ⬭ Make no change.

© Pearson Education, Inc., 3

Home Activity Your child prepared for taking tests on singular and plural nouns. With your child, take turns naming kinds of insects. Have your child write the plural form of each word.

Compound Words

Directions Identify the two words that make up each compound word. Write the words on the lines.

1. __sun__ + __glasses__ = sunglasses
2. __rail__ + __road__ = railroad
3. __hair__ + __cut__ = haircut
4. __fire__ + __house__ = firehouse
5. __pop__ + __corn__ = popcorn
6. __my__ + __self__ = myself
7. __green__ + __house__ = greenhouse
8. __back__ + __yard__ = backyard
9. __rain__ + __water__ = rainwater
10. __sun__ + __flower__ = sunflower

Directions Choose the compound word to complete each sentence. Write the word on the line. Draw a line between the two words that make up each compound word.

__grand/father__   **11.** My (grandfather/uncle) lives on a farm.

__when/ever__   **12.** I help him take care of his animals (whenever/when) I visit.

__snow/storm__   **13.** Last winter I was with him during a terrible (snowstorm/blizzard).

__out/side__   **14.** We had to work (outside/quickly) in the cold and snow.

__some/times__   **15.** It's (sometimes/often) difficult to be a farmer.

Home Activity Your child wrote compound words—words formed by joining two shorter words—such as *homework*. With your child, read advertisements to find compound words (such as *everyday*, *something*, and *everyone*). Have your child identify the two words that make up each compound word.

Draw Conclusions

- A **conclusion** is a decision or opinion that makes sense based on facts and details.
- When you use new information you read or information you already know to make decisions, you are **drawing conclusions.**

Directions Read the following article.

Many people feel nervous when they're surrounded by clutter. They waste lots of time searching for what they need. If you need to get organized, follow these steps:

1. Discard or give away items you no longer need.

2. Sort the objects that are left into categories. For example, group your shirts, pants, and shoes and put your homework supplies in a special place.

3. Take a few minutes each day to make sure your belongings are in their certain places.

You'll spend less time searching and more time doing what you want to do.

Directions Complete the graphic organizer by using the information from the article to write a conclusion.

Fact or detail from article
People surrounded by clutter often waste their time searching for the things they need.

Fact or detail from article
People who organize their belongings usually have more time to spend on activities they enjoy.

Conclusion:
Organized people have more time for fun.

© Pearson Education, Inc., 3

School + Home

Home Activity Your child drew a conclusion from information presented in a text. With your child, read a how-to article in a magazine or on the Internet. Have your child draw conclusions about the information and identify the facts and/or details that helped him or her reach those conclusions.

Writing • Persuasive Advertisement

Key Features of a Persuasive Advertisement

- states why a person would want to go somewhere or buy something
- gives reasons and details to support statements
- uses descriptive words and phrases
- connects with a reader's feelings

"The Prudy Museum of Indescribable Wonderment"

Where can you go to find ribbon collections, plastic lizards, and the most dog hair you've ever seen? You can go to The Prudy Museum of Indescribable Wonderment. It is the most interesting museum in the world. You will never see a collection like the one at the Prudy Museum.

Many museums have art or dinosaur bones. This museum is special. You can see amazing collections of gym socks, scarves, souvenir postcards, leaves, and old candy boxes. They have been carefully collected and organized by one young girl. This museum is the biggest tourist attraction in town and even includes a gift shop.

A visit to The Prudy Museum of Indescribable Wonderment will put you in a good mood. After your visit, you will see beauty in things you see around your house every day.

1. Read the advertisement. What is one statement made about the museum? What reasons and details support this statement?

   It is the most interesting museum in the world. It is special and unlike any other museum. For example, it has unusual collections you don't usually see in a museum, like gym socks, plastic lizards, and dog hair.

2. How does the advertisement try to connect with readers' feelings?

   It says people will be in a good mood. They will learn to see beauty in everyday items.

Vocabulary

Directions Choose the vocabulary word from the box and write it next to its meaning.

> ### Check the Words You Know
> ___enormous ___shoelaces
> ___strain ___scattered
> ___collection ___butterflies

scattered 1. spread over a large area

collection 2. a group of similar things a person gets and saves

butterflies 3. insects with brightly colored wings

strain 4. to stretch too much

enormous 5. very big; huge

Directions Each sentence has a word missing. Circle the word at the end of each sentence that fits the meaning.

6. She brought new blue _____ for her old shoes. (shoelaces) butterflies

7. My sister _____ her leg in the race. enormous (strained)

8. We _____ the grass seed all over the front yard. (scattered) strained

9. The _____ dictionary in the library is too heavy to lift.
collection (enormous)

10. My brother has a large _____ of baseball cards. strain (collection)

Write an Advertisement

On a separate sheet of paper, write an advertisement describing an item for sale. Tell why a person would want it in a collection. Use as many vocabulary words as possible.

Students should use vocabulary to describe something collectible.

Home Activity Your child identified and used vocabulary words from *Prudy's Problem and How She Solved It*. Ask your child to explain Prudy's problem to you and how it was solved. Encourage your child to use as many vocabulary words as possible.

Name _____

Irregular Plural Nouns

A plural noun names more than one person, place, or thing. Most nouns add -s to form the plural. An **irregular plural noun** has a special form for the plural.

Singular Nouns   A <u>goose</u> and a <u>deer</u> ate a <u>leaf</u>.
Irregular Plural Nouns Some <u>geese</u> and some <u>deer</u> ate some <u>leaves</u>.

Some nouns and their irregular plural forms are *child/children, deer/deer, foot/feet, goose/geese, leaf/leaves, life/lives, man/men, mouse/mice, ox/oxen, sheep/sheep, tooth/teeth,* and *woman/women.*

Directions Write *S* if the underlined noun is singular. Write *P* if the underlined noun is plural.

1. The <u>children</u> had a messy room. __**P**__

2. Aunt Rose would not put a <u>foot</u> into the room. __**S**__

3. There were <u>leaves</u> on the floor. __**P**__

4. I've never seen such a sight in my <u>life</u>! __**S**__

5. <u>Mice</u> could make a nest in there. __**P**__

Directions Write the plural nouns in each sentence.

6. The men on the farm had a problem.

men
_____

7. Deer were eating vegetables from their fields.

deer, vegetables, fields
_____

8. The farmers found holes in the lettuce leaves.

farmers, holes, leaves
_____

9. The women tried to think of clever solutions.

women, solutions
_____

 Home Activity Your child learned about irregular plural nouns. Say the words goose, mouse, and child and have your child say the plural form of each word.

Compound Words

Missing Words Write the missing list word.

Spelling Words

sunglasses
football
homework
haircut
popcorn
railroad
snowstorm
earring

scarecrow
blueberry
butterflies
lawnmower
campground
sandbox
toothbrush

1. I squeezed toothpaste onto

   my __toothbrush__ .

2. Do you like __blueberry__ muffins?

3. School was cancelled because of the

   __snowstorm__ .

4. Our teacher asked us to turn in __homework__ .

5. She felt her ear and discovered she had lost an

   __earring__ .

6. A good pair of __sunglasses__ will protect

   your eyes.

7. The __scarecrow__ wore an old straw hat.

Combinations Underline the two words in the sentence that should be combined into a compound word. Write the compound word.

8. Carrie's mom gave her a <u>hair cut</u>.   8. __haircut__

9. I ate <u>pop corn</u> at the theater.   9. __popcorn__

10. The <u>lawn mower</u> needs to be fixed.   10. __lawnmower__

11. Look at the big blue <u>butter flies</u>!   11. __butterflies__

12. We should take our pails out of the <u>sand box</u>.   12. __sandbox__

13. Do you want to play <u>foot ball</u> after school?   13. __football__

14. A train blocked the <u>rail road</u> crossing.   14. __railroad__

15. We set up our tent at a great <u>camp ground</u>.   15. __campground__

© Pearson Education, Inc., 3

Home Activity Your child wrote compound words. Remind your child that no letters are dropped from the two words that are combined to make a compound word.

Name _____

Outline Form A

Title _____

A. _____

   1. _____

   2 _____

   3. _____

B. _____

   1. _____

   2. _____

   3. _____

C. _____

   1. _____

   2. _____

   3. _____

Vocabulary • Compound Words

- Sometimes you may come across words you do not know. You can look to see if the word is a **compound word,** a word made up of two small words. Each word can stand on its own and still have meaning.

Directions Read the sentences and underline each compound word. Then write the words that make the compound word on the lines.

1. My <u>grandmother</u> lives in Florida.   **grand** + **mother**

2. Florida's <u>nickname</u> is the <u>Sunshine</u> State.   **nick** + **name**

          sun + **shine**

3. Gram always wears <u>sunglasses</u> when she goes out.   **sun** + **glasses**

4. She is teaching me to <u>waterski</u>.   **water** + **ski**

5. She says I should be careful not to get a <u>sunburn</u>.   **sun** + **burn**

6. Gram makes me put on <u>sunscreen</u>, too.   **sun** + **screen**

7. After supper we watch <u>videotapes</u>.   **video** + **tapes**

8. Sometimes we make <u>popcorn</u>.   **pop** + **corn**

Directions Read the clues. Think of a compound word that matches the clue and write it on the line.

9. You use it to cut the grass.   **lawnmower**

10. These keep your sneakers on your feet.   **shoelaces**

11. Some caterpillars turn into these.   **butterflies**

12. This is jewelry you wear in your ear.   **earrings**

13. You use this to keep your teeth clean.   **toothbrush**

14. You sit in this to take a bath.   **bathtub**

15. This berry is small and blue, and good to eat.   **blueberry**

© Pearson Education, Inc., 3

Home Activity Your child identified and used compound words. Give your child words that are part of compounds, such as *sun, snow,* and *butter.* Have your child list as many compound words as possible that can be made from those words.

Magazine

Directions Read the magazine article. Use it to answer the questions below.

Collector's Monthly	
How to Manage Your Collectibles *by Sara Vega* We all love our collectibles, but often there are too many items to manage. Here are some suggestions: • Set a goal or purpose for your collection. Get rid of items that don't meet this goal or purpose. • Buy or make storage containers. You want to be able to view each item. • Make a list of each item in your collection. Add and remove items from the list as needed. You may want to keep your list on a computer.	**FOR SALE** **Action Figures** More than 100 favorites. Call Mike 430-1874. **Rare Coins** Many hard-to-find U.S. coins. 555-7372 Ask for Marcia.

1. What is the title of the magazine?

   Collector's Monthly

2. What is the title of the article?

   How to Manage Your Collectibles

3. What is the article about?

   The article gives suggestions for organizing

   a collection of items.

4. Who might buy this magazine?

   Possible response: someone who

   wants to buy or sell items for a collection

5. If you were looking for a rare coin or action figure, how might you use this magazine?

   I would look at the For Sale section to see what

   coins or action figures are being sold.

Home Activity Your child read a magazine page and answered questions about it. Look through a children's magazine. Ask your child to point out the different parts. Have him or her suggest other articles or materials that might be found in a magazine like this.

Compound Words

Proofread a Description Ann wrote about a family reunion. Underline two words that should have been a compound word. Circle three other spelling mistakes. Write the words correctly. Add the missing comma.

> All my relatives met at a <u>camp ground</u>. The grownups talked while the kids played football and chased (butterflys). Then (evryone) ate chicken popcorn, (bluebery) pie, and other good food. Nobody wanted to say goodnight.

1. __campground__   2. __butterflies__

3. __everyone__   4. __blueberry__

Spelling Words

sunglasses
football
homework
haircut
popcorn
railroad
snowstorm
earring

scarecrow
blueberry
butterflies
lawnmower
campground
sandbox
toothbrush

Proofread Words Fill in the circle to show the correctly spelled word.

Frequently Misspelled Words

outside
everyone
something
sometimes

5. Our family always has ____ on Sunday night.
   ● popcorn   ○ pop korn   ○ pop corn

6. Manuel's grandma has a ____ in her garden.
   ● scarecrow   ○ scarcrow   ○ scare crow

7. I do my ____ right after school.
   ○ homwork   ○ home work   ● homework

8. Let's build a castle in the ____ .
   ● sandbox   ○ sand box   ○ sandbocks

Home Activity Your child identified misspelled compound words. Have your child draw a line to divide each list word into its two parts.

Irregular Plural Nouns

Directions Read the selection. Then read each question that follows the selection. Decide which is the best answer to each question. Mark the space for the answer you have chosen.

Different Collections

(1) All the <u>child</u> collect something. (2) Carlo has 20 <u>foot</u> of string. (3) Jo has 8 stuffed <u>mouse</u>. (4) Nick has all his baby <u>tooth</u>. (5) Jake has 100 toy army <u>man</u>. (6) Maria has 20 plastic <u>sheep</u>. (7) Nan has 15 pictures of fall <u>leaf</u>.

1 What is the plural form of the underlined noun in sentence 1?
- ⬭ childs
- ⬬ children
- ⬭ childe
- ⬭ childen

2 What is the plural form of the underlined noun in sentence 2?
- ⬭ foots
- ⬭ foves
- ⬭ fice
- ⬬ feet

3 What is the plural form of the underlined noun in sentence 3?
- ⬬ mice
- ⬭ mouses
- ⬭ meese
- ⬭ mousen

4 What is the plural form of the underlined noun in sentence 5?
- ⬭ manen
- ⬭ mans
- ⬬ men
- ⬭ manes

5 What is the plural form of the underlined noun in sentence 6?
- ⬬ sheep
- ⬭ sheeps
- ⬭ sheepes
- ⬭ shep

Home Activity Your child prepared for taking tests on irregular plural nouns. Have a discussion with your child about the families in your neighborhood. Ask your child to use the singular and plural forms of *man*, *woman*, and *child*.

Name _____

Consonant Blends

Directions Read the story. Underline the words with the three-letter blends **squ, spl, thr,** and **str.** Then write the underlined words on the lines.

Emily <u>threw</u> on her coat and ran down the <u>street</u>. As she got to the town <u>square</u>, she saw <u>three</u> friends <u>throwing</u> water balloons at one another. Each time a balloon <u>struck</u> the ground, it <u>split</u> open. Water <u>splashed</u> everywhere. Then someone tossed a balloon with such <u>strength</u> that it flew <u>through</u> an open car window. Emily knew they had to find the owner and tell what they had done.

1. _____**threw**_____

2. _____**street**_____

3. _____**square**_____

4. _____**three**_____

5. _____**throwing**_____

6. _____**struck**_____

7. _____**split**_____

8. _____**splashed**_____

9. _____**strength**_____

10. _____**through**_____

Directions Read each word and listen for the three-letter blend. Then write two more words that start with the same blend. Underline the three-letter blend in each word you write. **Students' answers will vary.**

11. straw _____<u>stri</u>pe_____ _____<u>str</u>ong_____

12. splurge _____<u>spl</u>int_____ _____<u>spl</u>endid_____

13. squeak _____<u>squ</u>int_____ _____<u>squ</u>ash_____

14. thread _____<u>thr</u>oat_____ _____<u>thr</u>one_____

15. straight _____<u>str</u>ict_____ _____<u>str</u>ange_____

© Pearson Education, Inc., 3

Home Activity Your child wrote words that begin with the three-letter blends *spl* (as in *splash*), *squ* (as in *square*), *str* (as in *strike*), and *thr* (as in *throw*). Challenge your child to name additional words that begin with these three-letter blends. For help in identifying words with these starting letters, you can use a dictionary.

Author's Purpose

- An **author's purpose** is the author's reason for writing. An author may write to inform or teach, to entertain, to persuade, or to express thoughts and feelings.

Directions Read the following passage.

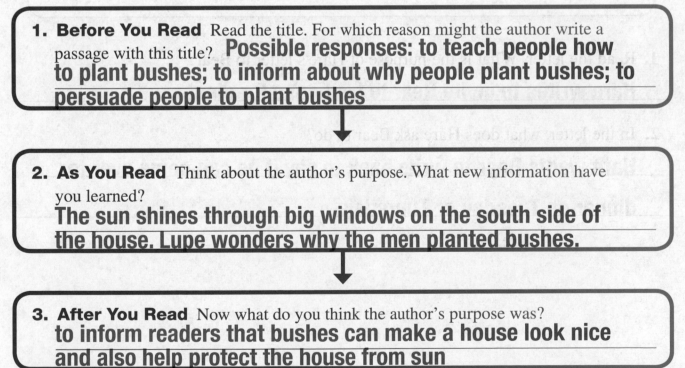

Planting Bushes

STOP and answer Question 1 below.

The Lopez family had just built a nice house in the desert. The only problem was that the hot sun shone through the huge windows on the south side.

Early one morning, Dad and Grandpa planted bushes along the south side of the house.

"I wonder why they did that," thought Lupe.

STOP and answer Question 2 below.

Every day, Dad or Grandpa watered the bushes. They began to grow. Soon the bushes got so tall they blocked the sun from coming in the windows.

"Now I know why they did that!" thought Lupe.

Directions Complete the graphic organizer to determine the author's purpose.

1. **Before You Read** Read the title. For which reason might the author write a passage with this title? **Possible responses: to teach people how to plant bushes; to inform about why people plant bushes; to persuade people to plant bushes**

2. **As You Read** Think about the author's purpose. What new information have you learned? **The sun shines through big windows on the south side of the house. Lupe wonders why the men planted bushes.**

3. **After You Read** Now what do you think the author's purpose was? **to inform readers that bushes can make a house look nice and also help protect the house from sun**

Home Activity Your child determined the author's purpose for writing a story. Purposes include to inform, to persuade, to entertain, or to express feelings or ideas. Talk about the author's purpose for writing tales your child is familiar with. Ask your child to give reasons for his or her answers.

Writing • Friendly Letter

Key Features of a Friendly Letter

- includes a date, salutation, and closing
- written in a friendly tone
- usually written to someone you know

September 15, 2008

Dear Bear,

I worked hard to grow vegetables this year. Now I have a lot of carrots and corn. I have enough to share with you. Would you like to come over for dinner?

We will have corn and carrots. We will have corn bread, too. Then we will have carrot cake for dessert. The cake's frosting will be sweet and creamy.

Please write back. Tell me if you want to come Tuesday or Thursday.

Your friend,
Hare

---

1. Read the letter. What is the purpose of Hare's letter to Bear?

Hare writes to invite Bear to his house for dinner.

2. In the letter, what does Hare ask Bear to do?

Hare wants Bear to write back to say if he can come over for dinner on Tuesday or Thursday.

© Pearson Education, Inc., 3

Vocabulary

Directions Each sentence has an underlined word. Circle the word at the end of the sentence with the same meaning as the underlined word.

```
┌─────────────────────────────────────────┐
│       Check the Words You Know           │
│                                          │
│   ___lazy            ___bottom           │
│   ___crops           ___clever           │
│   ___cheated         ___partners         │
│   ___wealth                              │
└─────────────────────────────────────────┘
```

1. My <u>lazy</u> brother hates to do his chores. (idle) young

2. Jill put the cookies on the <u>bottom</u> shelf. (lowest) long

3. Juan and I are <u>partners</u> in a lawn-mowing business. (co-workers) a class

4. Jim does well in school because he is very <u>clever</u>. lazy (smart)

5. A person with lots of money has lots of <u>wealth</u>. (riches) need

Directions Write a word from the box to complete each sentence below.

6. The farmer plants many _____**crops**_____ , including corn and wheat.

7. A farmer cannot be _____**lazy**_____ because farming takes lots of work.

8. Ann is an honest student, so I don't think she _____**cheated**_____ on the test.

9. The rich man had so much _____**wealth**_____ , he owned five houses.

10. We will work together as _____**partners**_____ to build a business.

Write a Story

On a separate sheet of paper, write about two farmers working together on something special. Describe them and what happens. Use as many vocabulary words as possible.

Students should use vocabulary to describe partners, what they do, and what happens.

Home Activity Your child identified and used vocabulary words from *Tops and Bottoms*. Visit the supermarket produce aisle together and have your child identify the vegetables whose tops or bottoms we eat. Encourage using as many vocabulary words as possible.

Singular Possessive Nouns

To show that one person, animal, or thing owns something, use a **singular possessive noun.** Add an apostrophe (') and the letter *s* to a singular noun to make it possessive.

Singular Noun	The <u>hare</u> planted corn.
Singular Possessive Noun	The bear wanted the <u>hare's</u> corn.

Directions Write the possessive noun in each sentence.

1. Aesop's fables tell stories about people and animals. __**Aesop's**__

2. A fox takes a crow's cheese. __**crow's**__

3. A mouse frees a lion's paw. __**lion's**__

4. A wolf wears a sheep's fur. __**sheep's**__

5. People enjoy each story's lesson. __**story's**__

Directions Write the possessive form of the underlined noun in each sentence.

6. <u>Jeff</u> favorite fable is about the wind and the sun. __**Jeff's**__

7. The wind challenges the <u>sun</u> power. __**sun's**__

8. Which one can remove a <u>man</u> coat? __**man's**__

9. The man feels the <u>wind</u> chill, and he buttons his coat. __**wind's**__

10. He pulls up his <u>coat</u> collar. __**coat's**__

11. The <u>sun</u> heat makes the man warm, and he takes off his coat. __**sun's**__

12. What do you think is the <u>fable</u> lesson? __**fable's**__

© Pearson Education, Inc., 3

Home Activity Your child learned about singular possessive nouns. Have your child name objects in your home and use a possessive phrase to tell who they belong to, for example, *Dad's book.*

Words with *spl, thr, squ, str, scr*

Spelling Words				
splash	throw	three	square	scream
strike	street	split	splurge	thrill
strength	squeak	throne	scratch	squeeze

Rhyming Pairs Finish the sentence with a list word that rhymes with the underlined word.

1. He has a <u>batch</u> of itches to **scratch** .

2. Skiing down that <u>hill</u> was a **thrill** !

3. I don't think he has the **strength** to swim the <u>length</u> of the pool.

4. See if you can **throw** the ball to the <u>row</u> of trees.

5. The town **square** was <u>bare</u>.

6. The **throne** has been occupied by six men and a <u>lone</u> woman.

7. There are **three** squirrels playing in the <u>tree</u>.

8. Let's <u>dash</u> into the water and make a big **splash** .

Missing Blends Add a three-letter blend to finish the list word. Write the word.

9. The scared girl let out a **s c r** eam.   **9.** **scream**

10. The pitcher threw a **s t r** ike.   **10.** **strike**

11. Don't play in the **s t r** eet.   **11.** **street**

12. I'd love to **s p l** urge on an expensive gift.   **12.** **splurge**

13. Let's **s p l** it the last piece of pizza.   **13.** **split**

14. Mom gave my hand a big **s q u** eeze.   **14.** **squeeze**

15. We heard the hinges **s q u** eak.   **15.** **squeak**

© Pearson Education, Inc., 3

Home Activity Your child wrote words with three-letter blends (*spl, thr, squ, str,* and *scr*). Have your child circle and pronounce the three-letter blends in the list words.

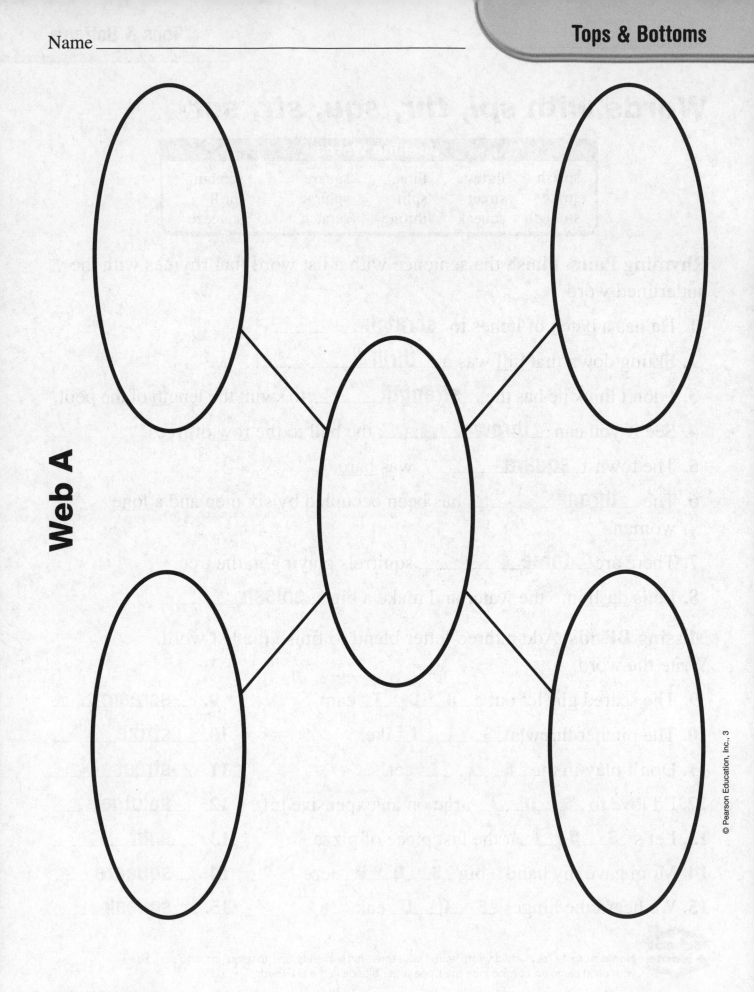

Web A

Vocabulary • Antonyms

- Sometimes you come across a word you don't know. The author may use a word with the opposite meaning—an **antonym**—as a clue to the word's meaning.
- Use **antonyms** as context clues to figure out the meaning of unfamiliar words.

Directions Read each sentence. One word is underlined. Circle the antonym of the underlined word. Write the meaning of the underlined word on the line.

1. Sue is always so busy that no one can say she is <u>lazy</u>.

   not willing to work or move fast

2. Put the glass on the top shelf because your sister may break it if it's on the <u>bottom</u>.

   lowest or last

3. Danny is so <u>clever</u>, he would never do a silly thing like that.

   bright; intelligent; having a quick mind

4. The cat was <u>asleep</u>, but the dog was awake.

   not awake; sleeping

5. Months after planting the seeds, the farmer can <u>harvest</u> the corn.

   to gather crops

6. Do not scatter the papers, but <u>gather</u> them into one pile.

   to bring or come together in one place; collect

7. You look so nice when you smile that you should never <u>scowl</u>.

   to look at someone in an angry way; frown

8. Whisper the secret in my ear, don't <u>holler</u> it out loud.

   to cry or shout loudly

Home Activity Your child identified and used new words by understanding antonyms used in context. Read a story together and encourage identifying unfamiliar words. Then help look for antonyms in the text that might help figure out the words' meanings.

© Pearson Education, Inc., 3

Encyclopedia

An **encyclopedia** is a set of books, or **volumes,** that has **entries** and articles on many subjects. Volumes and entries are arranged in alphabetical order. **Guide words** show the first and last entries on a page or facing pages. **Electronic encyclopedias** display links to articles on subjects for which you search.

Directions Use the information above to answer the questions.

1. What word or words would you use to find information about the climate of the northeastern United States? Write the volume number you would use.

Possible response: Look under United States in Volume 14.

2. The entry *tortoise* might be found between which guide words: **tidal wave/tiger, tornado/town,** or **toy/trampoline?** Write the volume number in which it would be found.

tornado/town, Volume 13

3. You want to compare an alligator and a crocodile. Which volumes will you use?

Volume 1 and Volume 2

4. How many different articles on rabbits are shown in the electronic encyclopedia window? _____**4**_____

5. Which article will you read to learn about the size of a rabbit?

The Body of a Rabbit

Home Activity Your child identified words and volume numbers to locate answers to questions about using an encyclopedia. Help your child write four or five questions about a topic of interest. Have your child use an encyclopedia, either print or electronic, to answer the questions.

Name _____

Words with *spl, thr, squ, str, scr*

Proofread a Report Circle four spelling mistakes in this report about the gray fox. Write the words correctly. Write the word that should be used instead of **don't** in the last sentence.

A gray fox has a white belly. It can run fast and climb trees. It may splash into the water and swim if it is (skared) and needs to escape. It can also let out a high-pitched (screem). When hunting, it listens for the (sqeak) of a mouse. If it sees movement, it (srikes) quickly. Sometimes, in bad weather, a gray fox don't leave its den for three or four days.

Spelling Words

splash
throw
three
square
scream
strike
street
split

splurge
thrill
strength
squeak
throne
scratch
squeeze

1. **scared**   2. **scream**
3. **squeak**   4. **strikes**
5. **doesn't**

Frequently Misspelled Words

scared
brother

Proofread Words Fill in the circle to show the correctly spelled word.

6. ○ thril   ● thrill   ○ thill
7. ○ squeze   ○ sqeeze   ● squeeze
8. ○ scatch   ● scratch   ○ scrach
9. ● throne   ○ trone   ○ throan
10. ○ stength   ○ strentgh   ● strength
11. ○ streat   ○ steet   ● street
12. ○ sqare   ● square   ○ squar

© Pearson Education, Inc., 3

School + Home   **Home Activity** Your child identified misspelled words with three-letter blends (*spl, thr, squ, str* and *scr*). Ask your child to use some of the list words to tell a story about a mouse.

Singular Possessive Nouns

Directions Read the selection. Then read each question that follows the selection. Decide which is the best answer to each question. Mark the space for the answer you have chosen.

A Favorite Fable

(1) Jeff favorite fable is about the wind and the sun. (2) In the story, the wind challenges the sun for power. (3) Which one can remove a man coat? (4) The wind blows hard to try to get the coat to fly off. (5) The man feels the wind chill, but it only makes him button his coat tighter. (6) He pulls up his coat collar. (7) The sun heat makes the man warm, and he pulls off his coat.

1 What change, if any, should be made to sentence 1?

- Change *Jeff* to **Jeff's**
- Change *fable* to **fables**
- Change *wind* to **wind's**
- Make no change.

2 What change, if any, should be made to sentence 3?

- Change *one* to **one's**
- Change *man* to **men's**
- Change *man* to **man's**
- Make no change.

3 What change, if any, should be made to sentence 4?

- Change *blows* to **blow's**
- Change *wind* to **winds**
- Change *wind blows* to **wind's blow**
- Make no change.

4 What change, if any, should be made to sentence 5?

- Change *feels* to **feel's**
- Change *wind* to **wind's**
- Change *coat* to **coat's**
- Make no change.

5 What change, if any, should be made to sentence 7?

- Change *man* to **man's**
- Change *pulls* to **pull's**
- Change *sun* to **sun's**
- Make no change.

Home Activity Your child prepared for taking tests on singular possessive nouns. Have your child think of a friend's name and something that friend owns and make up a sentence using the possessive form of the friend's name.

© Pearson Education, Inc., 3

Consonant Digraphs

Directions Write **sh, th, ph, ch, tch,** or **ng** to complete each word. Write the whole word on the line to the left.

___**purchased**___   **1.** Maria's family pur__ch__ased a house.

___**mother**___   **2.** Her mo__th__er decided to paint it.

___**brushes**___   **3.** She went to the store and bought bru__sh__es and buckets.

___**clothing**___   **4.** When she came home she put on old clo__th__ing.

___**patched**___   **5.** Then she pa__tch__ed the cracks and nail holes.

___**going**___   **6.** Maria didn't know what color her room was goi__ng__ to be.

___**phoned**___   **7.** She __ph__oned her friend to talk about it.

___**choice**___   **8.** Her friend helped Maria make the __ch__oice.

___**shade**___   **9.** Maria picked a beautiful __sh__ade of peach.

Directions Say the name of each picture. Write **sh, th, wh, ph, tch,** or **ng** to complete each word.

10. tro__ph__y

11. wa__tch__

12. a__th__lete

13. __wh__ale

14. swi__ng__

15. spla__sh__

School + Home

Home Activity Your child wrote words with the consonants *sh (English), th (father), wh (wheel), ph (trophy), ch (chapter), tch (watch),* and *ng (wing).* Have your child read the words on the page above. Ask your child to change one or more letters in some of the words to form new words. For example, substituting *t* for *p* in *peach* forms *teach.*

© Pearson Education, Inc., 3

Name _____

Main Idea and Details

The **main idea** answers the question, "What is this story all about?" **Details** are small pieces of information that help tell what the story is about.

Directions Read the following passage.

John went into the woods on a snowy day, and his boots made tracks where he walked.

I can follow my tracks back out, thought John, so he didn't pay attention to where he was going.

But the sun came out and melted the snow, and when John wanted to leave, he couldn't see any tracks.

Then John saw an eagle overhead. "Eagle," said John, "please help me find my way out."

The eagle flew south, then west. John followed until he was out of the woods.

Directions Complete the graphic organizer to tell what the story is all about.

Detail

1. John thinks he will follow his tracks to leave the woods.

Detail

2. The sun melts the snow, and the tracks disappear.

Detail

3. John asks an eagle to help him.

What This Story Is All About

4. When John gets lost, an eagle helps him find his way out of the woods.

School + Home

Home Activity Your child found the main idea of a story. The main idea is a sentence that sums up what the story is all about. Read a story such as the one above with your child. Ask your child to name details from the story and then tell what the story is all about.

Writing • Directions

Key Features of Directions

• gives a step-by-step explanation of how to perform a specific task

• provides necessary information and details

• explains a task fully

• often uses commands and sequence words

How to Make Pancakes

Pancakes are delicious, and they're not that hard to make. Let's find out how to make them in a few simple steps. Making pancakes requires using a hot stove, which can be dangerous. Be sure to have an adult help you with any steps that involve using the stove.

First, we should collect the ingredients and supplies we need. To mix the pancake batter, we want a bowl and a mixer. To cook the pancakes, we'll need a frying pan and a spatula. We also want a measuring cup to measure ingredients. The ingredients you need to make the pancakes are simple:

• 3 cups of flour   • ½ cup milk
• 1 cup of sugar   • water
• 1 egg   • butter

Next, we want to prepare the batter. Combine the flour, sugar, egg, and milk in the bowl. Mix them together until they form a smooth batter. Add water as necessary to make sure that the batter is not too thick. Stir through the batter carefully to make sure there are no lumps.

Now it's time to cook our pancakes. Again, be sure that there's an adult present. Put the frying pan on a lit burner and add a pat of butter. Once the butter has melted, pour the batter into the pan in order to form a pancake. If your pan is big enough, you can make more than one pancake at a time.

Once the pancakes begin to form bubbles and become dry on top, use the spatula to flip them over. Let the other side cook for two or three minutes. Then you can slide the pancakes out of the pan and onto your plate. Add some butter and syrup, and enjoy your breakfast!

1. What supplies do you need in order to make pancakes?

   A bowl, mixer, frying pan, spatula, measuring cup, 3 cups flour, 1 cup sugar, ½ cup milk, one egg, water, and butter.

2. Put the following steps in making pancakes in the proper order:

   4, 3, 1, 2

   1. Pour batter into pan.
   2. Eat pancakes.
   3. Mix batter.
   4. Gather supplies.

Vocabulary

Check the Words You Know

___bill   ___platform
___goo   ___tons
___hunters   ___twigs
___material

Directions Match the word with its meaning. Draw a line from the word to its definition.

1. bill   units of weight equal to 2,000 pounds

2. twigs   the hard part of a bird's mouth; beak

3. material   a raised level surface for people to stand or sit on

4. platform   very small branches of a tree or bush

5. tons   what a thing is made of

Directions Write the word from the box that best completes each sentence.

6. The mayor stood on the _____**platform**_____ to make his speech.

7. This bridge is strong enough to hold ten _____**tons**_____.

8. The rabbit hid from foxes and other _____**hunters**_____.

9. I put my hand into the sticky _____**goo**_____.

10. The bird had a cherry in its _____**bill**_____.

Write a Journal Entry

Imagine you are watching a bird building its nest. On a separate piece of paper, write a journal entry telling about what the bird did. Use as many vocabulary words as you can in your writing. **Students should use vocabulary in a description of a bird building its nest.**

© Pearson Education, Inc., 3

Home Activity Your child identified and used vocabulary words from the selection *Amazing Bird Nests.* Find a library book on the same subject and read it together. Talk about the book using the week's vocabulary words.

Name _____

Plural Possessive Nouns

To show that two or more people share or own something, use a **plural possessive noun.**

Plural Noun	The birds built nests.
Singular Possessive Noun	One bird's nest was made of twigs.
Plural Possessive Noun	Some birds' nests are made of grass.

Add an apostrophe (') to plural nouns that end in *-s, -es,* or *-ies* to make them possessive. To make plural nouns that do not end in *-s, -es,* or *-ies* possessive, add an apostrophe and an *s*.

children   children's toys   women   women's books

Directions Write the plural possessive noun in each sentence.

1. Eagles' nests are huge. __**Eagles'**__

2. Hummingbirds' nests hold their eggs. __**Hummingbirds'**__

3. The parents' job is to protect their chicks. __**parents'**__

4. The trees' holes were made by woodpeckers. __**trees'**__

5. The forest's trees are full of animals' homes. __**animals'**__

Directions Write the possessive form of the underlined plural noun in each sentence.

6. There are good places for our <u>cities</u> birds to nest. __**cities'**__

7. Some <u>pigeons</u> homes are on window ledges. __**pigeons'**__

8. Sometimes they get in <u>people</u> way. __**people's**__

9. Their <u>babies</u> lives can be full of danger. __**babies'**__

10. Some animals destroy the bird <u>families</u> homes. __**families'**__

School + Home **Home Activity** Your child learned about plural possessive nouns. Name some families in your neighborhood. Have your child make up sentences using the plural possessive form of each noun, such as *The Smiths' dog likes to play ball.*

Consonant Digraphs

Spelling Words				
father	chapter	other	alphabet	watch
English	weather	catch	fashion	shrink
pitcher	flash	athlete	trophy	nephew

Rhyme Clues Read the clue. Write the list word.

1. It rhymes with *patch,* but starts like *can.*   **catch**

2. It rhymes with *link,* but starts like *shred.*   **shrink**

3. It rhymes with *feather,* but starts like *win.*   **weather**

4. It rhymes with *mother,* but starts like *olive.*   **other**

5. It rhymes with *dash,* but starts like *flag.*   **flash**

6. It rhymes with *stitcher,* but starts like *pencil.*   **pitcher**

Making Connections Write a list word to fit each definition.

7. It's a list of letters.   **alphabet**

8. It's something you might win.   **trophy**

9. It's a parent. It's not a mother.   **father**

10. It helps you tell the time.   **watch**

11. It's a section of a book.   **chapter**

12. It's a sister's child. It's not a girl.   **nephew**

13. It's often spoken in Australia.   **English**

14. It could be a swimmer, a boxer, or a gymnast.   **athlete**

15. It's a trend in clothing.   **fashion**

© Pearson Education, Inc., 3

School + Home
Home Activity Your child wrote words with *sh, th, ph, ch,* and *tch.* Point to a list word on this page. Ask your child to read the word and then look away and spell it correctly.

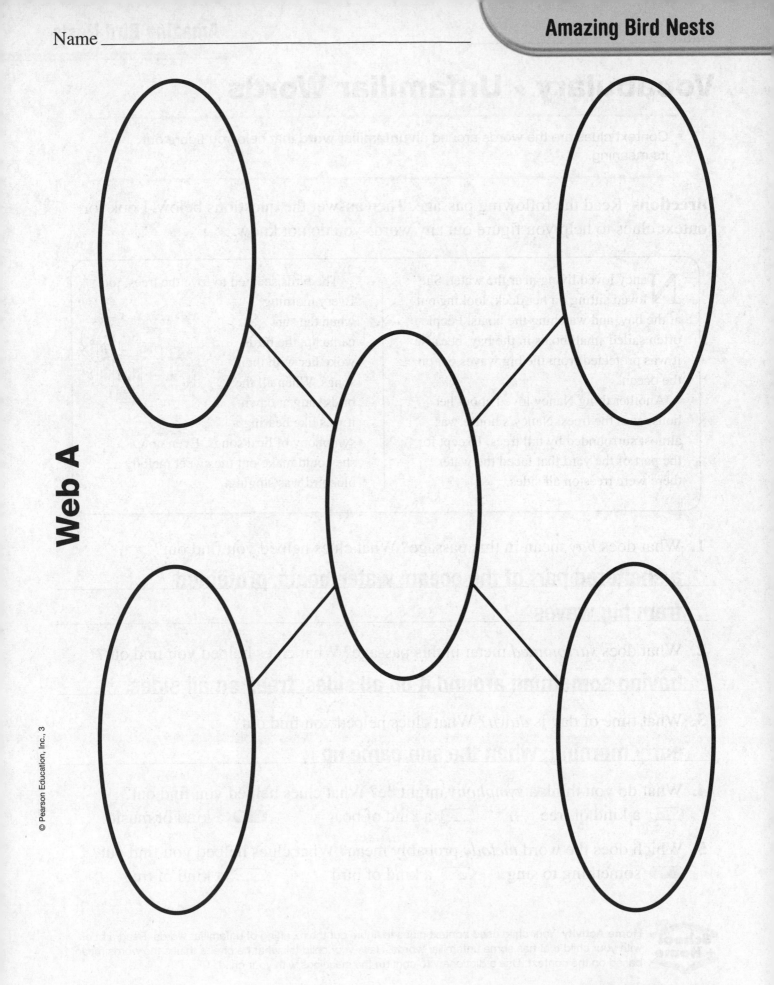

Web A

Vocabulary • Unfamiliar Words

- Context clues are the words around an **unfamiliar word** that help you figure out its meaning.

Directions Read the following passage. Then answer the questions below. Look for context clues to help you figure out any words you do not know.

Nancy loved living near the water. She loved sitting on her deck, looking out at the bay, and watching the boats. People often sailed small boats in the bay, because it was protected from the big waves out on the ocean.

Another thing Nancy loved about her house was the trees. Nancy's house was almost surrounded by tall trees. Except for the part of the yard that faced the water, there were trees on all sides.

The birds seemed to love the trees, too. Every morning when the sun came up, the birds woke her with their songs. When all the birds sang at dawn, it was like hearing a symphony of bird songs. Even now she could make out the sweet melody a bluebird was singing.

1. What does *bay* mean in this passage? What clues helped you find out?

   a sheltered part of the ocean; water, boats, protected from big waves

2. What does *surrounded* mean in this passage? What clues helped you find out?

   having something around it on all sides; trees on all sides.

3. What time of day is *dawn?* What clues helped you find out?

   early morning; when the sun came up

4. What do you think a *symphony* might be? What clues helped you find out?
   - ⬭ a kind of tree   ⬭ a kind of boat   ⬬ a kind of music

5. Which does the word *melody* probably mean? What clues helped you find out?
   - ⬬ something to sing   ⬭ a kind of bird   ⬭ a kind of tree

© Pearson Education, Inc., 3

Home Activity Your child used context clues to figure out the meaning of unfamiliar words. Read a book with your child that has some unfamiliar words. Have your child tell what he or she thinks the words mean, based on the context. Use a dictionary to confirm the meanings with your child.

Paraphrase Sources

- To **paraphrase** means to restate something in other words.

Directions Read the encyclopedia entry. Then paraphrase the information on the lines below.

Northern Mockingbird
(*Mimus polyglottos*)

The Northern Mockingbird is a medium-sized bird known for its unusual voice. Mockingbirds can imitate the songs of many kinds of birds, as well as other common sounds. Both male and female mockingbirds sing, although the males, especially males that are looking for a mate, sing most often. Unmated males may even sing at night. Male and female mockingbirds look alike. Both are gray on top and white underneath. Both have white patches on their wings and tails that can be seen when the bird is flying. Mockingbirds eat fruits and vegetables, but they also eat harmful insects. These birds are plentiful and are commonly found in a variety of habitats all over North America. The mockingbird is a popular bird that has been chosen as official state bird by Texas, Florida, and other states.

Responses will vary. Children may occasionally use short phrases from the encyclopedia entry but should not copy entire sentences. They should substitute synonyms for words from the article whenever appropriate.

_____

_____

Home Activity Your child read an encyclopedia entry about the Texas state bird and then paraphrased the information. Read another encyclopedia entry together and have your child tell about what you read in his or her own words.

Name _____

Consonant Digraphs

Proofread Safety Tips Chad wrote some weather safety tips. Circle four spelling mistakes and one capitalization error. Write the words correctly.

➤ Don't let bad (weatter) (cach) you off guard. Listen to the forecast.

➤ Be ready to go to a basement if (their) is a tornado watch.

➤ Take shelter when you hear thunder. Don't wait for a flash of lightning.

➤ (wear) a cap, mittens, and (othr) warm clothes in freezing weather.

Spelling Words
father
chapter
other
alphabet
watch
English
weather
catch
fashion
shrink
pitcher
flash
athlete
trophy
nephew

1. __weather__   2. __catch__

3. __there__   4. __other__

5. __Wear__

Proofread Words Circle the correctly spelled word. Write the word.

Frequently Misspelled Words
they
there
their

6. fashsun   (fashion)   6. __fashion__

7. (pitcher)   picher   7. __pitcher__

8. (trophy)   trofy   8. __trophy__

9. english   (English)   9. __English__

10. (shrink)   shink   10. __shrink__

11. atlete   (athlete)   11. __athlete__

12. alpabet   (alphabet)   12. __alphabet__

© Pearson Education, Inc., 3

 School + Home **Home Activity** Your child identified misspelled words with *sh*, *th*, *ph*, *ch*, and *tch*. Have your child underline and pronounce these letter combinations in the list words.

Plural Possessive Nouns

Directions Read the selection. Then read each question that follows the selection. Decide which is the best answer to each question. Mark the space for the answer you have chosen.

City Birds

(1) There are good places for many <u>cities</u> birds to nest. (2) Some <u>pigeons</u> homes are on window ledges. (3) Robins' nests can be found under highways. (4) Living in the city can also be dangerous for a bird. (5) Sometimes these birds get in <u>people</u> way. (6) Their <u>babies</u> lives can be full of danger. (7) Some animals destroy bird families homes.

1 What is the possessive form of the underlined noun in sentence 1?

- ⬭ cities
- ⬭ city's
- ⬭ citys'
- ⬬ cities'

2 What is the possessive form of the underlined noun in sentence 2?

- ⬬ pigeons'
- ⬭ pigeon's
- ⬭ pigeons
- ⬭ pigeons's

3 What is the correct form of the underlined noun in sentence 5?

- ⬭ peoples
- ⬬ people's
- ⬭ peoples'
- ⬭ peoples's

4 What is the possessive form of the underlined noun in sentence 6?

- ⬭ babie's
- ⬭ babys'
- ⬬ babies'
- ⬭ baby's

5 What change, if any, should be made to sentence 7?

- ⬭ Change *animals* to **animal's**
- ⬭ Change *animals* to **animals'**
- ⬬ Change *families* to **families'**
- ⬭ Change *families* to **familie's**

Home Activity Your child prepared for taking tests on plural possessive nouns. Name some kinds of animals. Have your child write sentences using the plural possessive form of each animal name, such as *Zebras' stripes are black and white.*

Syllables V/CV, VC/V

Spelling Words				
finish	pilot	even	wagon	music
silent	rapid	female	lemon	pupil
focus	robot	tulip	camel	salad

Crossword Puzzle Read each clue. Write the list word in the puzzle.

Across

2. to complete something
4. an animal with one or more humps
5. a sour fruit
8. a person who flies a plane
10. often made with lettuce
12. a kind of machine
13. very fast

Down

1. not odd but ____
2. the opposite of *male*
3. make no noise
6. songs
7. a toy with four wheels
8. a student
9. a spring flower
11. to adjust a camera lens

© Pearson Education, Inc., 3

Home Activity Your child has been learning to spell words with long and short vowel sounds with these syllable patterns: V/CV VC/V. Give clues about a word from the list. Ask your child to guess the word and then spell it.

Common and Proper Nouns

Directions Write *C* if the underlined noun is a common noun. Write *P* if the underlined noun is a proper noun.

1. Antarctica is an unusual <u>continent</u>. _____C_____

2. The <u>South Pole</u> is found there. _____P_____

3. The <u>weather</u> is harsh. _____C_____

4. It is one of the coldest places in the <u>world</u>. _____C_____

5. Yet some animals build <u>nests</u> on the land. _____C_____

6. The islands of <u>Antarctica</u> are home to many birds. _____P_____

7. Some <u>birds</u> live on the ocean. _____C_____

8. They find <u>fish</u> for food. _____C_____

9. Interesting birds live along the seashore of <u>America</u>. _____P_____

10. Gulls and terns nest on the <u>coast</u> and fish at sea. _____C_____

Directions Underline the common nouns and circle the proper nouns in the sentences.

11. <u>Ducks</u> and <u>geese</u> make <u>nests</u> near the (North Pole.)

12. The <u>animals</u> come to the <u>shores</u> of (North America) in <u>winter</u>.

13. Many <u>gulls</u> live near the <u>ocean</u> in (Canada.)

14. They follow <u>ships</u> and eat <u>trash</u> that <u>people</u> throw out.

15. These <u>birds</u> also live on the (Great Lakes.)

Final Syllable -*le*

Spelling Words				
handle	trouble	simple	people	middle
table	little	gentle	poodle	pickle
noodle	saddle	juggle	uncle	riddle

Rhymes Write the list word that rhymes with the word shown.

1. nickel   **p i c k l e**

2. doodle   **n o o d l e** or poodle

3. label   **t a b l e**

4. paddle   **s a d d l e**

5. bubble   **t r o u b l e**

6. steeple   **p e o p l e**

7. fiddle   **r i d d l e** or middle

8. dimple   **s i m p l e**

Missing Words Write the list word that completes each phrase.

9. a door **handle**

10. not rough but **gentle**

11. a barking **poodle**

12. not my aunt but my **uncle**

13. sit in the **middle**

14. **juggle** the balls

15. just a **little** bit more

handle	poodle
little	uncle
gentle	middle
juggle	

© Pearson Education, Inc., 3

 Home Activity Your child is learning to spell words that end in -*le*. Together, say each word, spell it, clap, and loudly say "l, e" when you get to the end of a word.

Singular and Plural Nouns

Directions Write *S* if the underlined noun is a singular noun. Write *P* if the underlined noun is a plural noun.

1. The desert is home to many animals. **S**

2. Kittens are common house pets. **P**

3. Mikey wants to give Alex his iguana. **S**

4. A large animal needs a large house. **S**

5. Lizards eat flies and other insects. **P**

Directions Write the plural nouns in each sentence.

6. Cats and kittens make good pets.

   cats, kittens, pets

7. Birds live in special cages.

   birds, cages

8. Different animals eat different foods.

   animals, foods

9. Hamsters and gerbils are furry friends.

   hamsters, gerbils, friends

10. Tiny sharks swim in special tanks.

    sharks, tanks

11. Pet owners have different jobs.

    owners, jobs

12. We groom our dogs using brushes made for pets.

    dogs, brushes, pets

© Pearson Education, Inc., 3

Compound Words

Spelling Words				
sunglasses	football	homework	haircut	popcorn
railroad	snowstorm	earring	scarecrow	blueberry
butterflies	lawnmower	campground	sandbox	toothbrush

Compound Match Up Draw a line to connect two words to make a compound word. Write the compound word.

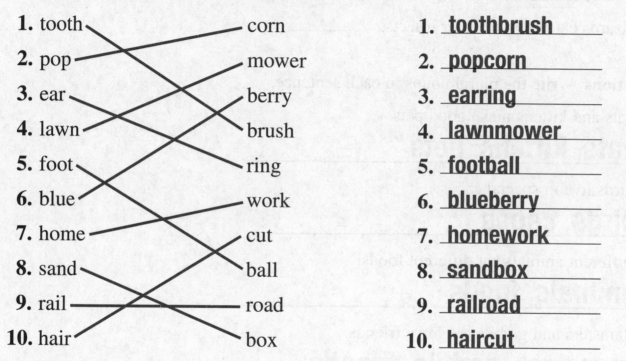

1. tooth	corn		1.	**toothbrush**
2. pop	mower		2.	**popcorn**
3. ear	berry		3.	**earring**
4. lawn	brush		4.	**lawnmower**
5. foot	ring		5.	**football**
6. blue	work		6.	**blueberry**
7. home	cut		7.	**homework**
8. sand	ball		8.	**sandbox**
9. rail	road		9.	**railroad**
10. hair	box		10.	**haircut**

Dividing Compounds Draw a line between the two words in each compound word. Write each word.

11. snow|storm   11. **snow** + **storm**

12. camp|ground   12. **camp** + **ground**

13. sun|glasses   13. **sun** + **glasses**

14. scare|crow   14. **scare** + **crow**

15. butter|flies 15. **butter** + **flies**

School + Home **Home Activity** Your child has been spelling compound words. Together, look for compound words in a favorite book. Ask your child to name the two words that make up each compound word.

Irregular Plural Nouns

Directions Write *S* if the underlined noun is singular. Write *P* if the underlined noun is plural.

1. The <u>women</u> next door had a problem in their barn. __P__

2. Some <u>mice</u> had made homes there. __P__

3. The little animals bothered the big <u>oxen</u> in the barn. __P__

4. A noisy <u>goose</u> went into the barn. __S__

5. Soon there were no mice under the people's <u>feet</u>. __P__

Directions Write the plural nouns in each sentence.

6. The children had problems.

children, problems

7. They had loose teeth.

teeth

8. They could not eat apples or carrots.

apples, carrots

9. Soon their teeth fell out, and their mouths felt better.

teeth, mouths

10. They could eat snacks again.

snacks

Words with *spl, thr, squ, str, scr*

Spelling Words				
splash	throw	three	square	scream
strike	street	split	splurge	thrill
strength	squeak	throne	scratch	squeeze

Question Clues Write the list word that answers each question.

1. How do you stop an itch?   1. **scratch**

2. What is the name of that shape?   2. **square**

3. What sound does a mouse make?   3. **squeak**

4. Where does a queen sit?   4. **throne**

5. Where might you park a car?   5. **street**

6. What might you do at a haunted house?   6. **scream**

7. What does a pitcher do with a ball?   7. **throw**

8. What number comes before four?   8. **three**

9. What is it called when a batter swings and misses?   9. **strike**

10. What do you do to get toothpaste out of a tube?   10. **squeeze**

Proofreading Circle the list word that is spelled correctly. Write it.

11. splesh (splash)   11. **splash**

12. (thrill) thril   12. **thrill**

13. stregth (strength)   13. **strength**

14. splutt (split)   14. **split**

15. (splurge) splurje   15. **splurge**

School + Home **Home Activity** Your child learned words with the three-letter blends *spl, thr, squ, str,* and *scr*. Divide a sheet of paper into four sections. Ask your child to sort and write the words according to their beginning blends.

© Pearson Education, Inc., 3

Singular Possessive Nouns

Directions Write the singular possessive noun in each sentence.

1. The little hen used the farmer's wheat for bread.

farmer's _____

2. The hen asked for each animal's help.

animal's _____

3. Each friend's answer was no.

friend's _____

4. The animals wanted the hen's good bread.

hen's _____

5. The hen enjoyed the bread's taste alone.

bread's _____

Directions Write the possessive form of the underlined singular noun in each sentence.

6. What is that <u>story</u> lesson?

story's _____

7. Good bread comes from the <u>baker</u> hard work.

baker's _____

8. Everyone wants the <u>worker</u> food.

worker's _____

9. No one helps in the <u>cook</u> kitchen.

cook's _____

10. Each <u>person</u> help is needed.

person's _____

Consonant Digraphs

Spelling Words				
father	chapter	other	alphabet	watch
English	weather	catch	fashion	shrink
pitcher	flash	athlete	trophy	nephew

Meaning Clues Read the clue. Write the list word the clue tells about. The letters in the boxes will answer this riddle:

What do you call cheese that's not yours?

1. get smaller   s h r i [n] k

2. the ABCs   a l p h [a] b e t

3. a clock for the wrist   w a t [c] h

4. a prize   t r o p [h] y

5. a clothing trend   f a s h i [o] n

6. something that can hold water   p i t [c] h e r

7. not a niece but a _____   n e p [h] e w

8. a dad   f a t h [e] r

9. part of a book   c h a p t [e] r

10. a language   E n g l i [s] h

11. what it's like outside   w e a t h [e] r

Word Parts Write the list word that contains each small word.

12. ash   f l a s h   or fashion

13. her   o t h e r   or father, pitcher, weather

14. let   a t h l e t e

15. cat   c a t c h

 Home Activity Your child learned to spell words with *sh, th, ph, ch,* and *tch*. Point to a word on the word list. Ask your child to circle the *sh, th, ph, ch,* or *tch* in the word. Then cover the word and have your child spell it out loud.

Name _____

Plural Possessive Nouns

Directions Write the plural possessive noun in each sentence.

1. The chicks' fur is so soft.

   chicks' _____

2. Hummingbirds' bills are long and thin.

   Hummingbirds' _____

3. Weaverbirds' nests are cleverly built.

   Weaverbirds' _____

4. The robins' eggs lie safely in nests.

   robins' _____

5. Building nests is the females' job.

   females' _____

Directions Write the possessive form of the underlined plural noun in each sentence.

6. The students saw eagles nests in the treetops.

   eagles' _____

7. They found woodpeckers eggs in tree trunks.

   woodpeckers' _____

8. Take pictures of some sparrows nests.

   sparrows' _____

9. Look carefully at the nests materials.

   nests' _____

10. Some animals homes are lined with feathers.

    animals' _____

11. The feathers colors are black and brown.

    feathers' _____

12. The students day was full of interesting sights.

    students' _____

© Pearson Education, Inc., 3

Name _____

How-to Chart

Directions Fill in the graphic organizer with information about your project.

Task __Answers should include details about__

Materials __each part of the how-to report.__

Introduction _____

_____

_____

_____

Steps _____

_____

_____

_____

Conclusion _____

_____

_____

_____

Time-Order Words

Directions Add a time-order word to each of the five steps below. Write each sentence. Then add a final sentence using a time-order word. Tell what you could do with the flowers. **Possible answers:**

1. Find a pretty vase.

   First, find a pretty vase.

   _____

2. Pick some wildflowers from a field.

   Second, pick some wildflowers from a field.

3. Put water in the vase.

   Next, put water in the vase.

   _____

4. Place the flowers in the water.

   Then place the flowers in the water.

   _____

5. Arrange the flowers in an attractive pattern.

   Finally, arrange the flowers in an attractive pattern.

6. **Later, place the flowers on a table or windowsill and enjoy them.**

Vivid Words

When you write, use vivid, precise words to make your how-to report clearer and easier to follow.

General Words   Watch that kite <u>go</u> in the <u>air</u>.

Precise Words   Watch that kite <u>soar</u> up in the <u>clouds</u>.

Directions Replace each underlined word with a vivid, precise word. Write each sentence. **Possible answers:**

1. Cut paper for your kite in a <u>shape</u>.

   Cut paper for your kite in a triangle.

2. <u>Make</u> your kite a <u>good</u> <u>color</u>.

   Paint your kite a brilliant red.

3. <u>Put</u> some sticks on your kite.

   Glue some sticks on your kite.

4. <u>Put</u> your kite high in the air.

   Float your kite high in the air.

5. <u>Use</u> your kite with some <u>people</u>.

   Fly your kite with some good friends.

Peer and Teacher Conferencing
How-to Report

Directions Read your partner's report. Refer to the Revising Checklist as you write your comments or questions. Offer compliments as well as revision suggestions. Then take turns talking about each other's draft. Give your partner your notes. After you and your teacher talk about your report, add your teacher's comments to the notes.

Revising Checklist

Focus/Ideas

☐ Is the how-to report focused on explaining one task or activity?

☐ Are there enough details in the steps to explain the process?

Organization

☐ Are the steps of the process arranged in a logical order?

☐ Does the report have opening and concluding paragraphs?

Voice

☐ Does the writer show enthusiasm and knowledge?

Word Choice

☐ Do time-order words and vivid, precise words help make the steps and their sequence clear and coherent to the audience?

Sentences

☐ Are commands with strong verbs used to explain the steps?

Things I Thought Were Good _____

_____

Things I Thought Could Be Improved _____

_____

Teacher's Comments _____

_____

Contractions

Directions Use each pair of words to make a contraction. Write the contraction on the line.

haven't	1. have not	**I'd**	8. I would
when's	2. when is	**let's**	9. let us
didn't	3. did not	**they're**	10. they are
they'll	4. they will	**that's**	11. that is
she's	5. she is	**he'd**	12. he would
you'll	6. you will	**wasn't**	13. was not
we'd	7. we would	**you'd**	14. you would

Directions: Use the words in ( ) to make a contraction to complete each sentence. Write the contraction on the line.

hasn't   15. Judy (has not) planted a garden before.

she'd   16. This year she decided (she would) like to grow some plants.

they'd   17. Her mom said that (they would) work together.

wasn't   18. Judy's mom told her that it (was not) yet time to plant the garden.

it's   19. She explained that seeds can't grow if (it is) too cold.

wouldn't   20. She also said that plants (would not) grow without water.

Home Activity Your child formed contractions by using an apostrophe to take the place of letters that are left out. Ask your child to think of at least ten other word pairs that can be used to form contractions, such as *she is (she's), we will (we'll),* and *are not (aren't).* Ask your child to write sentences using these contractions.

Draw Conclusions

- A **conclusion** is a decision you reach after thinking about facts and details you read.
- You can also use what you already know to help draw a **conclusion.**
- Then ask yourself, "Does my **conclusion** make sense?"

Directions Read the following passage. Then complete the chart to draw a conclusion.

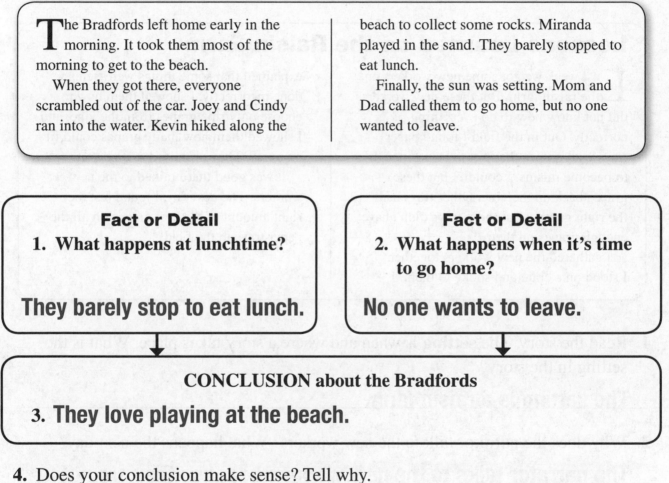

The Bradfords left home early in the morning. It took them most of the morning to get to the beach.

When they got there, everyone scrambled out of the car. Joey and Cindy ran into the water. Kevin hiked along the beach to collect some rocks. Miranda played in the sand. They barely stopped to eat lunch.

Finally, the sun was setting. Mom and Dad called them to go home, but no one wanted to leave.

Fact or Detail
1. What happens at lunchtime?

They barely stop to eat lunch.

Fact or Detail
2. What happens when it's time to go home?

No one wants to leave.

CONCLUSION about the Bradfords

3. **They love playing at the beach.**

4. Does your conclusion make sense? Tell why.

Yes, I know that when I don't want to stop doing something, it's because I'm having a great time.

Home Activity Your child drew a conclusion by using two facts or details from a story. Good readers draw conclusions as they read, using both facts in the story and their own prior knowledge. Provide your child with two facts or details, such as "Sam fills up a tub with water" and "the dog runs away." Ask your child to use the information to draw a conclusion. (The dog does not want to have a bath.)

Writing • Fiction

Key Features of Fiction

- tells an imagined story
- includes characters
- includes a setting
- follows a sequence of events that builds up to a climax

Lessons Learned on the Raisin Farm

Last week we got some new workers on the raisin farm. But these new workers did not know how to do everything correctly. Out in the field I found paper trays with grapes that weren't ripe enough to become raisins. I couldn't put these grapes back on the vine. Other trays had the right grapes. But these trays didn't have enough grapes on them.

I gathered the new workers together. I stood on a crate and spoke to them. I explained that some things were being done incorrectly. I showed them how to choose only ripe grapes from the vine, and I showed them how many grapes could fit on a tray. They promised to do better.

It was good that I talked to the new workers. The next day, I found just the right amount of the best grapes on all the paper trays in the field!

1. Read the story. The **setting** is when and where a story takes place. What is the setting in the story?

   The setting is a raisin farm.

2. Why does the narrator talk to the new workers? What happens the next day?

   The narrator talks to the new workers because they are not always choosing the best grapes to become raisins, and sometimes the workers are not putting enough grapes on the paper trays. The next day, the workers pick the correct grapes and put the right amount of each paper tray.

Vocabulary

Directions Fill in the blank with the word from the box that fits the meaning of the sentence.

1. Most natural foods are healthier than _____**artificial**_____ ones.

2. When you _____**raise**_____ your own crops, you know exactly what you are getting.

3. If the _____**area**_____ has warm winters, people grow food all year.

4. They don't need ___**preservatives**___ to keep their food fresh.

5. They can pull grapes off the _____**grapevine**_____, wash them, and eat them right away.

Directions Draw a line from the word to its meaning.

6. raisin   not found in nature

7. raise   additive that keeps food from spoiling too quickly

8. proof   a dried grape

9. preservative   evidence that shows that a fact is true

10. artificial   to grow, as on a farm

Write a Commercial

Write a commercial for raisins. Use as many of this week's vocabulary words as you can.
Students' writing should incorporate the lesson vocabulary in a commercial they write about raisins.

Home Activity Your child identified and used vocabulary words from *How Do You Raise a Raisin?* Talk with your child about foods in your kitchen or at the grocery store. Use the vocabulary words on this page.

© Pearson Education, Inc., 3

Action and Linking Verbs

A **verb** is a word that tells what someone or something is or does. **Action verbs** are words that show action. **Linking verbs,** such as *am, is, are, was,* and *were,* do not show action. They link a subject to a word or words in the predicate.

Action Verb	Grapes <u>grow</u> on tall vines.
Linking Verb	The grapes <u>are</u> red and juicy.

Directions One of the underlined words in each sentence is a verb. Write that word.

1. Amy <u>puts</u> the <u>seed</u> in the ground. _____**puts**_____

2. She <u>covers</u> it with <u>dirt</u>. _____**covers**_____

3. It <u>is</u> a pumpkin seed. _____**is**_____

4. Pumpkins <u>grow</u> in <u>summer</u>. _____**grow**_____

5. They <u>are</u> good <u>for</u> decorations. _____**are**_____

Directions Write the sentences. Underline the verb in each sentence.

6. Farmers grow grapes in warm places.

Farmers <u>grow</u> grapes in warm places.

7. They cut the ripe grapes from the vines.

They <u>cut</u> the ripe grapes from the vines.

8. Many people gather the grapes.

Many people <u>gather</u> the grapes.

9. Raisins are dried grapes.

Raisins <u>are</u> dried grapes.

10. We buy raisins at the supermarket.

We <u>buy</u> raisins at the supermarket.

Home Activity Your child learned about action verbs and linking verbs. Have your child name some action verbs that describe something you have done or are doing together today.

Contractions

Spelling Words				
let's	he'd	you'll	can't	I'd
won't	haven't	hasn't	she'd	they'll
when's	we'd	should've	wasn't	didn't

Contractions Write the underlined words as a contraction.

1. I wish <u>she had</u> stayed a few more days.   1. __she'd__

2. If <u>you will</u> build a doghouse, I'll paint it.   2. __you'll__

3. I <u>will not</u> be going to the party.   3. __won't__

4. I <u>can not</u> reach the top shelf.   4. __can't__

5. He <u>did not</u> go to the library.   5. __didn't__

6. I knew <u>we had</u> put too much water in the paint.   6. __we'd__

7. She <u>has not</u> finished writing the invitations.   7. __hasn't__

8. We <u>have not</u> played softball since Monday.   8. __haven't__

Joining Words Write the contraction.

9.	let + us	**9.**	__let's__
10.	they + will	**10.**	__they'll__
11.	he + would	**11.**	__he'd__
12.	when + is	**12.**	__when's__
13.	should + have	**13.**	__should've__
14.	was + not	**14.**	__wasn't__
15.	I + would	**15.**	__I'd__

Home Activity Your child wrote contractions. Pronounce a list word. Have your child name the words that were combined and then spell the contraction.

© Pearson Education, Inc., 3

Story Sequence B

Title	
Characters	**Setting**

Events **1. First**	

2. Next	

3. Then	

4. Last	

Vocabulary • Homophones

- **Homophones** are words that sound the same but have different spellings and meanings.
- Use the words and sentences around the homophone to help you figure out what it means.

---

knead to work dough with the hands
need to be unable to do without something

does plural of *doe,* a female deer
doze to sleep lightly

scent odor or smell
sent the past tense of *send*

peace calmness
piece a part of

flour the fine powder or meal made by grinding wheat or other grains
flower the part of a plant that produces seeds

Directions In each sentence below, underline the word in the ( ) that makes sense in the sentence. Use context clues to help you choose the right word.

1. Plants (knead, <u>need</u>) water and nutrients to live.

2. The rose is my favorite (flour, <u>flower</u>).

3. The rose has a beautiful (<u>scent</u>, sent).

4. You have to (<u>knead</u>, need) the dough twice to make good bread.

5. Sometimes I like a little (<u>peace</u>, piece) and quiet.

6. There were two (<u>does</u>, doze) and two fawns in my backyard.

7. Put the (<u>flour</u>, flower) into a large bowl and add the milk and eggs.

8. My dad likes to (does, <u>doze</u>) in his chair after dinner.

9. We (scent, <u>sent</u>) the photos of the party to Grandma in an e-mail.

10. Do you want a (peace, <u>piece</u>) of pie?

Home Activity Your child used sentence context to identify the meanings of homophones, words which sound alike but are spelled differently and have different meanings. Take turns with your child naming words that sound alike (such as *read* and *red*) and making up sentences to show the meaning.

Card Catalog

Libraries use a **card catalog** or a computerized **library database** to organize their materials. You can search for a book using the **author, title,** or **subject.** Look for the author's last name followed by the first name. When the book is located, either on the card or computer, there will be a **call number.** Each book in the library has its own call number that appears on the spine of the book.

Directions A database entry for a book on gardening is shown below. Use the entry to answer the questions.

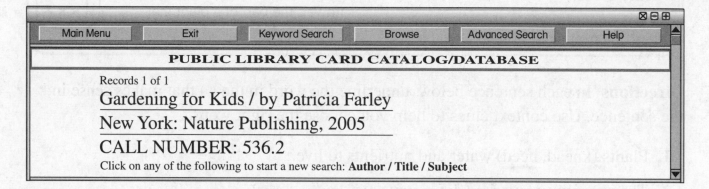

| Main Menu | Exit | Keyword Search | Browse | Advanced Search | Help |

PUBLIC LIBRARY CARD CATALOG/DATABASE

Records 1 of 1
Gardening for Kids / by Patricia Farley
New York: Nature Publishing, 2005
CALL NUMBER: 536.2
Click on any of the following to start a new search: **Author / Title / Subject**

1. What would you type to search the database by author to find this book?

   Farley, Patricia

2. What is the call number for this book?

   536.2

3. What would you type to search the database by subject to find this book?

   gardening

4. You want to find a book about gardening. Which word will you click on to begin your search?

   subject

5. In which year was this book published?

   2005

Home Activity Your child answered questions about a library database. If possible, visit the library with your child to review the computerized database. If not, look at some books and have your child tell how to search for it by subject, author, and title.

Name _____

Contractions

Proofread a Report To find out what happened in a playground accident, Tim's teacher had everyone write about it. Circle four spelling mistakes in Tim's report. Write the words correctly. Rewrite the compound sentence with a comma.

Spelling Words

let's
he'd
you'll
can't
I'd
won't
haven't

hasn't
she'd
they'll
when's
we'd
should've
wasn't
didn't

I (havn't) been playing ball lately, so I (did'nt) see the accident with the bat. I was playing tag with Dan. He said (hed) been playing ball earlier.

I'd tell you more but (thats) all I know. I hope Julian wasn't hurt badly.

1. __**haven't**__   2. __**didn't**__

3. __**he'd**__   4. __**that's**__

5. __**I'd tell you more, but that's all I know.**__

_____

Frequently Misspelled Words

that's
they're
didn't
it's

Proofread Words Circle the correct word and write it on the line.

6. Do you think (**we'd**) **we'ld** like the movie?   6. __**we'd**__

7. I **cant** (**can't**) play right now.   7. __**can't**__

8. Before we go, **lets'** (**let's**) say goodbye.   8. __**let's**__

9. I know (**they'll**) **theyl'l** love this gift!   9. __**they'll**__

10. He **has'nt** (**hasn't**) found his dog yet.   10. __**hasn't**__

11. I think (**you'll**) **you'l** be the winner.   11. __**you'll**__

12. The team (**won't**) **wo'nt** make the playoffs.   12. __**won't**__

School + Home **Home Activity** Your child identified misspelled contractions. Point to a spelling word. Ask your child to name the letters that were replaced by the apostrophe (').

Spelling Contractions   **187**

Action and Linking Verbs

Directions Read the selection. Then read each question that follows the selection. Decide which is the best answer to each question. Mark the space for the answer you have chosen.

Raisins: From Farms to Markets

(1) Farmers grow grapes in warm places. (2) When it is time, they cut the ripe grapes from the vine. (3) It takes many people to gather the grapes. (4) Some grapes are dried. (5) This is how they become raisins. (6) Farmers ship raisins off to stores. (7) We buy raisins at the supermarket, and they are delicious.

1 What is the verb in sentence 1? Is it an action verb or a linking verb?

- ⬭ in; linking
- ⬛ grow; action
- ⬭ grow; linking
- ⬭ in; action

2 What is the action verb in sentence 2?

- ⬛ cut
- ⬭ is
- ⬭ they
- ⬭ from

3 What is the verb in sentence 4? Is it an action verb or a linking verb?

- ⬭ grapes; linking
- ⬭ grapes; action
- ⬭ are; action
- ⬛ are; linking

4 What is the action verb in sentence 6?

- ⬛ ship
- ⬭ farmers
- ⬭ off
- ⬭ to

5 What is the linking verb in sentence 7?

- ⬭ buy
- ⬭ raisins
- ⬭ they
- ⬛ are

© Pearson Education, Inc., 3

Home Activity Your child prepared for taking tests on action verbs and linking verbs. Have your child make up some sentences about a job that interests him or her. Have your child identify the verb in each sentence.

Prefixes *un-, re-, mis-, dis-, non-*

Directions Add the prefix **un-, re-, mis-, non-,** or **dis-** to each base word. Write the new word on the line.

1. un- + load = **unload**
2. re- + learn = **relearn**
3. mis- + direct = **misdirect**
4. non- + sense = **nonsense**
5. dis- + like = **dislike**

Directions Write the word from the box that best fits each definition.

misspell 6. to spell wrong

nonstop 7. without stopping

unknown 8. not known

rewrite 9. to write again

dishonest 10. not honest

> nonstop
> dishonest
> misspell
> rewrite
> unknown

Directions Add the prefix **un-, re-, mis-,** or **dis-** to the word in ( ) to complete each sentence. Write the new word on the line.

unable 11. Last night I was (able) to see the stars.

disappeared 12. The sky was so dark, I thought they had (appeared).

misplaced 13. I couldn't find the telescope. Someone had (placed) it.

recall 14. When I asked who had used the telescope last, no one could (call).

unlikely 15. It's (likely) that I will see the stars tonight.

Home Activity Your child wrote words with the prefixes *un- (unhappy)*, *re- (recall)*, *mis- (mistake)*, *non- (nonsense)*, and *dis- (dislike)*. Ask your child to choose words from the box above and use them in sentences. Then ask your child to remove the prefix from each word and use the new words in sentences.

Character, Setting, and Plot

- **Characters** are the people or animals in a story.
- We can learn about characters by what they do and say.
- The **setting** is where and when a story takes place.

Directions Read the following play. Then answer the questions below.

NARRATOR: Maureen and Lynn help Ms. Kominski clean the classroom whenever they can. One Friday after school, they were helping to clean the bookcases, when someone came to call Ms. Kominski to the office.

MS. KOMINSKI: I'll be right back, girls.

NARRATOR: The two girls kept working, dusting the bookcase and straightening the books. Suddenly Maureen bumped into Lynn, and Lynn's arm hit the vase of flowers. The vase went crashing to the floor and broke!

LYNN: Oh, no! Quick, let's leave before Ms. Kominski comes back.

MAUREEN: That's silly! She will know it was us! Let's just tell her.

LYNN: You're right.

NARRATOR: Just then Ms. Kominski returned, and Lynn and Maureen told her what had happened. They offered to buy a new vase.

MS. KOMINSKI: I'm glad you told me. The vase was not expensive, so we won't worry about your paying for it. Just help me clean up the spilled water.

---

1. What is the setting of this story? __a classroom after school__

2. How do you know the girls like their teacher and enjoyed helping her?

   __They are staying after school. They offer to help whenever they can.__

3. Why do you think Lynn says they should leave when the vase breaks?

   __She probably feels embarassed and sorry.__

4. Why did the girls offer to pay for the vase?

   __They felt bad about breaking it and thought that would make up for it.__

5. How do you think they felt after Ms. Kominski said the vase was not expensive?

   __They probably felt relieved and glad they had told the truth.__

Home Activity Your child answered questions about characters in a story. Read a story together, or watch a television program, and discuss why the characters did the things they did in the story.

Writing • Play

Key Features of a Play

• has characters with speaking and sometimes nonspeaking parts who act out the story

• speaking characters have lines to say called *dialogue*

• includes a description of the setting

• has a central problem that must be solved (plot)

The Moose and the Gadfly

[Setting: At the riverbank. Moose is drinking from the river. Beaver, Bear, Duck, and Gadfly are gathered nearby.]

Narrator: The animals were worried. Moose had been drinking from the river for a very long time, and they were concerned that he would soon drink the river dry. Then Beaver would have no place to build his dam, Bear would have no fish to catch, and Duck would have no place to swim.

Beaver: What else can we do to stop Moose from drinking the river? The logs I rolled down the river only bounced off of him.

Bear: My angry growls don't frighten him.

Duck: And my furious quacks Moose ignores.

Gadfly: I will stop Moose from drinking the river dry!

Beaver, Bear, and Duck: What! How can a little fly frighten away a big moose? You are not clever, or strong, or brave!

Gadfly: [*buzzes toward Moose*] You'll see!

Narrator: As the other animals watched in disbelief, Moose suddenly stopped drinking the river. He began to swish his tail and gnaw his neck, and finally became so angry at Gadfly's biting that Moose ran far away, stomping his great feet and creating deep holes in the river as he went. This is how the Grand Canyon was formed, with steep sides and the river at the bottom. When Gadfly returned, all the animals cheered for him and never doubted the little fly again.

---

1. What is the problem in the story? Circle the paragraph that tells you.

The animals are afraid Moose will drink all the water. The Narrator's first paragraph tell us this.

2. How is the problem solved? Circle the paragraph that tells you.

Gadfly bit Moose and made him run away. The Narrator's last paragraph tells us this.

Vocabulary

Check the Words You Know

___overhead   ___poked
___imagined   ___narrator
___antlers   ___languages

Directions Write the vocabulary word from the box next to its meaning.

poked 1. jabbed with a finger or stick

narrator 2. someone who tells a story

antlers 3. bonelike growths on an animal's head, such as a deer

languages 4. the words and grammar people use to communicate

imagined 5. formed a picture in your mind about something

Directions Fill in the word from the box that fits the meaning of the sentence.

6. The deer had huge, pointed **antlers** on its head.

7. We looked at the clouds **overhead** to see if it would rain.

8. The boy **imagined** that he would grow up to be a great ball player.

9. My brother **poked** me in the arm to wake me up.

10. Rafael speaks two **languages**, English and Spanish.

Write a Poem

On a separate sheet of paper, write a poem about something wonderful you imagine. Use as many vocabulary words as possible.

Students' writing should incorporate the lesson vocabulary in a poem that's about something good they imagine.

Home Activity Your child has identified and used vocabulary words from *Pushing Up the Sky*. Play a game with your child in which you take turns imagining something, with each of you adding to what the other imagined. Use as many vocabulary words as you can.

Main Verbs and Helping Verbs

A **verb phrase** is a verb that has more than one word. The **main verb** shows action. A **helping verb** shows the time of the action. In the following sentence, *planting* is the main verb, and *are* is the helping verb.

The girls are planting corn with the women.

The helping verbs *am, is,* and *are* show present time. *Was* and *were* show past time. *Will* shows future time. The helping verbs *has, have,* and *had* show that an action happened in the past. In the following sentences, *had* and *will* are helping verbs.

They had planted in spring. We will harvest in fall.

Directions Underline the verb phrase in each sentence.

1. The chief is carving a beautiful pole.

2. He will place it at the entrance of the village.

3. The little boys are learning from the chief.

4. Someday they will carve a pole.

5. They have made many small animals already.

Directions Look at the underlined verb in each sentence. Write *M* if it is a main verb. Write *H* if it is a helping verb.

6. Everyone in the village is helping with the crops. _____**M**_____

7. The women had planted the seeds. _____**H**_____

8. The girls have watered the plants. _____**M**_____

9. The boys are picking the beans. _____**H**_____

10. The men will plow the fields. _____**H**_____

© Pearson Education, Inc., 3

School + Home **Home Activity** Your child learned about main verbs and helping verbs. Have your child answer the following question: *What were you doing at 3:00 today?* Then have your child identify the main verb and the helping verb in the answer.

Prefixes

Spelling Words				
unhappy	recall	disappear	unload	mistake
misspell	dislike	replace	mislead	disagree
rewrite	unroll	unknown	dishonest	react

Adding Prefixes Add a prefix to the underlined base word to make a list word. Write the list word. Read the sentence both ways.

1. Let's all help <u>load</u> the truck.　　1. **unload**

2. Our coach really knows how to <u>lead</u> the team.　2. **mislead**

3. We all <u>like</u> getting an allowance.　3. **dislike**

4. The class will <u>agree</u> with whatever you say.　4. **disagree**

5. I know I can <u>spell</u> that word.　5. **misspell**

6. You can count on that salesman to be <u>honest</u>.　6. **dishonest**

7. I like to <u>write</u> letters.　7. **rewrite**

8. Did you see the rabbit <u>appear</u> in the hat?　8. **disappear**

Word Meanings Write the list word that means almost the same thing as each word or phrase.

		react
9. unfamiliar	9. **unknown**	mistake
10. error	10. **mistake**	recall
11. remember	11. **recall**	unhappy
12. spread out	12. **unroll**	unknown
13. respond	13. **react**	replace
14. get another	14. **replace**	unroll
15. sad	15. **unhappy**	

© Pearson Education, Inc., 3

School + Home

Home Activity Your child spelled words with the prefixes *un-*, *re-*, *mis-*, and *dis-*. Point to a list word. Have your child spell the prefix and the base word separately.

Three-Column Chart

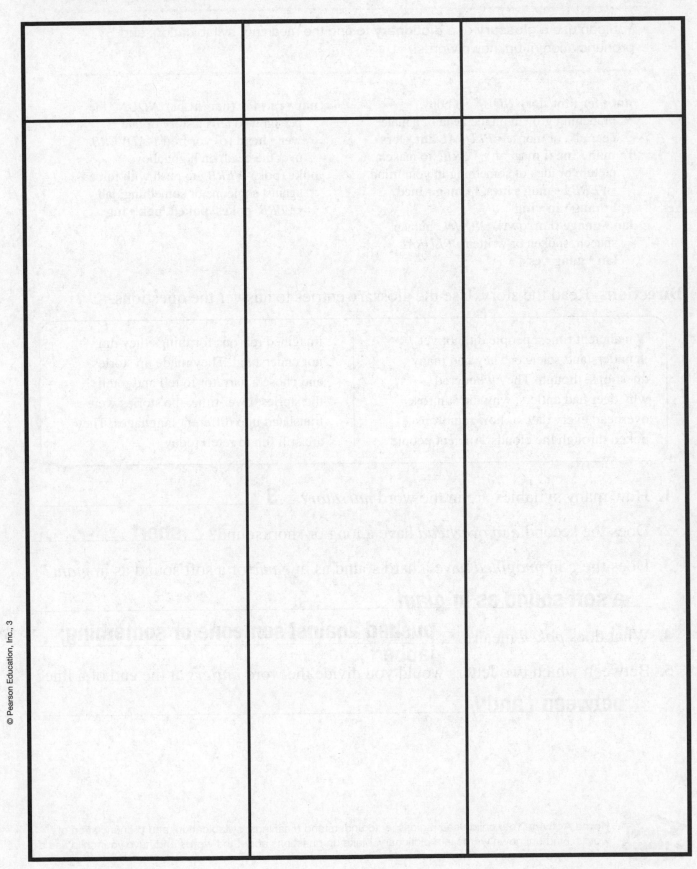

Vocabulary: Dictionary/Glossary

- You can use a **glossary** or a **dictionary** to find the meaning, syllabication, and pronunciation of unknown words.

ant • ler (ant′ lər) *NOUN.* a bony, branching growth on the head of a male deer elk, or moose • *PLURAL* ant • lers

i • mag • ine (i maj′ ən) *VERB.* to make a picture or idea of something in your mind • *VERB* i • mag • ines, i • mag • ined, i • mag • in • ing

lan • guage (lan′ gwij) *NOUN.* human speech, spoken or written • *PLURAL* lan • guag • es

nar • ra • tor (nar′ āt ər) *NOUN.* the person who tells a story or tale

o • ver • head (ō′ vər hed′) *ADVERB.* over the head; on high; above

poke (pōk) *VERB.* to push with force against someone or something; jab • *VERB* pokes, poked, pok • ing

Directions Read the story. Use the glossary entries to answer the questions.

In ancient times, people did not yet understand science. They had many questions, though. They wondered why deer had antlers, why the sun rose overhead every day, or how raindrops poked through the clouds. Ancient people imagined reasons for things they did not understand. They made up stories and chose a narrator to tell and retell the stories. Over time, the stories were translated into different languages. They are still fun to retell today.

1. How many syllables are in the word *narrator*? __**3**__

2. Does the second *e* in *overhead* have a long or short sound? __**short**__

3. Does the *g* in *imagined* have a hard sound as in *game* or a soft sound as in *giant*?

   __**a soft sound as in *giant***__

4. What does *poked* mean? __**pushed against someone or something; jabbed**__

5. Between which two letters would you divide the word *antlers* at the end of a line?

   __**between *t* and *l***__

Home Activity Your child used a glossary to understand meanings, syllabication, and pronunciation of words. Find unknown words in a dictionary. Make up questions about the words and have your child use a dictionary or glossary to find the answers.

Name _____

Thesaurus

A **thesaurus** includes entry words with synonyms (words with the same or similar meanings) and antonyms (words with opposite meanings). Most word processing programs have a thesaurus to help you choose just the right word.

Directions Use the thesaurus entry to answer the questions.

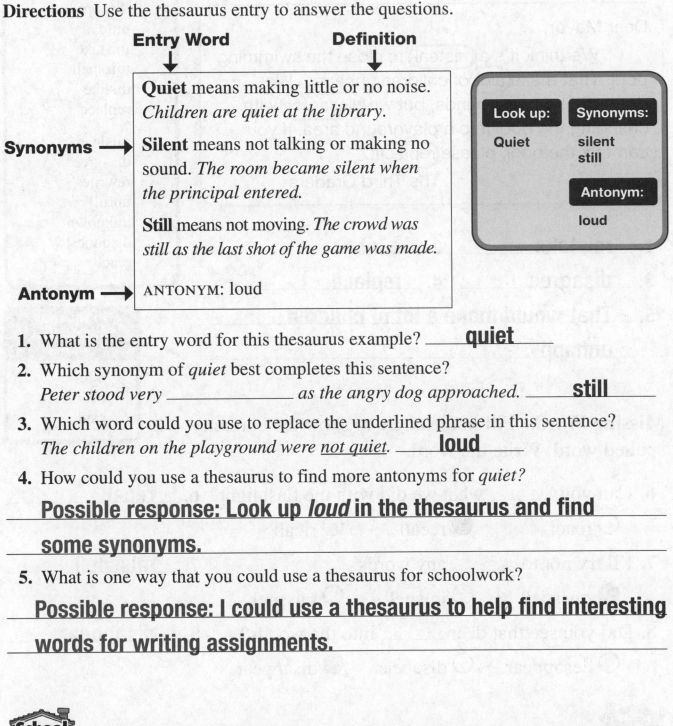

Entry Word   **Definition**

Quiet means making little or no noise. *Children are quiet at the library.*

Synonyms → **Silent** means not talking or making no sound. *The room became silent when the principal entered.*

Still means not moving. *The crowd was still as the last shot of the game was made.*

Antonym → ANTONYM: loud

Look up: Quiet
Synonyms: silent, still
Antonym: loud

1. What is the entry word for this thesaurus example? __**quiet**__

2. Which synonym of *quiet* best completes this sentence?
Peter stood very _____ as the angry dog approached. __**still**__

3. Which word could you use to replace the underlined phrase in this sentence?
The children on the playground were <u>not quiet</u>. __**loud**__

4. How could you use a thesaurus to find more antonyms for *quiet*?
__**Possible response: Look up *loud* in the thesaurus and find some synonyms.**__

5. What is one way that you could use a thesaurus for schoolwork?
__**Possible response: I could use a thesaurus to help find interesting words for writing assignments.**__

© Pearson Education, Inc., 3

School + Home **Home Activity** Your child answered questions about a thesaurus entry. Read a book or story with your child. Select appropriate words for him or her to look up in a thesaurus to find synonyms and antonyms.

Name _____

Prefixes

Proofread a Letter Circle four misspelled words and write them correctly. Rewrite the second sentence, adding the missing helping verb.

Dear Mayor,

We think it's a (misteak) to close the swimming pool. That make (alot) of children unhappy. We don't dislike playgrounds, but we (dissagree) with changing the pool into a playground area. If you can't fix the pool, please (replac) it.

The Third Graders

1. **mistake**   2. **a lot**

3. **disagree**   4. **replace**

5. **That would make a lot of children unhappy.**

Missing Words Fill in the circle to show the correctly spelled word. Write the word.

6. Can you _____ what we did with the flashlight?   6. **recall**
   ○ reacl   ● recall   ○ ricall

7. I'll try not to _____ any words.   7. **misspell**
   ● misspell   ○ mispell   ○ misspel

8. Did you see that deer _____ into the woods?   8. **disappear**
   ○ desappear   ○ disapear   ● disappear

Home Activity Your child identified misspelled words with the prefixes *un-*, *re-*, *mis-*, and *dis-*. Name a base word. Have your child spell the list word.

© Pearson Education, Inc., 3

Main Verbs and Helping Verbs

Directions Read the selection. Then read each question that follows the selection. Decide which is the best answer to each question. Mark the space for the answer you have chosen.

In the Village

(1) The chief is carving a beautiful pole. (2) He will place it at the entrance of the village. (3) The little boys are learning from the chief. (4) Someday they will carve a pole. (5) The children have made many small animal carvings already. (6) The village is famous for its poles. (7) People have come from all around to see their poles.

1 What is the main verb in sentence 1?

- ○ chief
- ○ is
- ● carving
- ○ pole

2 What is the helping verb in sentence 2?

- ● will
- ○ place
- ○ it
- ○ of

3 What word could you use to replace the main verb in sentence 4?

- ○ are
- ○ is
- ● make
- ○ made

4 What is the helping verb in sentence 5?

- ○ made
- ● have
- ○ many
- ○ carvings

5 The helping verb in sentence 7 shows that the action took place in what time?

- ● past
- ○ present
- ○ future
- ○ It does not show time.

Home Activity Your child prepared for taking tests on main verbs and helping verbs. Have your child make up two sentences about what he or she will do next weekend. Ask your child to identify the main verb and the helping verb in each sentence.

© Pearson Education, Inc., 3

Spellings of /j/, /k/, /s/

Directions Underline the letter or letters that stand for the sound /j/ in **jar**, **large**, and **edge**. Then write a sentence using each word.   **Possible responses are given.**

1. dama<u>ge</u>

   __The car had little damage from the crash._____

2. bri<u>dge</u>

   __The bridge goes across the river._____

3. ban<u>j</u>o

   __I would like to play the banjo._____

4. villa<u>ge</u>

   __The story takes place in a small village._____

Directions Circle the words in the box that have the sound /k/ spelled *k*, *c*, *ck*, and *ch* as in **mar<u>k</u>**, **<u>c</u>ost**, **pi<u>ck</u>**, and **s<u>ch</u>ool**. Write the words on the lines below.

(brake) branch cellar decide (locket)
merchant peaceful (stomach) stretch (stuck)

5. ___**brake**___   7. ___**stomach**___

6. ___**locket**___   8. ___**stuck**___

Directions Choose the words with the sound /s/ as in **per<u>s</u>on** and **pen<u>c</u>il**. Write the word on the line.

___**acid**___   9. acid   is   picture

___**inside**___   10. become   catch   inside

___**dance**___   11. coat   dance   was

___**once**___   12. account   bacon   once

© Pearson Education, Inc., 3

School + Home   **Home Activity** Your child wrote words with the /j/ sound in *jar*, *large*, and *edge*, the /s/ sound in *person* and *pencil*, and the /k/ sound in *mark*, *cost*, *pick*, and *chorus*. Encourage your child to identify other words with the /j/, /s/, or /k/ sounds. Together, make a list of these words and use them in sentences.

Graphic Sources

- **Graphic sources** include maps, charts, illustrations, and captions.
- Graphic sources help you understand information in the text.

Directions Read the following passage. Study the graphic source.

There are many things to see in the sky. In the daytime, you can see the Sun. On a clear night, you might see the Moon and lots of stars. You might also see some of the planets.

The Sun seems to travel around Earth, but that is not true. Earth is a planet, and planets orbit the Sun. The Sun, like other stars, stays in one place.

Directions Complete the chart to tell how the illustration and caption help you understand the text.

Type of Graphic Source	What It Shows	How It Helps You Understand Information
illustration	the name of each planet	shows how many planets there are
illustration	the path each planet travels	**Possible answer: illustrates what the word *orbit* means**
caption	**Possible answer: explains what the illustration shows**	helps readers understand the difference between stars and planets

Home Activity Your child used graphic sources such as captions and illustrations to understand a short passage. Flip through magazines and nonfiction books with your child. Discuss different graphic supports and how they help in understanding the text.

Writing • Formal Letter

Key Features of a Formal Letter

- Are written in correct letter format: heading, inside address, salutation, body, closing, and signature
- Are short and to the point
- Have a respectful tone
- Have no unnecessary personal information

---

805 Oak Street
Pine Plains, NY 12523
January 24, 20 _____

Professor Anne Shea
Astronomy Museum
789 Main Street
Pine Plains, NY 12523

Dear Professor Anne Shea,

   My third grade class has been learning about stars. I am writing because I have a question about pulsating stars. Is it true that these stars can expand and contract like beating hearts? And so some of these stars pulse with steady beats while others pulse with uneven beats?

   I would appreciate it if you could please answer my questions about these stars. I would like to write a school report about them. Thank you for your time.

                                    Sincerely,

                                    Ben Chung

---

1. Which words make up the salutation?

Dear Professor Anne Shea,

2. Circle where the writer shows respect in the letter.

3. List two examples of subject-verb agreement in the letter.

My third grade class has been learning; I am

Vocabulary

Directions Choose the vocabulary word from the box and write it next to its meaning.

gigantic _____ **1.** very large

ladle _____ **2.** spoon with a deep bowl and a long handle

shine _____ **3.** to give off light

temperature _____ **4.** a measure of heat or cold

dim _____ **5.** poorly lit; hard to see

Check the Words You Know
___dim
___gas
___gigantic
___ladle
___patterns
___shine
___temperature

Directions Choose a word from the box that fits the meaning of the sentence and write it on the line.

6. Constellations are groups of stars that form _____**patterns**_____ in the sky.

7. Our sun gives off light because it is a ball of burning _____**gas**_____.

8. The Big Dipper is shaped like an ordinary kitchen _____**ladle**_____.

9. It's hard to believe stars are _____**gigantic**_____ when they look so small to us from Earth.

10. When daylight grows _____**dim**_____ as the sun sets, stars begin to appear in the sky.

Write a Description

On a separate sheet of paper, write a description of a constellation, such as the Big Dipper. Include information about its appearance and the stars that it contains. Use as many vocabulary words as you can in your writing.

Students should use vocabulary to describe a constellation.

Home Activity Your child identified and used new vocabulary words from *Seeing Stars.* Read an article about astronomy with your child. Use this week's vocabulary words to talk about the article.

© Pearson Education, Inc., 3

Subject-Verb Agreement

The subject and the verb in a sentence must work together, or **agree.** To make most present tense verbs agree with singular nouns or *he, she,* or *it,* add *-s.* If the subject is a plural noun or *I, you, we,* or *they,* the present tense verb does not end in *-s.*

Singular Subject   The <u>sun</u> <u>shines</u>. <u>It</u> <u>warms</u> the Earth.
Plural Subject   <u>Stars</u> <u>glow</u> at night. <u>They</u> <u>sparkle</u>.

A form of *be* in a sentence also must agree with the subject. Use *is* or *was* to agree with singular nouns. Use *are* or *were* to agree with plural nouns.

Singular Subject   A <u>star</u> <u>is</u> shining. <u>It</u> <u>was</u> millions of miles away.
Plural Subject   <u>People</u> <u>are</u> gazing at stars. <u>They</u> <u>were</u> interested in them.

Directions Choose the verb in ( ) that agrees with the subject. Write the verb.

1. I (see, sees) yellow stars. _____**see**_____

2. Yellow stars (is, are) very hot. _____**are**_____

3. Red stars (has, have) cooler temperatures. _____**have**_____

4. Stars (is, are) made of hot gas. _____**are**_____

5. The sun (appear, appears) very large. _____**appears**_____

Directions Choose the verb in ( ) that agrees with the subject. Write the sentence.

6. Earth (move, moves) around the sun.

Earth moves around the sun.

7. Our world (spin, spins) around once a day.

Our world spins around once a day.

8. We (see, sees) many stars at night.

We see many stars at night.

Home Activity Your child learned about subject-verb agreement. Have your child tell a sentence about something that happened in school and explain how the subject and verb agree.

© Pearson Education, Inc., 3

Spellings of /j/, /s/, /k/

Spelling Words

clock	large	page	mark	kitten
judge	crack	edge	pocket	brake
change	ridge	jacket	badge	orange

Context Clues Write the missing list word. It rhymes with the underlined word.

1. The _____ wouldn't <u>budge</u> on the sentence.

2. Don't go too near the _____ of the rock <u>ledge</u>.

3. A park ranger may scratch tree <u>bark</u> to _____ a path.

4. I placed the _____ on the <u>rock</u>.

5. We used the <u>bridge</u> to cross the _____ .

6. It's <u>strange</u> that he carries so much _____ .

7. When you are ready, <u>take</u> your foot off the _____.

8. This _____ tells how to build a <u>cage</u>.

9. The _____ likes to play with my <u>mitten</u>.

10. The old coat <u>rack</u> is starting to _____ .

11. I put my tennis <u>racket</u> under my _____ to keep it dry.

1. **judge**
2. **edge**
3. **mark**
4. **clock**
5. **ridge**
6. **change**
7. **brake**
8. **page**
9. **kitten**
10. **crack**
11. **jacket**

Missing Words Write list words to complete the description.

The firefighter is wearing a bright (12) **orange**

jacket and a (13) **large** hat. He has a

(14) **badge** on his (15) **pocket** .

© Pearson Education, Inc., 3

School + Home **Home Activity** Your child spelled words with the consonant sounds /j/ and /k/. Ask your child to identify the letter combinations *ge*, *dge*, *ck*, and *k* in the list words.

KWL Chart

Topic _____

What We **K**now	What We **W**ant to Know	What We **L**earned

© Pearson Education, Inc., 3

Name _____

Vocabulary: Reference Sources

- You can use a **glossary** or a **dictionary** to find the meanings of unknown words.
- Entries in glossaries and dictionaries are in **alphabetical order.** When two words have the same first and second letter, alphabetize by the third letter.

gigantic *ADJECTIVE.* huge
ginormous *ADJECTIVE.* so large that it is both gigantic and enormous

telescope *NOUN.* a tool to make distant objects appear nearer
temperature *NOUN.* the degree of heat or cold in something

Directions Put each set of words in alphabetical order. Use the glossary example above to help you. Then answer the questions.

shine   shapes   shrink
shoulder   shelf

thousands   these
that's   this   through

1. _____ shapes _____

2. _____ shelf _____

3. _____ shine _____

4. _____ shoulder _____

5. _____ shrink _____

6. _____ that's _____

7. _____ these _____

8. _____ this _____

9. _____ thousands _____

10. _____ through _____

11. Which word comes just before *shoulder* in the glossary?

shine

12. Which word comes just after *this* in the glossary?

thousands

© Pearson Education, Inc., 3

Home Activity Your child put words whose first two letters are the same in alphabetical order. Use a dictionary, glossary, or telephone book to find three words that begin with the same two letters, such as *star, stem,* and *sting.* Have your child put the words in alphabetical order.

Almanac

An **almanac** is a book of facts published once a year. There are two types of almanacs. The **farmer's almanac** contains facts about weather, astronomy, and the tides of the ocean. The **general information almanac** contains facts, figures, and information in many categories.

Directions Use the page from the almanac to answer the questions.

2007 Almanac

Awards and Prizes

The Newbery Medal, 2000–2006

The Newbery Medal of the American Library Association was first awarded in 1922. It is given to the author of the year's best children's book. Only American authors can win the Newbery Medal. The medal is named for John Newbery, the first English publisher of children's books.

2000   Christopher Paul Curtis, *Bud, Not Buddy*
2001   Richard Peck, *A Year Down Yonder*
2002   Linda Sue Park, *A Single Shard*
2003   Avi, *Crispin: The Cross of Lead*
2004   Kate DiCamillo, *The Tale of Despereaux*
2005   Cynthia Kadohata, *Kira-Kira*
2006   Lynne Rae Perkins, *Criss Cross*

1. Who won the Newbery Medal in 2001? **Richard Peck**

2. Under what broad category is this information listed?

Awards and Prizes

3. Is this page from a farmer's almanac or a general information almanac? How do you know?

general information alamanc; farmer's almanac only has

information about weather, tides, and astronomy

4. What was the title of the best children's book of 2005?

Kira-Kira

5. Name one fact you might find in a farmer's almanac.

Sample answer: You might find a sky map with labeled constellations.

Home Activity Your child answered questions about a page of information from an almanac. Show your child an almanac. Have your child examine the different sections, such as the index.

© Pearson Education, Inc., 3

Spellings of /j/, /s/, /k/

Proofread a Supply List Jon and Ted are organizing an overnight camping trip for the scouts. Circle four spelling mistakes. Write the words correctly. Write the item with the incorrect verb correctly.

Bring these things:
- (jackit)
- raincoat or (larg) plastic bag
- pocket compass if you has one
- a (chang) of clothing
- signed permission page

Jon and I will bring (are) tents.

Spelling Words

clock
large
page
mark
kitten
judge
crack
edge

pocket
brake
change
ridge
jacket
badge
orange

1. __jacket__   2. __large__

3. __change__   4. __our__

5. __pocket compass if you have one__

Frequently Misspelled Words

our
I
I'm
until

Proofread Words Circle the word that is spelled correctly. Write it.

6. citten   (kitten)   __kitten__

7. badg   (badge)   __badge__

8. (orange)   orandge   __orange__

9. rigde   (ridge)   __ridge__

10. (brake)   bracke   __brake__

11. poket   (pocket)   __pocket__

12. (edge)   edje   __edge__

School + Home **Home Activity** Your child spelled words with *ge*, *dge*, *ck*, and *k*. Give clues about a list word. Have your child guess and spell the word.

Subject-Verb Agreement

Directions Read the selection. Then read each question that follows the selection. Decide which is the best answer to each question. Mark the space for the answer you have chosen.

The Night Sky

(1) Juan <u>learn</u> all about stars. (2) He <u>use</u> his dad's telescope. (3) Juan's friends <u>is</u> interested in stars, too. (4) They <u>go</u> to the planetarium. (5) The planetarium has programs about the stars. (6) <u>Everyone</u> learn a lot on each visit.

1 What verb agrees with the subject in sentence 1?

- ⬭ learn
- ⬬ learns
- ⬭ learning
- ⬭ learnes

2 What verb agrees with the subject in sentence 2?

- ⬭ use
- ⬭ using
- ⬭ useses
- ⬬ uses

3 What verb agrees with the subject in sentence 3?

- ⬭ is
- ⬭ was
- ⬬ are
- ⬭ be

4 What verb agrees with the subject in sentence 4?

- ⬬ go
- ⬭ goes
- ⬭ going
- ⬭ gone

5 What subject agrees with the verb in sentence 6?

- ⬭ Everyone
- ⬭ Juan
- ⬭ Juan's dad
- ⬬ His friends

© Pearson Education, Inc., 3

Home Activity Your child prepared for taking tests on subject-verb agreement. Point out a sentence in a newspaper. Have your child identify the subject and verb in the sentence and explain why they agree.

Suffixes -*ly*, -*ful*, -*ness*, -*less*, -*able*, -*ible*

Directions Add the suffix **-ly, -ful, -ness, -able, -ible,** or **-less** to each base word. Write the new word on the line.

1. grace + -ful = **graceful**
2. bare + -ly = **barely**
3. depend + -able = **dependable**
4. fair + -ness = **fairness**
5. convert + -ible = **convertible**
6. wire + -less = **wireless**
7. rare + -ly = **rarely**
8. neat + -ness = **neatness**

Directions Add **-ly, -ful, -ness, -able,** or **-less** to the base word in ( ) to best complete each sentence. Use the word box for help. Write the new word on the line.

careful   careless   illness   quickly   safely   dependable   thickness

careless 9. A (care) mistake can cause an oil spill at sea.

quickly 10. This can (quick) cause problems for seabirds.

dependable 11. We can all help, by being (depend).

safely 12. If the oil is not (safe) removed, the birds cannot fly.

illness 13. If a seabird swallows oil, it can develop an (ill).

thickness 14. The (thick) of a bird's eggshell can also change.

careful 15. To protect the sea and its wildlife, ships' captains must be (care).

 Home Activity Your child wrote words with the suffixes *-ly (safely), -ful (playful), -ness (illness),* and *-less (worthless)*. Name some base words such as *slow, thank, harm, kind,* and *help*. Ask your child to make new words using the suffixes he or she practiced on this page.

© Pearson Education, Inc., 3

Name _____

Generalize

- Ideas in what you read are sometimes alike in several ways. To **generalize**, you can make a general statement about them together.

- Look for **clue words** such as *most*, *many*, *all*, *some*, or *few*.

Directions Read the following passage.

Mammals are animals that need to breathe air. Most mammals give birth to live babies. Mammal mothers also give milk to their babies.

Gray whales live in the ocean. Mothers-to-be find a safe place, such as a lagoon, to give birth. After the calf is born, a female helper pushes it up to the surface so it can breathe. Then the mother feeds the baby.

Directions Are gray whales mammals? Complete the chart. Make a generalization.

Example

1. Do gray whales breathe air?

Yes

Example

2. Do gray whales give birth to babies?

Yes

Example

3. Do gray whales nurse their young?

Yes

Generalization

4. Gray whales are _____**mammals**_____.

5. How did answering the questions in the examples help you make a generalization?

It helped me see how gray whales are mammals.

Home Activity Your child made a generalization by finding examples of the ways things are alike. Draw a graphic organizer like the one above. Write examples about the ways dogs are alike in the three example boxes (dogs bark, wag tails, have hair). Then help your child write a generalization about dogs.

Writing • News Article

Key Features of a News Article

- has a headline and a short introduction that grab attention
- answers the five Ws and How?
- describes a current event and includes important information about the event

Baby Finds New Home by Jess Salvatore

Diego Salvatore didn't know what it was at first. It was small and pink. It was lying at the bottom of the tree in his backyard. It looked like it needed his help.

Saturday Surprise
Diego found the baby animal on Saturday morning. He wrapped it carefully in an old towel, and he placed it in a shoebox. He talked to other kids on his street, but none of them knew what it was. "I thought it was a puppy," Diego's friend Brandon said. They decided to show it to Mrs. Sing. Mrs. Sing lives next door to Diego. She loves

animals. She has many birds, fish, and a tank of hermit crabs.

Mystery Solved
Mrs. Sing told them the animal was a baby squirrel. She called the Wildlife Center. The Center said they would care for the squirrel. "We rescue many baby squirrels each spring," said Alice, who works at the Center. "They often fall out of their nests."

After lunch, Mrs. Sing and Diego drove to the Center. They left the baby squirrel with Alice. They also made a donation to the Center. Their donation will help the Center rescue more young and wounded animals.

1. What is the action verb in the headline? What parts of the introduction grab your attention?
   Finds **is the action verb in the headline. The parts of the introduction that grab my attention are the words** *didn't know what it was at first* **and** *It looked like it needed his help.*

2. Write the first sentence in the model that tells you **what** happened.
   Diego found the baby animal on Saturday morning.

3. Write the quotes from the news article. Put a star next to the name of the person who is an expert.
   "I thought it was a puppy," Diego's friend Brandon said; "We rescue many baby squirrels each spring," said Alice*, who works at the Center. "They often fall out of their nests."

Vocabulary

Directions Read the pairs of sentences below. Use one word from the box to fill in the blank in each pair of sentences. Use context clues to help you fill in the correct word.

Check the Words You Know

___surrounded
___bay
___supplies
___chipped
___symphony
___channel
___blizzards
___anxiously
___melody

1. This winter was very snowy. We had four **blizzards** in December alone!

2. The bird sang a beautiful tune. The **melody** was sweet and sad.

3. The children gathered all around the teacher. She was **surrounded** by her class.

4. She was worried about her grade on the test. She waited **anxiously** as the tests were handed back.

5. The water flowed along a narrow stream. The stream was a **channel** that carried the water to the sea.

Directions In each sentence below, two words are underlined. Circle the word that makes sense. Use context clues in the sentence to help you choose the correct word.

6. The ship sailed into the large (bay) / blizzard that is near our town.

7. Before we went on the hike, I put a big bay /(supply) of water in my backpack.

8. Dan surrounded /(chipped) at the wood with a small ax.

9. We heard many musical instruments playing a beautiful (symphony)/ channel together.

10. I heard a song on the radio, and I have been humming the symphony /(melody) all day.

Write a Scene from a Play

On a separate sheet of paper, write a short scene from a play about a person communicating with an animal. Use as many vocabulary words as possible.

Students' writing should use lesson vocabulary in a play describing an animal and a human communicating.

Home Activity Your child identified and used vocabulary words from *A Symphony of Whales*. Read a story or article about animals to your child. Have your child point out unfamiliar words. Work together to try to figure out the meaning of each word by using other words that appear near it.

© Pearson Education, Inc., 3

Present, Past, and Future Tenses

Verbs can show when an action happens. This is called **tense.** Different verb tenses have different forms. Many present tense verbs end in *-s.* Form the past tense of many verbs by adding *-ed.* Add the helping verb *will* to a verb to make it a future tense verb.

Present Tense	A whale <u>stays</u> near the beach.
Past Tense	The whale <u>jumped</u> out of the water.
Future Tense	The other whales <u>will jump</u> out soon.

- When a verb ends with *e,* drop the *e* before adding *-ed: glide   glided*
- When a one-syllable verb ends with one vowel followed by one consonant, double the final consonant before adding *-ed: shop   shopped*
- When a verb ends with a consonant followed by *y,* change the *y* to *i* before adding *-ed: hurry   hurried*

Directions Tell the tense of the underlined verb in each sentence. Write *present, past,* or *future.*

1. I <u>like</u> the humpback whales. _____ **present**

2. You <u>will enjoy</u> the whales' music. _____ **future**

3. Those whales <u>traveled</u> from the Arctic Ocean. _____ **past**

4. They <u>will return</u> next year. _____ **future**

Directions Write the verb in ( ) that correctly completes each sentence.

5. Last year Sammy's class (learn, learned) about whales. _____ **learned**

6. Whales cannot breathe underwater, so they (jump, jumped) out of the water for air. _____ **jump**

7. Each time a mother whale gives birth, she (stays, stayed) close to the baby for a year. _____ **stays**

8. After a year, the baby (cared, will care) for itself. _____ **will care**

© Pearson Education, Inc., 3

School + Home **Home Activity** Your child learned about present, past, and future tenses. Ask your child to make up a sentence about something he or she saw on the way home from school and identify the tense of the sentence's verb.

Name _____

Suffixes

Spelling Words				
beautiful	safely	kindness	finally	spotless
worthless	illness	helpful	daily	suddenly
wireless	quietly	fairness	cheerful	painful

Word Endings Add an ending to the underlined word.
Then write the list word.

1. Do you floss your teeth <u>day</u>?   1. __**daily**__

2. We've <u>final</u> finished our treehouse!   2. __**finally**__

3. We sneaked <u>quiet</u> up the steps.   3. __**quietly**__

4. Cell phones are <u>wire</u>.   4. __**wireless**__

5. Isn't <u>fair</u> important in any game?   5. __**fairness**__

6. His bicycle was <u>spot</u>.   6. __**spotless**__

7. Holding the door open is a <u>help</u> thing to do.   7. __**helpful**__

8. His broken leg is <u>pain</u>.   8. __**painful**__

9. Her <u>kind</u> made everyone feel better.   9. __**kindness**__

10. Then <u>sudden</u> the boat turned over.   10. __**suddenly**__

11. She is always <u>cheer</u> when she gets up.   11. __**cheerful**__

Context Clues Write a list word to complete the phrase.

12. drive __**safely**__

13. __**worthless**__ as a wooden nickel

14. contagious __**illness**__

15. __**beautiful**__ as a swan

Home Activity Your child spelled words with the suffixes *-ly*, *-ful*, *-ness*, and *-less*. Have your child pronounce each list word and identify the suffix.

© Pearson Education, Inc., 3

Five Ws and How?

What happened?

Who was there?

Where did it happen?

When did it happen?

Why did it happen?

How did it happen?

Vocabulary: Unfamiliar Words/Context Clues

- **Context clues** are the words and sentences around an unfamiliar word.
- When you come to an unfamiliar word, read the words around the word you don't know and use them to figure out the word's meaning.

Directions Read the following passage about helping water birds. Then answer the questions below. Look for context clues as you read.

When a huge ship spilled oil into the bay, people in the nearby village rushed anxiously to the water. They were sad to see ducks surrounded by floating oil. Their feathers were covered with the black, slimy stuff. Without help, the ducks would die!

The people grabbed their supplies. They cleaned the ducks with soap and towels. After the ducks were rested and dry, the people took them back to the water. The school band played a happy melody while the ducks were released. Everyone cheered as the ducks swam away.

1. What words in the first sentence are clues that the word *bay* names a body of water?

   ship, water

2. Does *anxiously* mean "nervously" or "happily"? How do you know?

   nervously; People rushed to the water and when they got there, they felt sad.

3. Does *surrounded* mean "underneath" or "in the middle of"?

   in the middle of

4. What two words in the second paragraph are clues to the meaning of *supplies*?

   soap, towels

5. How can you tell that a melody is a tune?

   The paragraph says that the band played one.

Home Activity Your child used context clues to figure out the meanings of unfamiliar words. Read a story with your child. Stop when you come to an unfamiliar word and ask your child to use context clues to determine the word's meaning.

© Pearson Education, Inc., 3

Take Notes and Record Findings

As you research a subject, **taking notes** and **recording findings** of important information helps give your research a focus. You may want to organize your notes by main ideas and details or as answers to questions you have about the subject.

Directions Look at the chart below. Read the paragraph and highlight or underline important information as you read. Then record your findings in the lists to complete them.

Albino Animals

Imagine seeing an animal that looks like a deer, but it's different. It has white fur and pink eyes! The tail, the ears, and everything else look the same. Just the color is different. This animal is an albino deer. Albinos have a trait that is different from that of others of its species. An albino animal has no pigment in its skin, hair, or eyes. That's why the skin, fur, or feathers are white. Deer are not the only albino animals. Many others have been discovered. There are albino dogs, squirrels, leopards, and even birds.

Why It Is White	Features	Kinds of Animals
has different traits	looks like others	dogs
		leopards
1. **no pigment**	2. **white fur, skin, or feathers**	squirrels
	3. **pink eyes**	4. **deer**
		5. **birds**

Home Activity Your child read a paragraph and recorded important information about it in categories. Help your child find a paragraph in a reference book, nonfiction text, or from a Web site. Ask your child to take notes about the important information in the paragraph.

Suffixes

Spelling Words				
beautiful	safely	kindness	finally	spotless
worthless	illness	helpful	daily	suddenly
wireless	quietly	fairness	cheerful	painful

Proofread a Note Christy sent a note to her neighbor who is in the hospital. Circle four spelling mistakes. Write the words correctly. Add the missing punctuation mark.

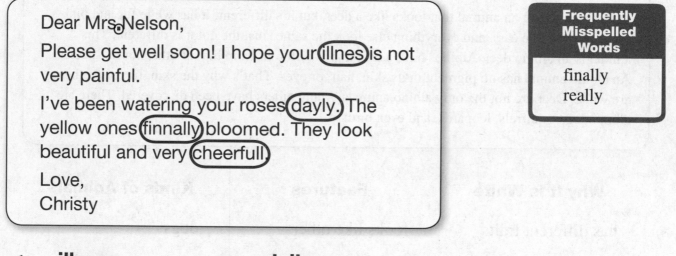

Dear Mrs. Nelson,

Please get well soon! I hope your (illnes) is not very painful.

I've been watering your roses (dayly.) The yellow ones (finnally) bloomed. They look beautiful and very (cheerfull.)

Love,
Christy

Frequently Misspelled Words

finally
really

1. __illness__   2. __daily__

3. __finally__   4. __cheerful__

Proofread Words Fill in the circle next to the word that is spelled correctly. Write the word.

5. ○ suddennly ● suddenly ○ suddenily   5. __suddenly__

6. ○ worthyles ○ worthles ● worthless   6. __worthless__

7. ○ safly ● safely ○ safelly   7. __safely__

8. ● quietly ○ quietily ○ qiuetly   8. __quietly__

9. ○ kindnes ○ kinness ● kindness   9. __kindness__

10. ● spotless ○ spotles ○ spottless   10. __spotless__

Home Activity Your child spelled words with the suffixes *-ly*, *-ful*, *-ness*, and *-less*. Have your child underline the base word in each list word. Remind your child to change *i* back to *y* when necessary.

© Pearson Education, Inc., 3

Present, Past, and Future Tenses

Directions Read the selection. Then read each question that follows the selection. Decide which is the best answer to each question. Mark the space for the answer you have chosen.

Whales

(1) I _____ humpback whales. (2) Last summer, I _____ to the ocean to see them. (3) My jaw _____ when I saw them. (4) The whales traveled from the Arctic Ocean. (5) They _____ thousands of miles every year. (6) They _____ next year.

1 What present tense verb can be used in sentence 1?

- ⬤ like
- ⬭ liked
- ⬭ would like
- ⬭ liking

2 What past tense verb can be used in sentence 2?

- ⬭ travel
- ⬭ traveling
- ⬤ traveled
- ⬭ will travel

3 What past tense verb can be used in sentence 3?

- ⬭ dropping
- ⬭ will drop
- ⬤ dropped
- ⬭ droped

4 What present tense verb can be used in sentence 5?

- ⬭ will swim
- ⬤ swim
- ⬭ swimmed
- ⬭ swimed

5 What future tense verb can be used in sentence 6?

- ⬭ return
- ⬭ returning
- ⬭ returned
- ⬤ will return

School + Home **Home Activity** Your child prepared for taking tests on present, past, and future tenses. Point out a sentence in a book you are reading together. Have your child tell whether the sentence is in present, past, or future tense.

Consonant Patterns *wr, kn, gn, st, mb*

Directions Choose the word in ( ) with the silent consonant, as in **wr, kn, st, mb,** or **gn,** to complete each sentence. Write the word on the line.

_____ **climb** _____ 1. It seemed like the perfect winter day for a (climb/hike) up the mountain.

_____ **knapsack** _____ 2. Jan packed water and snacks in a (cooler/knapsack).

_____ **knit** _____ 3. She put on her coat and (knit/new) cap.

_____ **design** _____ 4. She grabbed the scarf with the blue and yellow (design/stripes).

_____ **wrapped** _____ 5. Then she (tossed/wrapped) it around her neck.

_____ **fasten** _____ 6. Jan began to (close/fasten) her coat.

_____ **listen** _____ 7. The radio was on, and Jan stopped to (hear/listen).

_____ **signs** _____ 8. The reporter said there were (calls/signs) that a big snowstorm was on its way.

_____ **knew** _____ 9. Jan (learned/knew) she would have to go hiking another day.

Directions Circle each word in the box that has a silent consonant. Write the circled words in alphabetical order on the lines below.

| (gnaw) relax (castle) (wrong) basket no (comb) (knot) humid water trap (numb) |

10. _____ **castle** _____   13. _____ **knot** _____

11. _____ **comb** _____   14. _____ **numb** _____

12. _____ **gnaw** _____   15. _____ **wrong** _____

© Pearson Education, Inc., 3

Home Activity Your child wrote words with the silent consonants *wr (write), kn (knight), st (listen), mb (thumb),* and *gn (gnaw).* Work with your child to see how many words with those silent letters you can name together. Write the words and take turns making sentences using each word.

Name _____

Cause and Effect

- A **cause** tells why something happened.
- An **effect** is what happened.
- Words such as *because* and *so* are clues that can help you figure out a cause and its effect.

Directions Read the following article.

> Some people have backyards that are full of animals. Their yards are almost like private zoos. That's because these nature-loving people have taken the time and trouble to plant trees. The trees attract birds, so the birds rush to build nests in the branches. Squirrels like trees, too, so they'll often be seen climbing the trunks and leaping from branch to branch. When people plant trees, they can enjoy watching wildlife in their backyards for years to come.

Directions Fill in the chart to show cause and effect. Then list two clue words from the passage that helped you figure out the cause and effect.

Cause

1. Cause: People **plant trees**

Effects

2. Effect: so birds **come to build nests**

3. Effect: so squirrels **come to play**

4. Clue Word: <u>SO</u>

5. Clue Word: <u>because</u>

School + Home **Home Activity** Your child identified cause and effect in an article. Talk with your child about things that happen around your home every day. Talk about what causes those things to happen.

© Pearson Education, Inc., 3

Writing • Compare-and-Compare Composition

Key Features of a Compare-and-Contrast Composition

• shows how two things are similar and different

• includes supporting facts, details, and explanations

• ends with a concluding sentence or paragraph

A Tale of Two Playgrounds

There are two playgrounds I like to go to. The first is in Grant Park. The other one is in City Park. They have some things in common, but they also have differences.

The two playgrounds are the same in some ways. The Grant Park playground has a slide and swings. The slide is very tall. The playground also has a merry-go-round, which I like to spin really fast. The City Park playground also has a slide, merry-go-round, and swings. The slide is also tall, and the merry-go-round is just as fun.

The playgrounds have some differences too. Grant Park is near my house. We can walk to that playground. City Park is downtown, so we have to drive to get there. In the Grant Park playground, the ground is gravel. The City Park playground has sandy ground. The playgrounds are also different because the swings are different. The Grant Park playground uses soft swings that bend when you sit on them. The City Park playground uses hard, stiff swings.

So, the two playgrounds are the same in some ways and different in others. But most importantly, they are both fun!

1. What two things are being compared and contrasted?

   The two playgrounds: Grant Park and City Park.

2. What is one way that the playgrounds are the same? What is one way that they are different?

   Both playgrounds have the same equipment—slide, swings,

   and a merry-go-round. They are different because the swings in

   Grant Park are soft, but the swings in City Park are hard. Grant

   Park has a gravel ground, but City Park has a sandy ground.

Name _____

Vocabulary

Check the Words You Know

___incredible   ___survivors
___lofty   ___topic
___noble   ___unseen
___search   ___waterless
___stinging

Directions Draw a line from the word to its meaning.

1. incredible   without moisture; dry

2. noble   not noticed

3. lofty   unbelievable

4. unseen   high up

5. waterless   impressive

Directions Fill in the blank with the word from the box that fits the meaning of the sentence.

6. It's fun to go in _____**search**_____ of nature's secrets.

7. You may discover tricks animals use to be _____**survivors**_____ in a harsh world.

8. Some birds keep their babies safe by building nests in _____**lofty**_____ branches.

9. Some insects protect themselves by _____**stinging**_____ their enemies.

10. Nature is always a good _____**topic**_____ of conversation.

Write a Journal Entry

Write a journal entry about a day spent observing nature. Use as many vocabulary words from this week as you can.

Students' journal entries should use lesson vocabulary words.

Home Activity Your child identified and used new vocabulary words from *Around One Cactus*. Talk with your child about animals and plants in your neighborhood. Use the vocabulary words on this page.

Irregular Verbs

Usually you add -*ed* to a verb to show past tense. **Irregular verbs** do not follow this rule. Instead of having -*ed* forms to show past tense, irregular verbs change to other words.

Present Tense	We <u>do</u> a report on water.
Past Tense	We <u>did</u> a report on water.
Past with *has, have,* or *had*	We <u>have done</u> reports on water.

Irregular verbs have a special form when they are used with *has, have,* and *had.* Use the special past forms in the third column of the chart only with these helping verbs.

Here are some irregular verbs and their past forms:

Present Tense	Past Tense	Past with *has, have,* or *had*
begin	began	(*has, have, had*) begun
do	did	(*has, have, had*) done
find	found	(*has, have, had*) found
give	gave	(*has, have, had*) given
go	went	(*has, have, had*) gone
run	ran	(*has, have, had*) run
see	saw	(*has, have, had*) seen
take	took	(*has, have, had*) taken
think	thought	(*has, have, had*) thought
wear	wore	(*has, have, had*) worn

Directions Choose the correct form of the irregular verb in ( ) to complete each sentence. Write the verb on the line.

1. My family (went, gone) for a hike in the desert. _____**went**_____

2. We had (began, begun) hiking in the morning. _____**begun**_____

3. We (seen, saw) many desert creatures. _____**saw**_____

4. I had (think, thought) animals could not live there. _____**thought**_____

5. I (took, taken) lots of pictures. _____**took**_____

© Pearson Education, Inc., 3

School + Home **Home Activity** Your child learned about irregular verbs. Ask your child this question: *What did you wear to school today?* Have your child answer with a sentence using *wear* in the past tense (*wore*).

Consonant Patterns *wr, kn, gn, st, mb*

Spelling Words				
thumb	gnaw	written	know	climb
design	wrist	crumb	assign	wrench
knot	wrinkle	lamb	knob	knit

Words in Context Write the list word that completes each sentence.

1. A pup is a young dog. A __lamb__ is a young sheep.

2. Your leg bends at the ankle. Your arm bends at the __wrist__ .

3. You walk on a sidewalk. You __climb__ up a tree.

4. A bit of paper is a scrap. A bit of toast is a __crumb__ .

5. You can weave a tablecloth. You can __knit__ a sweater.

6. Your big toe is on your foot. Your __thumb__ is on your hand.

7. Music is composed. Books are __written__ .

8. Chickens peck at corn. Dogs __gnaw__ on bones.

9. A carpenter uses a hammer. A plumber uses a __wrench__ .

10. A gate has a latch. A door has a __knob__ .

Finishing Sentences Complete each sentence with a list word.

11. The artist painted a striped __design__ on the vase.

12. I __know__ how to dive.

13. He ironed every __wrinkle__ out of his shirt.

14. She tied her shoelace in a __knot__ .

15. My teachers never __assign__ a lot of homework.

© Pearson Education, Inc., 3

School + Home
Home Activity Your child spelled words with *wr, kn, mb,* and *gn.* Have your child pronounce each list word and identify the "silent letter" (*w* in *wr, k* in *kn, b* in *mb, g* in *gn*).

Scoring Rubric: Writing for Tests: Expository Composition

	4	3	2	1
Focus/Ideas	Strong composition; compares and contrasts effectively	Good composition; compares and contrasts	Weak composition; poorly compares and/or contrasts	Poor composition; neither compares nor contrasts
Organization	Similarities and differences in clear order; includes strong concluding statement	Similarities and differences in fairly clear order; includes concluding statement	Similarities and differences in confused order; vague or weak conclusion	No similarities and differences; no conclusion
Voice	Writer shows interest in the subject	Writer shows some interest in the subject	Writer shows very little interest in the subject	Writer shows no interest in the subject
Word Choice	Strong use of compare/contrast words	Good use of compare/contrast words	Weak use of compare/contrast words	Poor or no use of compare/contrast words
Sentences	Sentences with different lengths and beginnings	Sentences with a few different lengths and beginnings	Sentences with similar lengths and beginnings	No variety in sentence lengths and beginnings
Conventions	Few or no errors; strong use of irregular verbs	Several minor errors; use of irregular verbs	Many errors; weak use of irregular verbs	Numerous errors; no use of irregular verbs

Vocabulary: Word Structure

- A **prefix** is a syllable added at the beginning of a base word to change its meaning.
- A **suffix** is a syllable added to the end of a base word to change its meaning or the way it is used in a sentence.
- Recognizing prefixes and suffixes will help you figure out a word's meaning.

Directions Read the following passage about animals in hiding. Then answer the questions below. Look for prefixes and suffixes as you read.

Many animals hide so well that they remain unseen unless we know how to find them. Some land turtles that live in a waterless environment crawl slowly along the ground. The slow movements don't attract our attention. Large birds may sit in lofty perches at the tops of tall trees. They are hidden by leaves, and we have to look hard to see them. Animals that can stay out of sight are most likely to be survivors in the harsh world of nature.

1. Does *unseen* have a prefix or a suffix? What does *unseen* mean?

   It has a prefix. It means "not seen."

2. What is the base word in *waterless*? What does *waterless* mean?

   The base word is *water*. It means "without water."

3. What is the base word in *slowly*? What is the suffix?

   The base word is *slow*. The suffix is *ly*.

4. What is the suffix in *lofty*? What does *lofty* mean?

   The suffix is *y*. The meaning is "high up."

5. Is the *or* in *survivors* a prefix or suffix? What are survivors?

   Or is a suffix. *Survivors* are people or animals who are able to stay alive in a hard situation.

Home Activity Your child used prefixes and suffixes to read and define unfamiliar words. Read an article about nature with your child. Ask your child to point out words with prefixes or suffixes.

Newspaper

A **newspaper** is just what its name sounds like. It is the day's news printed on paper.

Directions Read the following article about newspapers. Then answer the questions.

Newspapers are printed on very large sheets of paper that are folded together in a packet. They include photographs and advertisements as well as articles. Advertisements pay for the cost of publishing newspapers.

There are many newspapers all across the country. Some are in big cities and some are in small towns. Some come out every day and others only publish once a week.

Every newspaper article has a headline. The headline is like the title of a book. It tells you in a few words what the article is about. Read the headline first to see if you want to read the article.

Newspapers are divided into sections by category. The front page usually contains a table of contents that gives the page numbers for each section. Sections usually include the following:

- **Front Page**—articles about important issues and events in the U.S. and the world
- **Local News**—articles about the city, town, or neighborhood in which the paper is published
- **Sports**—yesterday's scores and articles about games and athletes
- **Business**—articles about major events in the financial world
- **Entertainment**—movie reviews, entertainment stories, comic strips, crossword puzzles, and games

1. What is the purpose of a headline?

   It summarizes the article so you will know if you want to read it.

2. Underline the section where you might find an article about who won the election for your town's mayor.

3. Draw a box around the section where you would look for yesterday's baseball scores.

4. In which section might you find an article about a nationwide strike by airline pilots?

   front page

Home Activity Your child learned about the different sections of a newspaper. Show your child today's newspaper. Go through the sections together and have your child explain to you what he or she might find in each section.

Name _____

Consonant Patterns *wr, kn, gn, st, mb*

Proofread a Poster Circle four spelling mistakes on the poster. Write the words correctly. Then write the day and date correctly.

Spelling Words

thumb
gnaw
written
know
climb
design
wrist
crumb

assign
wrench
knot
wrinkle
lamb
knob
knit

Art Fair!
Choose from four projects!

a. Make a (wris) or ankle knot bracelet.
b. Design a kite.
c. Learn an easy way to (nit.)
d. Make a (thum) puppet.
   Where and (wen:) Room 103 on
   wednesday january, 15

1. **wrist**   2. **knit**

3. **thumb**   4. **when**

5. **Wednesday, January 15**

Frequently
Misspelled
Words

know
when
where
what

Proofread Words Circle the correct word and write it on the line.

6. Shall we (climb) clim to the top of the hill?   6. **climb**

7. I (know) kow where to find the glue.   7. **know**

8. The lam (lamb) slept by her mother.   8. **lamb**

9. He used a (wrench) rench to fix the leaky pipe.   9. **wrench**

10. Did Mr. Rice assin (assign) the entire page?   10. **assign**

11. You have a crum (crumb) on your chin.   11. **crumb**

12. The mouse will (gnaw) naw on the wires.   12. **gnaw**

© Pearson Education, Inc., 3

School + Home **Home Activity** Your child spelled words with *wr, kn, gn, st,* and *mb.* Have your child circle these letter combinations in the list words.

Irregular Verbs

Directions Read the selection. Then read each question that follows the selection. Decide which is the best answer to each question. Mark the space for the answer you have chosen.

Learning About the Desert

(1) Jamie has <u>see</u> the desert. (2) He <u>give</u> a speech about the desert in class. (3) He <u>take</u> pictures of the desert plants and animals. (4) He showed us a path where a river had <u>wear</u> through the desert. (5) I had <u>think</u> the desert was empty. (6) Now I understand how amazing the desert really is.

1 What irregular verb is correct in sentence 1?
- ⬭ saw
- ⬭ sees
- ⬮ seen
- ⬭ sawen

4 What irregular verb is correct in sentence 4?
- ⬭ wore
- ⬭ wearing
- ⬭ wored
- ⬮ worn

2 What irregular verb is correct in sentence 2?
- ⬭ has gave
- ⬮ gave
- ⬭ giving
- ⬭ will go

5 What irregular verb is correct in sentence 5?
- ⬭ thinked
- ⬮ thought
- ⬭ thinks
- ⬭ thoughted

3 What irregular verb is correct in sentence 3?
- ⬮ took
- ⬭ taken
- ⬭ taking
- ⬭ tooked

© Pearson Education, Inc., 3

Home Activity Your child prepared for taking tests on irregular verbs. In a magazine or newspaper, point out a verb. Have your child tell whether the verb is regular or irregular.

Contractions

Spelling Words				
let's	he'd	you'll	can't	I'd
won't	haven't	hasn't	she'd	they'll
when's	we'd	should've	wasn't	didn't

Making Contractions Write the contraction for each pair of words.

1. will not   w o n ' t
2. has not   h a s n ' t
3. when is   w h e n ' s
4. you will   y o u ' l l
5. he would   h e ' d
6. should have   s h o u l d ' v e
7. let us   l e t ' s

Mystery Contractions Look at the shaded boxes. Write the letters and the apostrophe to make another contraction. Then write the two words that make up the contraction.

8. __they'll__ = __they__ + __will__

Contraction Equations Write a contraction by solving each math word problem. Write an apostrophe in place of the letter or letters you subtract.

9. was + not – o = __wasn't__
10. I + would – woul = __I'd__
11. she + had – ha = __she'd__
12. have + not – o = __haven't__
13. can + not – no = __can't__
14. did + not – o = __didn't__
15. we + had – ha = __we'd__

 Home Activity Your child has been learning to spell contractions. Use a newspaper or a magazine to hunt for contractions together. See how many can be found and circled in five minutes. Work together to figure out what two words make up each contraction.

© Pearson Education, Inc., 3

Action and Linking Verbs

Directions Write the verb in each sentence.

1. Grandma plants bulbs every fall. **plants**
2. The plants grow in spring. **grow**
3. That plant is a lily. **is**
4. These lilies are white. **are**
5. This bulb is a tulip. **is**
6. Everyone loves Grandma's flowers. **loves**

Directions Write the verb in each sentence. Write *A* after an action verb. Write *L* after a linking verb.

7. A raisin is a dried grape. **is, L**
8. My uncle grows grapes in California. **grows, A**
9. I helped my uncle on the farm. **helped, A**
10. Plants need water and sunlight. **need, A**
11. The grapes were ripe on the vines. **were, L**
12. Workers laid them in the sun. **laid, A**
13. Raisins bake in the sun for two weeks. **bake, A**
14. Machines remove the dirt. **remove, A**
15. I packed some raisins. **packed, A**
16. The factory was busy. **was, L**
17. Raisins are good snacks. **are, L**
18. People buy my uncle's raisins. **buy, A**

© Pearson Education, Inc., 3

Prefixes

Spelling Words				
unhappy	recall	disappear	unload	mistake
misspell	dislike	replace	mislead	disagree
rewrite	unroll	unknown	dishonest	react

Context Clues Write the list word that correctly completes the sentence. Use the underlined word as a clue.

1. To not <u>spell</u> a word correctly is to _____**misspell**_____ it.

2. If you don't <u>like</u> something, you _____**dislike**_____ it.

3. To put something in its <u>place</u> again is to _____**replace**_____ it.

4. To not <u>agree</u> is to _____**disagree**_____.

5. To <u>call</u> back a memory of someone again is to _____**recall**_____ that person.

6. For something to <u>appear</u> and then to pass from sight is for it to _____**disappear**_____.

7. If you <u>take</u> something the wrong way, you _____**mistake**_____ it.

8. A person who is not <u>honest</u> is _____**dishonest**_____.

9. To <u>lead</u> someone the wrong way is to _____**mislead**_____ that person.

10. To <u>write</u> something over is to _____**rewrite**_____ it.

11. To <u>act</u> in response to something is to _____**react**_____.

Making Opposites Use the base form of a list word. Add the prefix *un-* to make a word with the opposite meaning.

known	roll	load	happy

12. Dennis will roll the towel and lay it on the sandy beach. **unroll**

13. Lily was happy about her broken computer. **unhappy**

14. The stranger is known to me. **unknown**

15. Please load the groceries and bring them into the house. **unload**

Home Activity Your child has been spelling words with the prefixes *un-*, *re-*, *mis-*, and *dis-*. To practice the words together, help your child write each list word as an equation, like this: un + roll = unroll.

Name _____

Main Verbs and Helping Verbs

Directions Write the main verb and the helping verb in each sentence.

1. The men are hunting for deer in the forest.

Main verb: **hunting**

Helping verb: **are**

2. The women have planted corn in the field.

Main verb: **planted**

Helping verb: **have**

3. The boys were fishing in the clear lake.

Main verb: **fishing**

Helping verb: **were**

4. The girl has sewn a pretty dress.

Main verb: **sewn**

Helping verb: **has**

5. I am learning about Native American life.

Main verb: **learning**

Helping verb: **am**

Directions Look at the underlined verb in each sentence. Write *M* if it is a main verb. Write *H* if it is a helping verb.

6. A woman was <u>weaving</u> a basket. **M**

7. She <u>will</u> make a necklace with beads. **H**

8. The girls had <u>cut</u> the deerskin in pieces. **M**

9. They are <u>making</u> shoes for everyone. **M**

10. The boy <u>is</u> gathering pretty feathers. **H**

Spellings of /j/, /s/, /k/

Spelling Words				
clock	large	page	mark	kitten
judge	crack	edge	pocket	brake
change	ridge	jacket	badge	orange

Silly Sentences Read each silly sentence. Write the list word that rhymes with the underlined word and makes sense in the sentence.

1. I looked at a <u>sock</u> to tell the time.

2. My <u>mitten</u> likes milk.

3. There is a big black <u>park</u> on my paper.

4. The <u>fudge</u> is in court right now.

5. There is a <u>barge</u> hippo in the zoo.

6. This book <u>stage</u> has many words on it.

7. My <u>racket</u> has a zipper and two pockets.

8. Dad stepped on the <u>rake</u> to stop the car.

9. Please <u>range</u> the TV channel.

10. I have a dime in my <u>rocket</u>.

1. **clock**

2. **kitten**

3. **mark**

4. **judge**

5. **large**

6. **page**

7. **jacket**

8. **brake**

9. **change**

10. **pocket**

Letter Directions Follow each direction. Write the new word.

11. Add **ge** to **bad**.

12. Add **o** to **range**.

13. Subtract **pl** from **pledge**.

14. Add **c** to **rack**.

15. Subtract **f** from **fridge**.

11. **badge**

12. **orange**

13. **edge**

14. **crack**

15. **ridge**

Home Activity Your child learned words spelled with *ge*, *dge*, *ck*, and *k*. To help you practice the list words with your child, say each word and ask your child to spell it. Then take turns naming words that rhyme with it.

© Pearson Education, Inc., 3

Subject-Verb Agreement

Direction Choose the verb in ( ) that agrees with the subject. Write the verb.

1. The city lights (hide, hides) the stars. **hide**
2. Stars (gleam, gleams) brightly in the country. **gleam**
3. They (seem, seems) close enough to touch. **seem**
4. The Big Dipper (look, looks) huge. **looks**
5. Our galaxy (is, are) amazing. **is**

Directions Choose the verb in ( ) that agrees with the subject. Write the sentence.

6. This telescope (work, works) well.
This telescope works well.

7. We (see, sees) millions of stars.
We see millions of stars.

8. Rigel (is, are) one of the brightest stars.
Rigel is one of the brightest stars.

9. Hot gases (make, makes) it sparkle.
Hot gases make it sparkle.

10. Astronomers often (find, finds) new stars.
Astronomers often find new stars.

© Pearson Education, Inc., 3

Name _____

Suffixes

Spelling Words				
beautiful	safely	kindness	finally	spotless
worthless	illness	helpful	daily	suddenly
wireless	quietly	fairness	cheerful	painful

Choosing Suffixes Circle the suffix needed to make a list word. Write the list word.

Base Word	**Suffix**		**List Word**
1. kind	ful	(ness)	1. __kindness__
2. quiet	(ly)	ful	2. __quietly__
3. cheer	(ful)	ness	3. __cheerful__
4. spot	ly	(less)	4. __spotless__
5. worth	(less)	ful	5. __worthless__
6. sudden	ful	(ly)	6. __suddenly__
7. ill	ly	(ness)	7. __illness__
8. safe	ful	(ly)	8. __safely__
9. help	(ful)	ness	9. __helpful__
10. final	less	(ly)	10. __finally__

Meaning Clues Write a list word for each meaning clue.

11. full of beauty   b e a u t i f u l

12. full of pain   p a i n f u l

13. done each day   d a i l y

14. with no wire   w i r e l e s s

Mystery Word Write the mystery word formed by the boxes. Then write the list word by adding the suffix *-ness* to the mystery word.

15. _____ **fair** _____   _____ **fairness** _____

Home Activity Your child is learning to spell words with the suffixes *-ly*, *-ful*, *-ness*, and *-less*. Help your child write list words with two different suffixes, such as *painless, painful* and *kindly, kindness*.

© Pearson Education, Inc., 3

Name _____

Present, Past, and Future Tenses

Directions Tell the tense of the underlined verb in each sentence.
Write *present, past,* or *future.*

1. Scientists <u>discovered</u> some smart mammals. **past**

2. The mammals <u>live</u> in the ocean. **present**

3. Many dolphins <u>learned</u> tricks. **past**

4. Scientists <u>will study</u> dolphins more. **future**

Directions Write the verb in ( ) that correctly completes each sentence.

5. These dolphins live at the sea park, and they (perform, performed) each day.
   perform

6. A few minutes ago, a dolphin (leaps, leaped) out of the water.
   leaped

7. Tomorrow the dolphins (invented, will invent) a new trick.
   will invent

8. In next week's show, a dolphin (tossed, will toss) a ball into a net.
   will toss

9. Yesterday the dolphins (played, play) happily with their trainers.
   played

10. I (enjoyed, will enjoy) dolphins in the future.
    will enjoy

11. In yesterday's show, a dolphin (pushed, will push) a ball across the pool.
    pushed

12. People watch the dolphins and (clapped, clap) loudly.
    clap

© Pearson Education, Inc., 3

240 **Conventions**

Consonant Patterns *wr, kn, gn, st, mb*

Spelling Words				
thumb	gnaw	written	know	climb
design	wrist	crumb	assign	wrench
knot	wrinkle	lamb	knob	knit

Word Search Circle the list words in the puzzle. Look across, down, and diagonally. Write the words you find.

1. __wrinkle__   6. __climb__   11. __lamb__

2. __know__   7. __assign__   12. __design__

3. __crumb__   8. __wrist__   13. __wrench__

4. __thumb__   9. __written__   14. __knob__

5. __gnaw__   10. __knot__   15. __knit__

Home Activity Your child practiced spelling words with *wr, kn, gn, st,* and *mb*. Ask your child to write each list word. Have him or her underline the *wr, kn, gn, st,* and *mb* in each word and to X out the letter in each pair that is silent.

Irregular Verbs

Directions Choose the correct form of the irregular verb in ( ) to complete each sentence. Write the verb.

1. Mae (saw, seen) plants and animals in the desert. **saw**

2. She had (think, thought) nothing lived there. **thought**

3. The cactus had (grew, grown) slowly. **grown**

4. A snake (began, begun) to rattle nearby. **began**

5. Mae (took, taken) many pictures. **took**

Directions Write each sentence. Use the correct past form of the verb in ( ).

6. Juan (go) to the desert.

Juan went to the desert.

7. He (do) a report on life in the desert.

He did a report on life in the desert.

8. He (find) out about desert plants and animals.

He found out about desert plants and animals.

9. We have not (go) to the desert.

We have not gone to the desert.

10. Rivers have (wear) paths through the desert.

Rivers have worn paths through the desert.

© Pearson Education, Inc., 3

Cause-and-Effect Chart

Directions Most events in nature have more than one cause and effect. Fill in the chart with each cause and effect that helps explain the event you are planning to write about in your essay.

Natural Event	
Answers should include details about the causes and effects for the student's cause-and-effect essay.	
Cause	**Effect**

Use Logical Order

Directions Choose a sentence from the box that logically follows each numbered sentence below. Write the letter of the second sentence on the line. Then write a third sentence that logically follows the first two sentences.

A. The house is very dirty.
B. The house was crowded.
C. The house is too small.

D. The house was completely dark.
E. The house was very quiet.
F. The house is vacant.

---

1. We lost our electricity for six hours last night.

   Second sentence: ___**D**___

   Logical conclusion:

   Possible third sentence: We couldn't watch television or play
   video games.

2. Our neighbors moved away last year.

   Second sentence: ___**F**___

   Logical conclusion:

   Possible third sentence: There are no lights on at night.

3. No one was home when Jim returned from baseball practice that morning.

   Second sentence: ___**E**___

   Logical conclusion:

   Possible third sentence: Jim could take a nice, long nap.

4. The vacuum cleaner has stopped working.

   Second sentence: ___**A**___

   Logical conclusion:

   Possible third sentence: Now is not the time to invite the
   neighbors over.

Combining Sentences

When you revise, you can combine two short simple sentences to make a compound sentence. Make sure the ideas in the two sentences are related. Use one of these conjunctions: *and, but,* or *or.* Put a comma before the conjunction.

Simple Sentences The fire lasted three days. Most of the forest was destroyed.
Compound Sentence The fire lasted three days, and most of the forest was destroyed.

Directions Combine each pair of simple sentences with the conjunction *and, but,* or *or* to make a compound sentence. Don't forget to add a comma.

1. Flames raced from tree to tree. Black smoke filled the sky.

Flames raced from tree to tree, and black smoke filled the sky.

2. People could stay in their homes. They could go to shelters.

People could stay in their homes, or they could go to shelters.

3. Firefighters worked day and night. They could not control the blaze.

Firefighters worked day and night, but they could not control the blaze.

4. No rain had fallen in weeks, and the forest was very dry.

No rain had fallen in weeks, and the forest was very dry.

5. The forest will return. It is hard to imagine trees growing here.

The forest will return, but it is hard to imagine trees growing here.

Editing 2

Directions Edit these sentences. Look for errors in spelling, grammar, and mechanics. Use proofreading marks to show the corrections.

Proofreading Marks	
Delete (Take out)	～
Add	∧
Spelling	⬭
Uppercase letter	≡
Lowercase letter	/

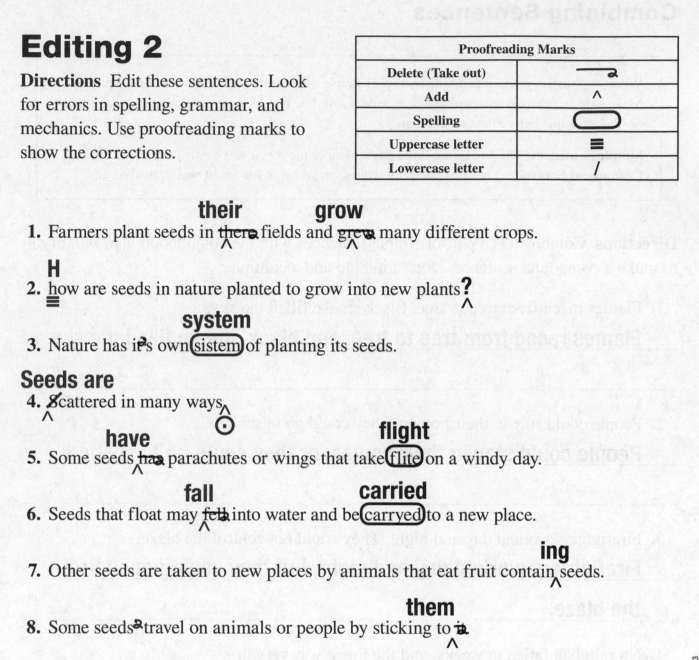

1. Farmers plant seeds in <u>there</u> fields and <u>grew</u> many different crops.
   their ∧   grow ∧

2. <u>how</u> are seeds in nature planted to grow into new plants_∧?
   H
   ≡

3. Nature has it's own (sistem) of planting its seeds.
   system

4. Scattered in many ways_∧⊙
   Seeds are
   ∧

5. Some seeds <u>has</u> parachutes or wings that take (flite) on a windy day.
   have ∧   flight

6. Seeds that float may <u>fell</u> into water and be (carryed) to a new place.
   fall ∧   carried

7. Other seeds are taken to new places by animals that eat fruit contain_∧ seeds.
   ing

8. Some seeds travel on animals or people by sticking to <u>it</u>.
   them ∧

Now you'll edit the draft of your cause-and-effect essay. Next, you'll use your revised and edited draft to make a final copy of your essay. Finally, you'll share your written work with your audience.

Irregular Plurals

Directions Use the plural form of each word in ( ) to complete each sentence. Write the word on the line.

mice   1. Timmy wasn't like the other (mouse).

teeth   2. He was missing all his (tooth).

loaves   3. He couldn't chew into the (loaf) of bread in the bakery where he lived.

feet   4. Using his (foot) to pull off tiny pieces of bread didn't work.

women   5. Of course the (woman) who worked in the bakery would never feed him.

men   6. When the delivery (man) came, Timmy would run and hide.

children   7. Timmy finally solved his problem when he saw some (child) dropping crumbs.

shelves   8. Now he stores the crumbs behind the (shelf) so he can eat them whenever he wants.

Directions Write the plural form of each word below.

9. wife **wives**

10. wolf **wolves**

11. scarf **scarves**

12. hero **heroes**

13. cuff **cuffs**

14. calf **calves**

15. banjo **banjos**

16. elf **elves**

17. half **halves**

18. goose **geese**

19. knife **knives**

20. sheep **sheep**

© Pearson Education, Inc., 3

Home Activity Your child wrote plurals—words naming more than one person, place, or thing. Ask your child to review the plural forms of the words on the page above. Work together to write a silly poem or song using these and other plural words.

Generalize

- An **autobiography** is a book in which the author tells the story of his or her own life. It is written in the **first person.** The author uses pronouns such as *I, me, my, our, us,* and *we.*

- A **biography** is a life story written about someone other than the author. It is written in the **second person.** The author uses pronouns such as *he, she, him, her, his, hers, they,* and *them.*

- When you read autobiographies, biographies, and other types of literature, you can sometimes use what you have read to make a **general statement,** or **generalization.** When you generalize, you use individual examples to make a general rule about a subject.

Directions Read the following life stories. Think about generalizations you can make from what you have read. Then answer the questions.

W hen she was little, Bonnie never sat still. She turned somersaults. She jumped on the bed. She did splits. Finally her mother took her to gymnastics class. Bonnie loved it. She practiced and practiced. She dreamed of being an Olympic star.

Dad bought a little basketball when I was born. Maybe that's why I grew up loving the game. I practiced all the time because I loved to play, but all that practice made me better and better. I began to wonder whether I could be a professional player.

1. Which passage is an autobiography?
the one about basketball

2. How do you know? **The author is the person the story is about. The author uses the pronoun _I_.**

3. Think about what you read in both passages. What generalization can you make about when many star athletes probably begin learning their sport?
Star athletes probably start when they are very young.

4. Think about what you read in both passages. What generalization can you make about what most star athletes probably do that makes them successful?
Most star athletes probably practice as much as they can.

5. Reread your answer to question 4. What generalization can you make about why star athletes do this?
They probably practice so much because they love their sports.

Home Activity Your child read a biographical passage and an autobiographical passage and used the ideas to make generalizations. With your child, read two or more biographical articles about successful people. Then ask your child to make a generalization about how people become successful.

© Pearson Education, Inc., 3

Writing Persuasive Text

Key Features of Persuasive Text
- take a position on a subject
- tries to influence the reader's opinion
- provides details to support the opinion
- might urge the reader to take action

Fun on the Ice

Curling is a fun, unique sport that everyone should try. It is a sport you play on an icy surface, such as a frozen pond or an ice rink. To play, one person throws a large, heavy stone toward a target called a "tee." Other players sweep the ice in front of the stone to make it go faster or slower.

Curling is a good sport for people who live in places with long winters. It is especially popular where ponds and lakes freeze over in the winter. If you like other winter sports like hockey, ice skating, or skiing, you will probably like curling.

In curling, sportsmanship is very important. Before you play, your team shakes hands with the other team and says "Good Curling." After you play, you shake hands again. You can learn a lot about being a good sport from curling.

Curling is also a good way to spend time with friends. You and your teammates have to practice a lot to become good at "throwing," sliding, the stones and getting them to stop in just the right places. Teams have to learn to work together.

So next time you want to have some fun on the ice, try curling!

1. What is the purpose of this persuasive essay?

   to convince readers to try curling

2. What reasons does the author use to achieve his or her purpose?

   Curling is a fun cold weather sport; it teaches you to be a good sport; it is a good way to spend time with friends.

3. Which reason do you think is most persuasive?

   Answers will vary

Vocabulary

Directions Draw a line from the word to its meaning.

Check the Words You Know

___basketball	___popular
___disease	___sports
___freeze	___study
___guard	___terrible

1. disease   enjoyed by many people

2. freeze   a game in which teams toss a ball into a basket

3. guard   illness

4. basketball   to keep an opponent from scoring points

5. popular   to get very, very cold

Directions Fill in the blank with the word from the box that fits the meaning of the sentence.

6. What are your favorite _____**sports**_____?

7. One of my favorites is _____**basketball**_____.

8. It is very _____**popular**_____ with my friends, too.

9. We _____**study**_____ our favorite players and then try to play the way they do.

10. A day when we can't play our favorite game is a _____**terrible**_____ day.

Write Copy for a Sports Card

Think about sports you like. Write about your favorite player. Use as many vocabulary words from this week as you can.

Students' writing should incorporate the lesson vocabulary in information for a sports card.

 Home Activity Your child identified and used new vocabulary words from *The Man Who Invented Basketball.* Talk with your child about favorite sports. Encourage your child to use the vocabulary words on this page.

© Pearson Education, Inc., 3

Singular and Plural Pronouns

Pronouns are words that take the place of nouns. Pronouns that take the place of singular nouns are **singular pronouns**. *I, me, he, she, him, her,* and *it* are singular pronouns.

  Singular Pronoun The <u>man</u> can run fast. <u>He</u> can run fast.

Pronouns that take the place of plural nouns are **plural pronouns**. *We, us, they,* and *them* are plural pronouns.

  Plural Pronoun <u>Turtles</u> cannot run. <u>They</u> cannot run.

You can be used as a singular and a plural pronoun.

  <u>Sam and Sara</u>, where do <u>you</u> like to run?

  <u>Sara</u>, <u>you</u> are the fastest runner.

Directions Write the pronoun in each sentence.

1. People like to have fun, so we invent games. _____**we**_____

2. Games and exercise are important to us. _____**us**_____

3. People long ago had ideas, and they created games. _____**they**_____

4. My sister and I invented a game. _____**I**_____

5. She is a lot of fun. _____**She**_____

Directions Write *S* if the underlined pronoun is singular. Write *P* if it is plural.

6. James Naismith was clever, and <u>he</u> invented a game. ___**S**___

7. The game was fast, and <u>it</u> was fun. ___**S**___

8. Two teams played the game, and <u>they</u> tried to make baskets. ___**P**___

9. <u>We</u> still play the game today. ___**P**___

10. Mike's team got new uniforms and wore <u>them</u> to the game. ___**P**___

School + Home **Home Activity** Your child learned about singular and plural pronouns. Make up sentences about one or more members of your family. Have your child repeat the sentences using pronouns in place of people's names.

Irregular Plurals

Spelling Words				
wolves	knives	feet	men	children
women	sheep	heroes	scarves	mice
geese	cuffs	elves	banjos	halves

Seeing Relationships Write list words to complete the comparisons.

1. arms and hands, legs and _____   1. __**feet**__

2. cats and lions, dogs and _____   2. __**wolves**__

3. feet and shoes, necks and _____   3. __**scarves**__

4. milk and cows, wool and _____   4. __**sheep**__

5. boys and girls, men and _____   5. __**women**__

6. tubas and trumpets, violins and _____   6. __**banjos**__

7. grown and adults, young and _____   7. __**children**__

8. fur and rabbits, feathers and _____   8. __**geese**__

9. leaders and followers, cowards and _____   9. __**heroes**__

10. four and fourths, two and _____   10. __**halves**__

Rhyming Plurals Write a list word that rhymes with the underlined word.

11. The _____ on my coat look like <u>puffs</u> of fur.   11. __**cuffs**__

12. The _____ in this story live on toy <u>shelves</u>.   12. __**elves**__

13. We've found _____ in the garage <u>twice</u>.   13. __**mice**__

14. The _____ put the cattle back in the <u>pen</u>.   14. __**men**__

15. They carry _____ on <u>dives</u> in dangerous water.   15. __**knives**__

© Pearson Education, Inc., 3

School + Home

Home Activity Your child spelled plural words. Name a list word. Ask your child to explain how the plural was formed.

Name _____

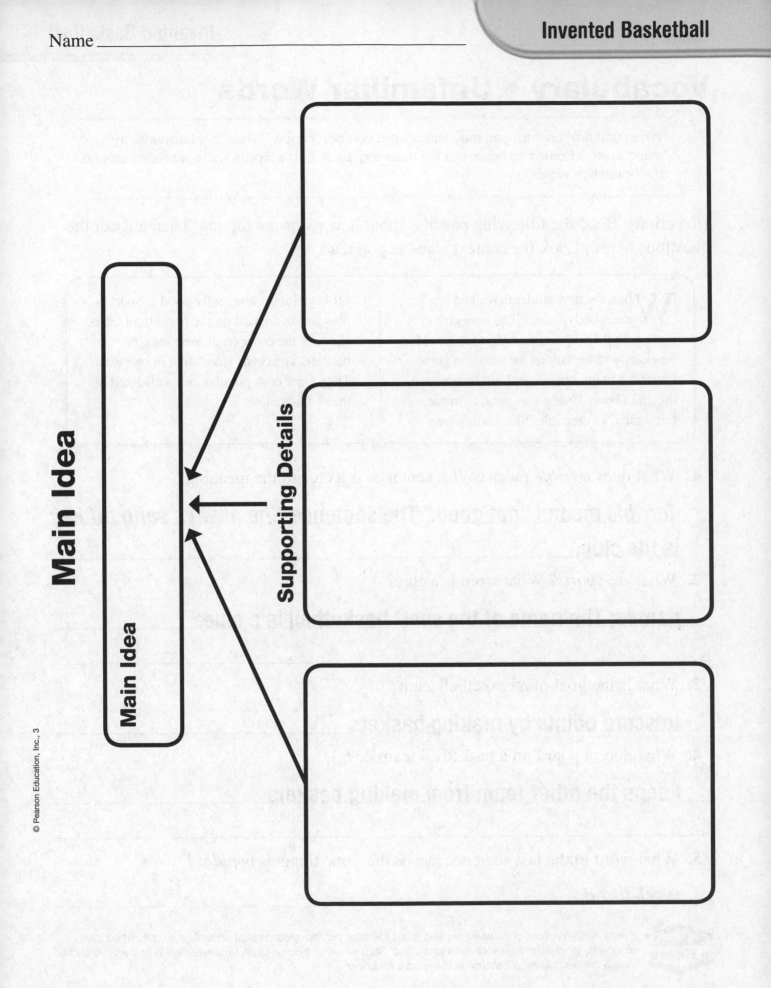

Main Idea

Main Idea

Supporting Details

Vocabulary • Unfamiliar Words

When you are reading, you may find a word you don't know. When this happens, try using **context clues** to figure out the meaning. Look at the words and sentences around the unfamiliar word.

Directions Read the following passage about how twins are unique. Then answer the questions below. Look for context clues as you read.

When the new students walked in, everybody stared. The new girls were twins! Everyone thought they would be exactly alike. But as the children got to know the twins, they found out how wrong they had been. Cindy was good at music, but Sandy was terrible. She always sang off key. Sandy was really good at sports, though. As a guard on the basketball team, she kept the other team from making baskets. The twins were alike in one way. They were both popular and well-liked by their classmates.

1. What does *terrible* mean? What sentence is a clue to the meaning?

Terrible means "not good." The sentence *She always sang off key* is the clue.

2. What are *sports*? What word is a clue?

games; The name of the sport basketball is a clue.

3. What is the goal of a basketball team?

to score points by making baskets

4. What does a guard on a basketball team do?

keeps the other team from making baskets

5. What word in the last sentence means the same thing as *popular*?

well-liked

 Home Activity Your child used context clues to figure out the meanings of unfamiliar words. Read a biography or character sketch with your child. Stop when you come to an unfamiliar word and ask your child to use context clues to determine the word's meaning.

Dictionary

- You can use a **dictionary** to find the meaning of unfamiliar words.
- The words in a dictionary are listed in **alphabetical order.**
- The **guide words** that appear at the top of the page show the first and last entries on that page.

Directions Read the sentences below. One word is underlined. Use the sample dictionary page to write the definition of the underlined word on the line.

---

gawk • whisper

gawk *v.* stare at in a rude way

nag *v.* annoy by complaining about something

snicker *v.* to laugh in a sly or silly way

swirl *v.* move along with a twisting motion; whirl

wag *v.* move from side to side or up and down

whisper *v.* to speak very softly and gently

---

1. I had to <u>whisper</u> so the baby wouldn't wake up.

   speak very softly and gently

2. Why did the children <u>gawk</u> at the clown in the supermarket?

   stare at in a rude way

3. I watched the snowflakes <u>swirl</u> in the air as they fell.

   move along with a twisting motion

4. When you see cats <u>wag</u> their tails, you know they are trying to make a decision about something.

   move from side to side or up and down

5. I put my hand over my mouth so no one would hear me <u>snicker</u>.

   to laugh in a sly or silly way

6. My sister likes to <u>nag</u> me to put my things away.

   annoy by complaining about something

© Pearson Education, Inc., 3

Home Activity Your child used a sample dictionary page to define unfamiliar words. Show your child a school dictionary. Play a game in which you cover up the page, showing only the guide words at the top. Have your child list and define five words that appear on the page.

Irregular Plurals

Proofread a Report Robbie wrote a report about the class field trip. Circle four misspelled words. Write them correctly. Write the verb Robbie should have used in his second sentence.

Our class went to the nature center. We (seen) sheep, (gese,) and even some wolves.

The two (wemen) who showed us around said wolves eat everything from big deer to little field (mouses)—but not children! Still, I wouldn't (wunt) to get too close to a wolf.

1. __saw__

2. __geese__

3. __women__

4. __mice__

5. __want__

Proofread Words Fill in a circle to show which word is spelled correctly. Write the word.

6. Two musicians played _____ for the square dance.
   ○ banjoes ● banjos ○ banjoys

6. __banjos__

7. We rolled up our _____ and went to work.
   ○ cuves ○ cuffes ● cuffs

7. __cuffs__

8. The _____ helped the shoemaker with his work.
   ● elves ○ elfs ○ elvies

8. __elves__

9. My mom has some pretty _____ .
   ● scarves ○ scarfs ○ scarvs

9. __scarves__

10. The police officers were _____ .
    ○ herros ● heroes ○ heros

10. __heroes__

© Pearson Education, Inc., 3

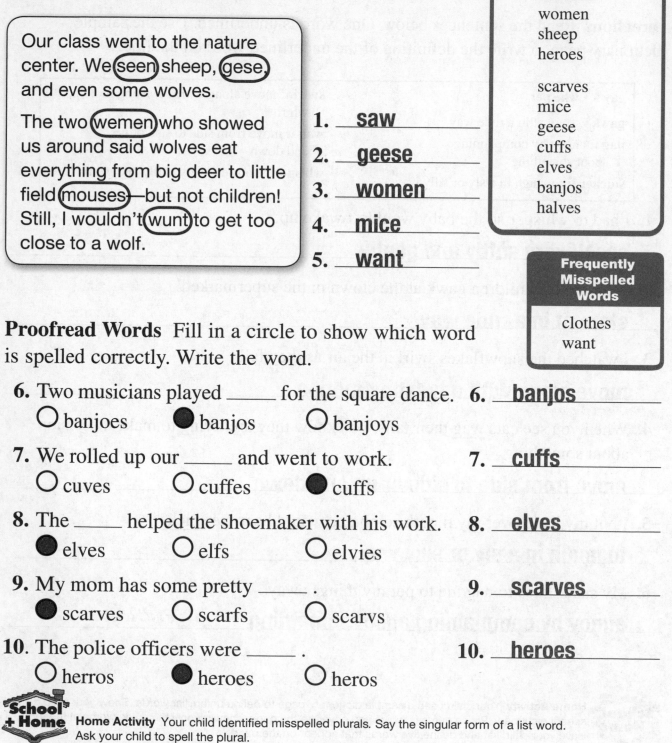

School + Home

Home Activity Your child identified misspelled plurals. Say the singular form of a list word. Ask your child to spell the plural.

Singular and Plural Pronouns

Directions Read the selection. Then read each question that follows the selection. Decide which is the best answer to each question. Mark the space for the answer you have chosen.

Basketball

(1) Basketball is a very popular game. (2) <u>Basketball</u> is played across the country. (3) James Naismith invented it, but <u>James</u> may not even recognize it anymore. (4) Fans fill thousands of seats every night to watch, and <u>the fans</u> love a good show. (5) Michael Jordan was a very popular player. (6) <u>Michael Jordan</u> led his team to 6 championships. (7) The game has female stars too, and many of <u>the female stars</u> are popular, too.

1 What pronoun can replace the noun in sentence 2?

- ⬭ They
- ⬭ He
- ⬬ It
- ⬭ I

2 What pronoun can replace the noun in sentence 3?

- ⬬ he
- ⬭ they
- ⬭ it
- ⬭ him

3 What pronoun can replace the noun in sentence 4?

- ⬭ he
- ⬭ her
- ⬭ she
- ⬬ they

4 What pronoun can replace the noun in sentence 6?

- ⬭ Him
- ⬬ He
- ⬭ They
- ⬭ It

5 What pronoun can replace the noun in sentence 7?

- ⬭ her
- ⬭ she
- ⬭ we
- ⬬ them

© Pearson Education, Inc., 3

School + Home **Home Activity** Your child prepared for taking tests on singular and plural pronouns. Read a book with your child. Point out several sentences with pronouns. Have your child identify the pronouns and tell whether they are singular or plural.

Vowels: *r*-Controlled /ėr/

Directions Circle the words in the box that have the vowel sound /ėr/ as in **bird**, **her**, **turn**, **earn**, and **work**. Then write the words you circled under the word that has the same vowel spelling.

(burst)	hear	corn	dear	(early)	there	(fern)
(fire)	flare	heart	(girl)	(hurry)	(learn)	pear
(perch)	(skirt)	tire	torn	(world)	(worm)	

bird
1. girl
2. skirt

her
3. fern
4. perch

turn
5. burst
6. hurry

earn
7. early
8. learn

work
9. world
10. worm

Directions Circle the word that has the same vowel sound as the first word. Then write a sentence that uses the word you circled.

11. **farm**   frame   (dart)   rare
Sample answer: The fish dart back and forth in the tank.

12. **short**   hoot   (horn)   shot
Sample answer: When you honk the horn, I'll come out.

13. **core**   cone   to   (shore)
Sample answer: The waves rolled up onto the shore.

14. **board**   boat   proud   (roar)
Sample answer: Did you hear the lion roar?

Home Activity Your child identified and wrote words with *r*-controlled vowels. With your child, write sentences for the answer words from items 1–10 above. Ask your child to underline the letters that stand for /ėr/.

© Pearson Education, Inc., 3

Graphic Sources

- A **graphic source** is an image that helps you understand what you read.
- There are many types of graphic sources. They include maps, photos, illustrations, graphs, and diagrams.

Directions Study the following graphic source. Then answer the questions below.

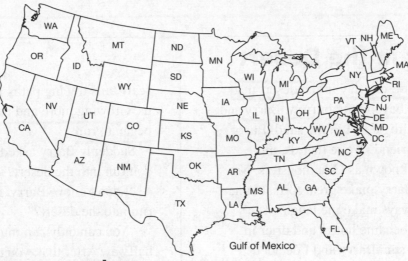

Gulf of Mexico

Sample answers are given.

1. What does this map show? How do you know?

   It shows the 48 states of the U.S. that are connected on land.

   I know from having seen other maps of the U.S.

2. Which state is the farthest east on the map?

   Maine is the farthest east.

3. Which state seems to be the largest?

   Texas looks larger than the other states.

4. Find your home state. Which states border on it?

   Answers will vary depending on student's home state.

5. Which state has the fewest border states? How many border states touch this state?

   Maine has the fewest. Only one state, New Hampshire, touches

   Maine.

Home Activity Your child looked at a graphic source and answered questions about it. Look at a map of your home town or city with your child. Have your child answer questions about the map.

Writing • Imaginative Story

Key Features of an Imaginative Story

- tells a made-up story that did not really happen
- has a plot that builds to a climax
- has characters—people or animals in the story
- has a setting—where and when the story takes place

A Day in the Desert

It was a hot, dry day in the desert that stretches beyond my burrow. Barry and I were building a fort in the sand. Barry is my best friend. We're lizards, more commonly known as Gila monsters. Not only does Barry make great forts, but he can also always make me laugh.

The day became hotter and drier in the midday sun. Barry and I decided to go home. But where was home? We both looked around, but nothing looked familiar. There were stretches of sandy soil in every direction. We had wandered too far into the desert.

"Let's start walking this way," I suggested. Soon we started trotting, our scaly tails tracing paths in the sand behind us. Growing more and more nervous, we began to run.

Suddenly Barry asked, "How far can you run into the desert?"

"I don't know, Barry. How far *can* you run into the desert?"

"You can only run into the desert halfway. After that, you're running *out* of the desert."

I started laughing so hard that I nearly ran into a cactus plant. When I finally looked up, there was a rocky outcrop— the same rocky outcrop that shades the entrance to my burrow—off in the distance.

1. Underline the sentence that is the most exciting part of the plot. **Students should underline *Growing more and more nervous, we began to run.***

2. Draw a circle around the characters in the story.
Students should circle *Barry* and *I*, the narrator.

3. Draw a box around the words that tell the setting.

Students should box the words *in the desert that stretches beyond my burrow.*

© Pearson Education, Inc., 3

Name_____

Vocabulary

Directions Draw a line from the word to its definition.

> ### Check the Words You Know
> ___outrun   ___tides
> ___deserts   ___waterfalls
> ___peak   ___average
> ___depth   ___erupted

1. average   violently sent out lava, ash, and gases

2. deserts   the very top of a mountain

3. depth   normal, usual

4. erupted   places with little rainfall

5. peak   having to do with how deep something is

Directions Write the word from the box that best matches each clue.

6. The winners of a race do this.   **outrun**

7. These falling waters are often shown on postcards.   **waterfalls**

8. Snow is often found on this part of a mountain.   **peak**

9. Cactus plants grow here.   **deserts**

10. These are related to ocean waters.   **tides**

Write a Travel Brochure

On a separate sheet of paper, write a travel brochure describing a place and the things people may see there. Use as many vocabulary words as possible.

Students' writing should use vocabulary in a brochure to describe a place people may visit.

Home Activity Your child identified and used vocabulary words from *Hottest, Coldest, Highest, Deepest*. With your child, read a story or nonfiction article about Earth science. Talk about landforms. Encourage your child to use vocabulary words in your conversation.

Subject and Object Pronouns

A pronoun used as the subject of a sentence is called a **subject pronoun.** A pronoun used after an action verb or as the object of a preposition is called an **object pronoun.**

- *I, you, he, she, it, we,* and *they* are subject pronouns.
- *Me, you, him, her, it, us,* and *them* are object pronouns.

Subject Pronouns <u>They</u> visited Mount Rainier. Sam and <u>I</u> went too.

Object Pronouns The mountain amazed <u>them</u>. They took pictures of Sam and <u>me</u>.

Directions Write the pronouns in each sentence.

1. She was on a high mountain, and the wind bothered her. ____**She, her**____

2. In the desert, the sun beats down on you. ____**you**____

3. The Mississippi is a long river, and it has many kinds of fish. ____**it**____

4. The huge waterfall impressed him. ____**him**____

5. He and I watched the tide come into shore. ____**He, I**____

Directions Write *SP* if the underlined pronoun is a subject pronoun. Write *OP* if it is an object pronoun.

6. Lake Superior is the largest of the Great Lakes. <u>It</u> is also the deepest. __**SP**__

7. The lake's size interested <u>us</u>. __**OP**__

8. Jamal visited Africa. There <u>he</u> saw the Nile River. __**SP**__

9. The rains in the tropical forest drenched <u>them</u>. __**OP**__

10. The deep snow on the mountain surprised Tina and <u>him</u>. __**OP**__

© Pearson Education, Inc., 3

School + Home **Home Activity** Your child learned about subject and object pronouns. Make up sentences about book and movie characters. Have your child repeat the sentences with pronouns in place of the characters' names.

Vowels: *r*-Controlled

Spelling Words				
third	early	world	certain	dirty
herself	earth	word	perfect	verb
nerve	worm	thirsty	workout	earn

Complete the Sentence Write a list word to complete the sentence.

1. This is really a _____ day!   1. **perfect**

2. He had a _____ at the gym.   2. **workout**

3. I put a _____ on my fishhook.   3. **worm**

4. May I have a _____ with you?   4. **word**

5. I'm so _____ I could drink a gallon of water!   5. **thirsty**

6. Don't lose your _____!   6. **nerve**

7. I'd like to travel around the _____ .   7. **world**

8. This is the _____ time we've won.   8. **third**

Opposites Write a list word that means the opposite.

9. late   9. **early**

10. unsure   10. **certain**

11. noun   11. **verb**

12. himself   12. **herself**

13. sky   13. **earth**

14. clean   14. **dirty**

15. win   15. **earn**

earth
certain
early
dirty
herself
verb
earn

School + Home

Home Activity Your child spelled words with *er*, *ir*, *or*, and *ear*. Have your child circle these letter combinations in the list words.

© Pearson Education, Inc., 3

Story Sequence B

Title	
Characters	**Setting**

↓

Events **1.** First	

↓

2. Next	

↓

3. Then	

↓

4. Last	

Vocabulary • Unknown Words

- You can use a glossary or a dictionary to find the meaning, syllabication, and pronunciation of **unknown words**.

---

av • er • age (av′ ər ij) *adj.* normal, usual
depth (depth) *n.* the distance from the
    top to the bottom
out • run (out run′) *v.* to move faster than
    someone or something

peak (pēk) *n.* the pointed top of a
    mountain or hill
tide (tīd) *n.* the rise and fall of the ocean
    about every twelve hours • *PLURAL*
    tides

Directions Read the passage. Use the glossary entries to answer the questions.

On an **average** summer day, some people like to wade far out into the ocean. This can be risky. Incoming **tides** change the **depth** of the water. The water level rises, and the beach disappears. If this happens to you, you can try to **outrun** the tide. Or you may be able to climb to the top of a tall, rocky **peak** in the water and wait until the tide goes out. The best thing to do, though, is to stay out of trouble by learning about tides.

1. How many syllables are in the word *average*?

   3

2. How many syllables are in the word *depth?*

   1

3. What are tides?

   the rise and fall of the ocean

4. Does the *e* in *peak* have a long or short sound?

   long

5. Which syllable should you stress when you say *outrun*?

   the second; *run*

Home Activity Your child used a glossary to understand meanings, syllabication, and pronunciation of words from *Hottest, Coldest, Highest, Deepest*. Read an article about nature with your child. Encourage your child to use a dictionary to find the meanings and pronunciations of unknown words.

Bar Graphs

Bar graphs compare amounts and numbers. The bars can go across or up and down. The words on the graph tell what is being compared. The ends of the bars line up to a number.

Directions The bar graph below shows the five longest distances thrown in a baseball throw event. Use the graph to answer each question.

1. What is the distance of the longest throw?

   90 feet

2. Which person threw the shortest distance?

   Gina

3. What distance did Ian throw the baseball?

   85 feet

4. Which two people threw the same distance?

   Lynn and Mario

5. What is the distance between the longest and shortest throws?

   15 feet

Home Activity Your child answered questions by interpreting data in a bar graph. Collect some data about your family, such as height, age, or shoe size. Help your child make a bar graph with this data.

Vowels: *r*-Controlled

Proofread Workout Tips Circle four misspelled words. Write them correctly. Cross out the incorrect end mark and write the correct one.

Workout Tips
- Some people plan a workout early in the day, but there's no (pirfect) time. Just be (ceartain) you do it!
- Drink extra water—even if you're not (thersty.)
- Do something you like. Have you (herd) that jogging is best ~~.~~ **?**

Spelling Words

third
early
world
certain
dirty
herself
earth
word

perfect
verb
nerve
worm
thirsty
workout
earn

1. __perfect__   2. __certain__

3. __thirsty__   4. __heard__

Proofread Words Circle the correctly spelled word. Write it.

5. nurve   (nerve)   5. __nerve__
6. (worm)   werm   6. __worm__
7. ern   (earn)   7. __earn__
8. (dirty)   durty   8. __dirty__
9. (third)   therd   9. __third__
10. hurself (herself)   10. __herself__
11. (workout) werkout   11. __workout__
12. vurb   (verb)   12. __verb__

Frequently Misspelled Words

another
brother
heard

School + Home **Home Activity** Your child identified misspelled words with *er*, *ir*, *or*, and *ear*. Pronounce a word. Ask your child to tell which letter combination it contains—*er*, *ir*, *or*, or *ear*.

Subjects and Object Pronouns

Directions Read the selection. Then read each question that follows the selection. Decide which is the best answer to each question. Mark the space for the answer you have chosen.

Mount Everest

(1) <u>Mount Everest</u> is the tallest mountain in the world. (2) Every year, <u>hundreds of people</u> try to climb it. (3) <u>Sir Edmond Hillary</u> was the first man to get to the top of Everest. (4) The mountain was important to <u>Edmond Hillary</u>. (5) But climbing <u>Mount Everest</u> remains very dangerous.

1 What pronoun can replace the noun in sentence 1?
- ⬭ You
- ⬭ He
- ⬭ Them
- ⬛ It

2 What pronoun can replace the noun in sentence 2?
- ⬭ he
- ⬛ they
- ⬭ it
- ⬭ him

3 What pronoun can replace the noun in sentence 3?
- ⬛ He
- ⬭ Him
- ⬭ It
- ⬭ They

4 What pronoun can replace the noun in sentence 4?
- ⬭ he
- ⬛ him
- ⬭ they
- ⬭ it

5 What pronoun can replace the noun in sentence 5?
- ⬭ him
- ⬭ they
- ⬛ it
- ⬭ them

© Pearson Education, Inc., 3

School + Home

Home Activity Your child prepared for taking tests on subject and object pronouns. Discuss a visit to a farm or zoo with your child. Have your child identify pronouns in the sentences and tell whether they are subject pronouns or object pronouns.

Prefixes *pre-, mid-, over-, bi-, out-, de-*

Directions Add the prefix **pre-, mid-, over-, out-,** or **de-** to each base word.
Write the new word on the line.

1. over- + load = **overload**

2. out- + going = **outgoing**

3. pre- + paid = **prepaid**

4. mid- + point = **midpoint**

5. de- + code = **decode**

Directions Choose the word from the box that best fits the definition. Write the word
on the line.

prefix _____ 6. a word part added to the beginning of a word

bicycle _____ 7. a vehicle with two wheels

outburst _____ 8. bursting forth

midweek _____ 9. the middle of the week

defrost _____ 10. to thaw something that is frozen

> bicycle
> midweek
> outburst
> defrost
> prefix

Directions Add the prefix **pre-, mid-, over-, bi-,** or **out-** to the base word in ( ) to
complete each sentence. Write the word on the line.

preschool _____ 11. Elena began to collect rocks when she was in (school).

outlast _____ 12. She thought this hobby would (last) any of her other hobbies.

overlook _____ 13. It is easy to (look) rocks during the day.

bicolor _____ 14. She found a (color) rock one day.

midnight _____ 15. Finding them at (night) is nearly impossible.

Home Activity Your child formed and wrote words with the prefixes *pre-, mid-, over-, bi-, out-,* and *de-*.
Work together to list other words with these prefixes, such as *pretest, midway, overhead, bilingual, outgrow,*
and *deflate.* Have your child use each word in a sentence.

© Pearson Education, Inc., 3

Fact and Opinion

- A **statement of fact** can be proved true or false.
- A **statement of opinion** gives someone's thoughts or feelings about something.
- Words that express feelings, such as *wise* and *wonderful*, are clues that a statement might be an opinion.

Directions Read the following biographical passage.

> Benjamin Franklin was a man of many interests. Franklin started his career as a printer, but printing was not his only accomplishment. Franklin also organized the first library and the first fire department. Benjamin Franklin was a wise and wonderful citizen. I think we are lucky that he was one of the founders of our country.

Directions Complete the chart by writing one more fact and one more opinion from the passage above. Then answer the question.

Facts	Opinions
Benjamin Franklin was a man of many interests.	Benjamin Franklin was a wise and wonderful citizen.
Franklin also organized the first library and the first fire department.	**I think we are lucky that he was one of the founders of our country.**

What facts support the idea the Franklin had many interests?

He was interested in printing, libraries, and fire departments.

Home Activity Your child identified facts and opinions in a biographical passage. Together with your child, read an article about a real person. Ask your child to find a statement of fact. Then use the Internet or a reference book to prove the fact is true.

© Pearson Education, Inc., 3

Writing • Biography

Key Features of a Biography

- tells about the life of a real person
- is usually told in time order
- uses words like he or she
- tells about the person's talents or important achievements

A Tinkering Man's Collection

As a boy, (Uncle Stefan) loved to tinker. He was good with his hands, and even better with tools. He could fix almost anything around the house, but his passion was working on his bicycle.

[Over time] Uncle Stefan began to build his own bikes, using spare parts from his workshop. That's how he began his one-of-a-kind bicycle collection. Have you ever seen a bicycle with a round steering wheel for handlebars and a plastic chair cushion for a seat? Uncle Stefan made a bike just like that for me!

[Now] Uncle Stefan has a shed full of bikes, and do you think they sit around collecting dust? Not on your life! Uncle loans them out to all of us neighborhood kids. And when the bikes start to squeak or show any signs of needing care, a big smile spreads across his face. It is time for Uncle Stefan to grab his toolbox and teach us how to tinker.

1. Find the person this biography tells about and circle his name. Then underline examples of the word *he* that refer to this man.

2. Draw a box around any words or phrases that give clues about when events happen.

Vocabulary

Check the Words You Know

___stamps	___spare
___chores	___attic
___labeled	___customer
___board	

Directions Write the word from the box that fits the meaning of each sentence.

1. I went to the post office to buy _____ **stamps** _____ for my letters.

2. The store owner _____ **labeled** _____ everything with a price.

3. We store things in the _____ **attic** _____ at the top of the house.

4. Al had a meeting with the _____ **board** _____ of directors at his company.

5. Taking out trash and washing dishes are my _____ **chores** _____ at home.

Directions Circle one word at the end of each sentence that fits the meaning.

6. I had a _____ pencil, so I gave one to my friend to use.
   (spare)   short

7. The salesman asked each _____ in the store if she needed any help.   custom (customer)

8. Walking the dog is one of my _____.   (chores)   chokes

9. We like to play upstairs in the _____.   attention (attic)

10. I need two _____ for my mail.
    steps (stamps)

Write an Advertisement

On a separate sheet of paper, use vocabulary words to write an advertisement for something you would like to sell if you owned a store.

Students' writing should use lesson vocabulary in an advertisement for something on sale in a store.

Home Activity Your child identified and used vocabulary words from *Rocks in His Head*. Visit a store with your child and have him or her describe the labels on items. Use as many of this week's vocabulary words as you can.

© Pearson Education, Inc., 3

Possessive Pronouns

Some pronouns show who or what owns, or possesses, something. This kind of pronoun is a **possessive pronoun.**

Possessive Pronouns   *My, mine, your, yours, her, hers, our, ours, his, their, theirs,* and *its* are possessive pronouns.

- This is <u>my</u> gold rock, and that is <u>hers</u>.

Directions Write the possessive pronouns in each sentence.

1. When Tracy visited her granddad, she looked for rocks on his farm.

   her, his

2. Her favorite rock was limestone. _____**Her**_____

3. Its color was pale gray. _____**Its**_____

4. Her brothers found rocks, and they put them in their granddad's study.

   Her, their

5. They had a shelf for theirs, and Tracy had a shelf for hers. **theirs, hers**

Directions Choose the possessive pronoun in ( ) that could replace the underlined words in each sentence. Write the sentence.

6. I found a piece of marble, and <u>the marble's</u> color was pink. (their, its)

   I found a piece of marble, and its color was pink.

7. Your favorite rock is quartz, and <u>my favorite rock</u> is marble. (mine, my)

   Your favorite rock is quartz, and mine is marble.

8. Is this quartz <u>the quartz you own</u>? (his, yours)

   Is this quartz yours?

Home Activity Your child learned about possessive pronouns. With your child, take turns using possessive pronouns in sentences about objects that family members collect. Have your child identify the possessive pronouns in the sentences.

Prefixes

Spelling Words				
prepaid	midnight	overflow	outdoors	outline
overgrown	prefix	Midwest	pretest	midpoint
outgoing	overtime	overdue	outside	outfield

Context Clues Write a list word that best completes each sentence.

1. Dad had to work **overtime** .

2. He stayed up until **midnight** .

3. The sink began to **overflow** .

4. My uncle is flying to the **Midwest** .

5. The word *midpoint* has a **prefix** .

6. My sister is **outgoing** .

7. Before you begin your report, make an **outline** .

8. The shrubs look **overgrown** .

9. Our teacher had us take a **pretest** .

10. My library book is **overdue** .

Missing Prefixes Write the prefix. Write the list word.

11. **out** doors   11. **outdoors**

12. **mid** point   12. **midpoint**

13. **pre** paid   13. **prepaid**

14. **out** side   14. **outside**

15. **out** field   15. **outfield**

Home Activity Your child spelled words with the prefixes *pre-*, *mid-*, *over-*, and *out-*. Have your child make up sentences using the answers to Exercises 11 to 15 on this page.

Story Sequence A

Title _____

Beginning

Middle

End

Vocabulary • Multiple-Meaning Words

- A **multiple-meaning** word has more than one meaning.
- If you see a word you know but the meaning does not make sense in the sentence, the word may be a multiple-meaning word. Try another meaning for the word in the sentence.

Directions Read the following passage about one child's special interests. Then answer the questions below. Look for multiple-meaning words as you read.

> My brother has had many hobbies. First he collected stamps. He filled his desk with envelopes full of stamps. Then he started building model airplanes. He hung the models from his ceiling and saved the spare parts in a big box. Now he's started to play chess. He always has a game set up on the floor.
>
> Mom complains about the clutter but she doesn't really mind. "Maybe someday he'll be president of a museum board," she says.

1. Does *stamps* mean "small, sticky papers that stand for postage paid" or "pounds one's foot loudly on the floor"?

   small, sticky papers that stand for postage paid

2. Does *spare* mean "a bowling score" or "extra"?

   extra

3. Does *play* mean "to act the part of a character in a drama" or "to join in on a game"?

   to join in on a game

4. Does *mind* mean "to obey someone" or "to be bothered by something"?

   to be bothered by something

5. Does *board* mean "a flat piece of wood" or "the group of people in charge of an organization?"

   the group of people in charge of an organization

Home Activity Your child chose the correct definitions for multiple-meaning words. See how many meanings of the word *run* you and you child can recall. Make up sentences for several different meanings.

Online Information

- You can go **online** to find **information** about almost any topic. You have to follow certain steps. First, you type in the URL. This is like an address. It takes you to the **home page,** or first page, of the Web site you want to use for reference.

- Next, you read the text on the home page and look at the images. Many of the words and images on the home page are **links.** When you click on a link, it takes you to a new page.

Directions Study the Web page and answer the questions that follow.

> ◀ ▶ C + http://www.url.here Q▾
>
> 🏠 **Home Page**   › **Contact Us**   › **Privacy**
>
> | LINCOLN | WASHINGTON | JACKSON | ROOSEVELT |
>
> **HOME**
> **HISTORY**
> **TOURS**
> **PETS**
> **TRADITIONS**
> **SPORTS**
> **PATRIOTISM**
>
> ★ HISTORY *History*
>
> America's presidents have represented many states, held different occupations and faced difficult challenges. However, each president answered the same call--the call to serve the American people. As you learn about the presidents, think about ways you can serve your neighbor, community or country today.
>
> ↘ **MEET THE PRESIDENTS**
> **Biographies**
> Read these presidential biographies put together by fifth-graders

1. What is the URL for this Web site? **www.url.here**

2. Which link can you click on to read about President Abraham Lincoln?

   Meet the Presidents or Lincoln

3. What might you find under the "Pets" link to the left?

   You might find out about the different animals that presidents had.

4. What is the purpose of this Web site?

   It is for kids who want to read about U.S. Presidents.

Home Activity Your child answered questions about an Internet site. Go online with your child to a United States government Web site. Spend some time looking through the site together. Click on the various links to visit other pages on the site. Help your child understand how to navigate the site.

© Pearson Education, Inc., 3

Prefixes

Proofread an Announcement Circle four misspelled words. Write them correctly. Rewrite the sentence that has an incorrect verb.

Night Hike

Learn about creatures of the night!

Meet outside the nature center. Dress for (outdores) and wear long pants. Some areas is (overgroan).

8 P.M. to (mid night)
Bring a (freind)!

Note: The $2 fee must be prepaid.

Spelling Words

prepaid
midnight
overflow
outdoors
outline
overgrown
prefix
Midwest

pretest
midpoint
outgoing
overtime
overdue
outside
outfield

1. __outdoors__   2. __overgrown__

3. __midnight__   4. __friend__

5. __Some areas are overgrown.__

Frequently Misspelled Words

outside
friend

Proofread Words Fill in a circle to show which word is spelled correctly. Write the word.

6. ○ middwest   ● Midwest   ○ midWest   __Midwest__

7. ○ overfloe   ● overflow   ○ ovrflow   __overflow__

8. ● outgoing   ○ ootgoing   ○ outtgoing   __outgoing__

9. ○ midpoin   ○ midpointe   ● midpoint   __midpoint__

10. ● outfield   ○ outfeild   ○ outfeeled   __outfield__

11. ○ pritest   ● pretest   ○ preetest   __pretest__

12. ○ ovrtime   ○ overrtime   ● overtime   __overtime__

Home Activity Your child identified misspelled words with the prefixes *pre-*, *mid-*, *over-*, and *out-*. Pronounce a word. Ask your child to identify the prefix and spell the word.

© Pearson Education, Inc., 3

Possessive Pronouns

Directions Read the selection. Then read each question that follows the selection. Decide which is the best answer to each question. Mark the space for the answer you have chosen.

Rock Collecting

(1) I have cool rocks in my collection. (2) Dad taught _____ family about rocks. (3) My dad gave me a rock from its collection. (4) The rock is odd, and its color is orange. (5) My sister Tara got down on her knees. (6) She found quartz on her first try. (7) Rock collecting is a good hobby, and it could be our.

1 Which word is the possessive pronoun in sentence 1?

- ⬭ I
- ⬭ rocks
- ⬬ my
- ⬭ in

2 Which pronoun correctly completes sentence 2?

- ⬬ our
- ⬭ mine
- ⬭ hers
- ⬭ its

3 What change, if any, should be made to sentence 3?

- ⬭ Change *its* to **he**
- ⬬ Change *its* to **his**
- ⬭ Change *its* to **mine**
- ⬭ Make no change

4 What change, if any, should be made to sentence 5?

- ⬭ Change *her knees.* to **hers knees.**
- ⬭ Change *her knees.* to **their knees.**
- ⬭ Change *her knees.* to **my knees.**
- ⬬ Make no change

5 What change, if any, should be made to sentence 7?

- ⬬ Change *our.* to **yours.**
- ⬭ Change *our.* to **him.**
- ⬭ Change *our.* to **its.**
- ⬭ Make no change

Home Activity Your child prepared for taking tests on possessive pronouns. Play a board game with your child. Have your child identify possessive pronouns used by any player as you play.

© Pearson Education, Inc., 3

Suffixes -er, -or, -ess, -ist

Directions Add the suffix to each base word. Write the new word on the line.

1. edit   +   -or   =   **editor** _____

2. art   +   -ist   =   **artist** _____

3. conduct   +   -or   =   **conductor** _____

4. lion   +   -ess   =   **lioness** _____

5. sell   +   -er   =   **seller** _____

Directions Write the word from the box that best fits each definition.

dentist _____ 6. a doctor who cares for your teeth

shipper _____ 7. one who ships packages

director _____ 8. one who directs

chemist _____ 9. a scientist in the field of chemistry

hostess _____ 10. a woman who greets restaurant guests

> chemist
> dentist
> hostess
> shipper
> director

Directions Add the suffix **-er, -or, -ess,** or **-ist** to the base word in ( ) to complete each sentence. Use the words in the box to help. Write the word on the line.

swimmer _____ 11. Gertrude Ederle was the first woman (swim) to swim across the English Channel.

instructor _____ 12. Many thought her coach was the greatest swimming (instruct) in the world.

actress _____ 13. After she became famous, Ederle was offered work as an (act), but she declined.

tourist _____ 14. Instead, she traveled as a (tour).

teacher _____ 15. Later, Ederle became a swimming (teach) for deaf children.

> actress
> instructor
> swimmer
> teacher
> tourist

© Pearson Education, Inc., 3

Home Activity Your child formed and wrote words with the suffixes *-er, -or, -ess,* and *-ist*. Together, think of additional job-related words that end with *-er, -or, -ess,* or *-ist* (such as *doctor, countess, biologist, police officer*). Help your child write a paragraph explaining which jobs sound most interesting to him or her and why.

Fact and Opinion

- A statement of **fact** tells something that can be proved true or false. You can prove it by reading or asking an expert.
- A statement of **opinion** tells someone's ideas or feelings. Words that tell feelings, such as *should* or *best,* are clues to opinions.

Directions Read the following passage. Then complete the diagram below.

Swimming is a sport that helps keep people in good shape. If you have any doubt, just ask Mark Spitz. He held the record for winning the most gold medals in swimming events at the Olympics until 2008.

In Germany, at the Olympics in 1972, Spitz won seven gold medals. He also set new world records in each of the seven events.

During those events, Spitz wore a mustache. The mustache distracted from his great performance. He should have shaved the mustache. That would have been best.

Fact	How to Prove
1. Spitz won most gold medals.	Ask expert or look it up.
2. Spitz set 7 world records.	Ask expert or look it up.

Opinion	Clue words
3. He should have shaved.	Should
4. That would have been best.	Best

5. How can you find out if Mark Spitz won seven gold medals at the Summer Olympics in 1972? _____
Check an encyclopedia, almanac, or the Internet.

Home Activity Your child identified fact and opinion in a nonfiction passage about swimming. Read another passage or editorial with your child and discuss whether the statements are fact or opinion. Have your child explain how to check to be sure seemingly true statements are really facts.

Writing • Autobiography

Key Features of an Autobiography

- tells the story of a person's own life
- may cover a person's whole life or only part of it
- written in first person

My Autobiography

I was born on August 29th, 2000, in Holland, MI. My mother has told me that when I was born, I cried less than any of the other children on the delivery floor. I guess I was just happy to be here!

A New Sister

My parents are Arthur and Tammy Garza. My father works as a social studies teacher at Brownsville High School. Someday I might even be one of his students! My mother is a lawyer who works for the city government. She helps to make sure that the city's plans will be safe for the environment.

When I was three years old, one of the biggest events in my life happened. My mother had to go away to the hospital for a few days, and my father told me that she'd come back with a big surprise. She came back with my baby sister! Her name is Teresa, and she's just starting school now. Teresa and I have our arguments, like any brother and sister, but I'm glad she's my sister.

Moving to Brownsville

A few years ago, my mother and father gave my sister and me some important news. My mother had gotten a new job in Brownsville, Texas, and so our family would be moving. At first, I couldn't believe what I was hearing. I would have to leave my friends behind, and the neighborhood where I grew up.

The time leading up to the move was full of preparations. Everything we owned was packed in brown boxes. Finally a big yellow truck pulled up outside and our furniture was loaded into it. We drove to Brownsville in my parents' car. When we arrived, our new house was bright and filled with sun.

1. Underline three sentences that tell you that this story is about the author's own life.

2. Circle the three examples of words that show the use of the first person point of view.

Students should circle words such as *I, my, me,* or *we.*

© Pearson Education, Inc., 3

Vocabulary

Check the Words You Know

___drowned   ___strokes
___medals   ___current
___continued   ___stirred
___celebrate

Directions Fill in the blank with a word from the box that fits the meaning of the sentence.

1. He ___**continued**___ to swim so that he could reach the shore.

2. The more she practiced, the stronger her swimming ___**strokes**___ became.

3. The swimmer won prizes and ___**medals**___ for every race she won.

4. The ocean ___**current**___ was strong, and he worked to swim against it.

5. The waves were high on the day she almost ___**drowned**___.

Directions Draw a line from the word to its meaning.

6. stirred   prizes or ribbons you win

7. celebrate   moved around

8. current   kept on going

9. medals   the movement of ocean water

10. continued   to have a party

Write a Newspaper Article

On a separate sheet of paper, write a newspaper article describing a swimming race. Use as many vocabulary words as possible.

Students' writing should use the lesson vocabulary in a description of a swimming race.

Home Activity Your child identified and used vocabulary words from *America's Champion Swimmer: Gertrude Ederle*. Read a sports article from a newspaper with your child. Encourage your child to discuss the article using this week's vocabulary words.

Contractions

A **contraction** is a word made by putting two words together. When words are joined in a contraction, an apostrophe shows where a letter or letters have been left out.

- Some contractions combine a pronoun and a verb: *I + am = I'm; he + is = he's; we + are = we're; you + will = you'll; we + will = we'll; they + are = they're.*
- Some contractions combine a verb and *not: can + not = can't; is + not = isn't; do + not = don't; will + not = won't; are + not = aren't.*

Contractions   They're swimming in the lake, but I can't see them.

Directions Read the sentence. Then write the contraction in each sentence.

1. Watch the Olympics, and you'll see some great swimmers. ___**you'll**___

2. The Americans think they'll win many medals. ___**they'll**___

3. I won't miss their big race tonight. ___**won't**___

4. I can't believe she broke the world record. ___**can't**___

5. Maybe we'll swim in the Olympics someday. ___**we'll**___

Directions Read the sentence. Write the contraction in each sentence. Then write the word or words that make up the contraction.

6. They're starting the race. ___**They're; They are**___

7. Jeremy is in this race, and he's in the first lane. ___**he's; he is**___

8. It's important to get a fast start. ___**It's; It is**___

9. Isn't a fast turn important also? ___**Isn't; Is not**___

10. The other swimmers can't beat Jeremy. ___**can't; cannot**___

Home Activity Your child learned about contractions. With your child, read an article in a local newspaper. Have your child identify the contractions and the words that make up each contraction.

Suffixes

Spelling Words				
dentist	editor	artist	hostess	actress
swimmer	seller	tutor	tourist	organist
lioness	shipper	chemist	investor	conductor

Definitions Write a list word to name each person.

1. a person who draws and paints
2. a person who takes care of teeth
3. a person who moves through water
4. a person who receives guests
5. a person who teaches
6. a person who works on books or magazines
7. a person who buys and sells stocks
8. a person who leads an orchestra
9. a person who plays an organ
10. a person who works with chemicals
11. a person who travels to new places

1. __artist__
2. __dentist__
3. __swimmer__
4. __hostess__
5. __tutor__
6. __editor__
7. __investor__
8. __conductor__
9. __organist__
10. __chemist__
11. __tourist__

Rhymes Write the missing word. It rhymes with the underlined word.

12. The _____ sent my sweater in a <u>zipper</u> bag.
13. He got a <u>propeller</u> from a model plane _____.
14. Did you see the <u>mess</u> the _____ left backstage?
15. The _____ eats <u>less</u> food than the lion.

12. __shipper__
13. __seller__
14. __actress__
15. __lioness__

Home Activity Your child spelled words with the suffixes -er, -or, -ess, and -ist. Many of the list words refer to people or occupations. Discuss any unfamiliar words with your child.

KWL Chart

Topic _____

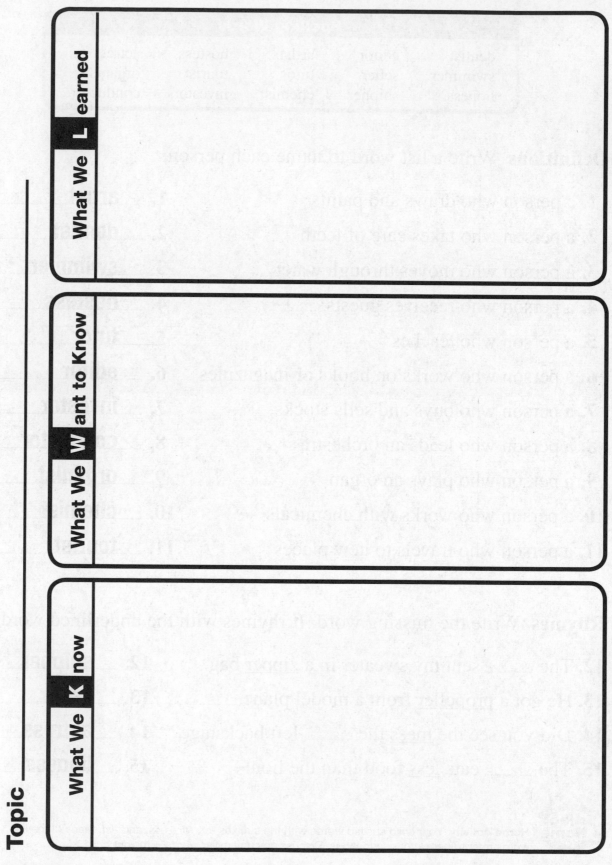

What We **K** now	What We **W** ant to Know	What We **L** earned

Vocabulary • Multiple-Meaning Words

- A **multiple-meaning** word has more than one meaning.
- If you see a word you know but the meaning does not make sense in the sentence, the word may be a multiple-meaning word. You can use **context clues** to figure out the word's meaning.

Directions Read the following passage about a child who was brave when it counted. Then answer the questions below. Look for context clues to help you with multiple-meaning words as you read.

Chad was afraid of water, but his dream was that he would get over his fear. One day Chad and his father saw a kitten stranded on a rock in the middle of a stream. The water was calm, but a small current swirled around the rock. "Go ahead," said Dad. "I'll be here if you need help."

Chad pulled off this cap and jumped in. He forgot to be afraid. With smooth strokes, he swam to the rock and brought the kitten back to shore. Chad was not afraid of water anymore

1. Does *dream* mean "an image in the mind of a sleeping person" or "a goal someone hopes to reach"?

   a goal someone hopes to reach

2. Does *calm* mean "without large waves" or "without strong feeling"?

   without large waves

3. Does *current* mean "movement of water in one direction" or "happening now"?

   movement of water in one direction

4. Does *cap* mean "to do something better than someone else" or "a head covering"?

   a head covering

5. Does *strokes* mean "motions used when swimming" or "motions used when petting an animal"?

   motions used when swimming

Home Activity Your child chose the correct definitions for multiple-meaning words. Read a story about a brave deed with your child. Then ask him or her to find multiple-meaning words and give their definitions.

Bar Graphs

- A **bar graph** allows you to compare amounts, dates, or other things. You can compare and contrast by looking at the heights of the bars on the graph.
- Bar graphs have two **axes**. The **horizontal axis** goes across the bottom of the graph. The **vertical axis** goes up the left-hand side of the graph. Each axis has a label to tell you what the numbers and categories in the graph mean.

Directions Use the bar graph to answer the questions.

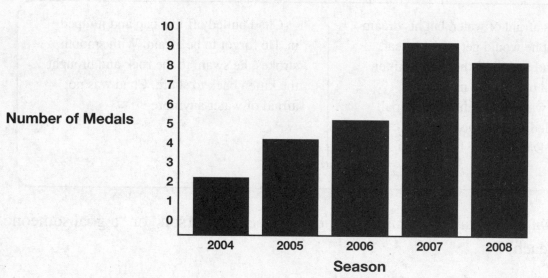

Gymnastics Medals Won

1. In which season did the gymnast win the most medals?

__2007__

2. How many medals did the gymnast win in her first season?

__2__

3. How many medals did the gymnast win in her last season?

__8__

4. In which season did the gymnast win a total of 5 medals?

__2006__

Home Activity Your child answered questions about a bar graph. Go through the sports page of the newspaper with your child. Find some data or statistics that will make a good bar graph. Help your child make a graph of the data.

Suffixes

Spelling Words				
dentist	editor	artist	hostess	actress
swimmer	seller	tutor	tourist	organist
lioness	shipper	chemist	investor	conductor

Proofread a Program Nick wrote the program for the school musical. Circle four misspelled words. Write them correctly. Add the missing punctuation mark.

The Cast

Mad chemist....Don Perlas

The ~~dentest~~.....Julie Blake

The tourist.......Kate Hanson

Music ~~conducter~~...Steve Carr

Scenery artist....Ann Morgan

We extend special thanks to the ~~editer~~ of the *Daily Press*, Mr. Pearson, ~~hoo~~ is our sponsor.

Frequently Misspelled Words

once
who
one

1. **dentist**
2. **conductor**
3. **editor**
4. **who**

Proofread Words Circle the word that is spelled correctly. Write the word.

5. Jake was a ticket (**seller**) **sellor**.

6. A **tudor** (**tutor**) helps Don with math.

7. Jean is a fast (**swimmer**) **swimer**.

8. The (**organist**) **organest** played softly.

9. We thanked our **hostes** (**hostess**)

10. The (**lioness**) **liones** paced back and forth.

5. **seller**
6. **tutor**
7. **swimmer**
8. **organist**
9. **hostess**
10. **lioness**

Home Activity Your child identified misspelled words with the suffixes *-er*, *-or*, *-ess*, and *-ist*. Ask your child to name the four hardest words. Have your child write these words.

© Pearson Education, Inc., 3

Contractions

Directions Read the selection. Then read each question that follows the selection. Decide which is the best answer to each question. Mark the space for the answer you have chosen.

Learning to Swim

(1) Swimming <u>is not</u> difficult. (2) <u>You will</u> learn some strokes. (3) <u>They are</u> your arm movements. (4) <u>I will</u> show you a kick. (5) <u>It is</u> the most popular kick. (6) <u>Don't</u> forget to breathe correctly. (7) Breathing <u>won't</u> be hard for you.

1 Which contraction is correct for sentence 1?
- ⬭ he's
- ⬭ don't
- ⬬ isn't
- ⬭ we'll

2 Which contraction is correct for sentence 2?
- ⬭ we're
- ⬭ I'm
- ⬭ won't
- ⬬ You'll

3 Which contraction is correct for sentence 3?
- ⬬ They're
- ⬭ Don't
- ⬭ We'll
- ⬭ can't

4 Which two words form the contraction in sentence 6?
- ⬭ I am
- ⬬ Do not
- ⬭ Are not
- ⬭ You will

5 Which two words form the contraction in sentence 7?
- ⬬ will not
- ⬭ can not
- ⬭ you will
- ⬭ are not

Home Activity Your child prepared for taking tests on contractions. Together, sort through the mail and have your child find contractions in advertisements and notices.

Syllables VCCCV

Directions Choose the word in ( ) with the VCCCV syllable pattern to finish each sentence. Write the word on the line.

children   **1.** The third grade (children/students) took a trip to the zoo.

surprise   **2.** Their teachers had a (surprise/special) assignment for them.

address   **3.** The zookeeper gave an (alert/address) to the students.

inspect   **4.** He told them to (inspect/watch) each animal's living space.

contrast   **5.** He suggested they (compare/contrast) different animals.

hundred   **6.** By the end of the day, the students had seen about one (dozen/hundred) animals.

Directions Circle the word that has the VCCCV syllable pattern. Then write a sentence on the line that uses the word you circled.

7. forgive   (monster)   wonder

Possible response: I read a book about a scary monster.

8. human   (fortress)   winner

Possible response: John built a fortress out of blocks.

9. (complain)   number   writer

Possible response: Some people complain about everything.

10. (constant)   planet   signal

Possible response: The noise from the machine was constant.

11. beyond   robin   (sample)

Possible response: The store gave everyone a free sample.

12. chosen   (control)   copper

Possible response: That dog is out of control.

Home Activity Your child wrote words with the VCCCV syllable pattern found in *mon/ster*. Ask your child to read each of the words he or she wrote on the page above. Take turns making up additional sentences using these words. Help your child write the sentences and underline the words with the VCCCV syllable pattern.

© Pearson Education, Inc., 3

Cause and Effect

- A **cause** tells why something happened.
- An **effect** is what happened.
- Words such as *because* and *so* are clues that can help you figure out a cause and its effect. Sometimes a clue word is not used.

Directions Read the following passage.

Camouflage is color or covering that blends with surroundings. Because it is so hard for animals to survive in the wild, some animals use camouflage to keep their enemies from noticing them. A baby deer, or fawn, has a tan coat with light spots. The spots provide camouflage in the sun-dappled forest. Other animals use tricks to protect themselves. The opossum tricks other animals by pretending to be dead. It does this because most other animals will not eat animals they have not killed. Wild animals would not last long if they had no way to hide. They have to be smart so they can find food for themselves and avoid becoming food for other animals.

Directions Fill in the chart to identify cause and effect.

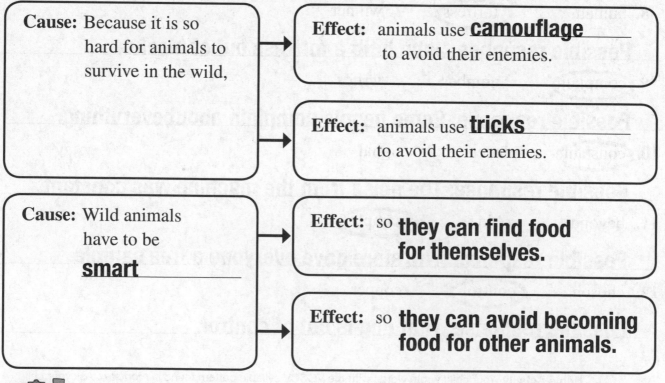

Cause: Because it is so hard for animals to survive in the wild,

→ **Effect:** animals use **camouflage** to avoid their enemies.

→ **Effect:** animals use **tricks** to avoid their enemies.

Cause: Wild animals have to be **smart**

→ **Effect:** so **they can find food for themselves.**

→ **Effect:** so **they can avoid becoming food for other animals.**

School + Home

Home Activity Your child identified cause and effect. Read an article about an animal with your child. Talk about causes and effects.

Writing • Summary

Key Features of a Summary

- retells a piece of writing
- includes only the most important information
- shorter than the original

Summary of Why the Dog Wags His Tail

Long ago, all the animals could speak and understood all the secrets of how things worked in the world. One special animal, Dog, knew all the secrets of the King. One day, Dog told the other animals to follow him because he was going to reveal all the King's secrets. So, many animals followed Dog to the cave.

Dog spoke for a long time telling many incredible secrets. Next, Raven raced to the palace to report to the King what Dog did. After, the King decided to teach Dog a lesson by taking away the Dog's power to speak. Ever since then, when Dog wants to say something he wags his tail—not his tongue.

1. Read the summary. Who are the main characters?

   Dog, Raven, and the King are the main characters.

2. What happens at the end of the story?

   The King takes away Dog's power to speak.

Vocabulary

Check the Words You Know
___scrambled   ___valley ___echoed   ___clutched ___reeds   ___thatch ___gully

Directions Read each sentence. Write a word from the box to complete each sentence.

1. The boy _____**scrambled**_____ over the rocks as quickly as he could.

2. The sound of thunder _____**echoed**_____ through the night.

3. We walked down the mountain into the _____**valley**_____ below.

4. The bird seemed to disappear in the tall _____**reeds**_____ near the lake.

5. We walked up the side of a small _____**gully**_____ to the top of the hill.

Directions Choose the word from the box that best matches each clue. Write the word on the line.

6. held tightly   **clutched**

7. ditch   **gully**

8. use straw or leaves as a roof   **thatch**

9. repeated, as a sound does   **echoed**

10. tall grasses   **reeds**

Write a Scene from a Play

On a separate sheet of paper, write a scene in which a child finds a baby animal and wants to take care of it. Use as many vocabulary words as possible.

Students' writing should use lesson vocabulary in a scene from a play about a child who wants to raise an orphan animal.

Home Activity Your child identified and used vocabulary words from *Fly, Eagle, Fly!* With your child, read a story or nonfiction article about nature. Discuss the setting. Encourage your child to use vocabulary words in your conversation.

Prepositions

A **preposition** is the first word in a group of words called a prepositional phrase. A **prepositional phrase** ends with a noun or pronoun called the **object of the preposition.** A prepositional phrase tells more about other words in a sentence.

Preposition	The eagle flew <u>in</u> a circle.
Prepositional Phrase	The eagle flew <u>in a circle</u>.
Object of Preposition	The eagle flew in a <u>circle</u>.

Common Prepositions

Here are some prepositions: *about, above, across, after, against, along, among, around, at, before, behind, below, beneath, beside, between, beyond, by, down, during, except, for, from, in, inside, into, near, of, off, on, onto, out, outside, over, past, since, through, throughout, to, toward, under, underneath, until, up, upon, with, within, without.*

Directions Write the preposition in each sentence.

1. Our class read a book about eagles. **about** _____

2. Bald eagles live in the United States. **in** _____

3. Bald eagles can grab fish from the water. **from** _____

4. The bald eagle population decreased during the 1970s. **during** _____

Directions Write the prepositional phrase in each sentence. Underline the preposition.

5. Another eagle within the United States is the golden eagle.

<u>within</u> the United States _____

6. Golden eagles have golden brown feathers on their necks.

<u>on</u> their necks _____

© Pearson Education, Inc., 3

Home Activity Your child learned about prepositions. With your child, look at ads. Have your child identify five prepositional phrases.

Syllables VCCCV

Spelling Words				
monster	surprise	hundred	complete	control
sample	instant	inspect	pilgrim	contrast
explode	district	address	substance	children

Missing Words Write the missing list word to complete each sentence.

1. That was a ____!

2. Would you like a ____ of lime yogurt?

3. That balloon will ____ if you keep blowing.

4. The ____ went on a long journey.

5. I couldn't ____ my tears.

6. My little sister thinks a ____ lives under her bed.

7. Many officials ____ the coal mine every year.

8. My best friend is not in my school ____.

1. __surprise__

2. __sample__

3. __explode__

4. __pilgrim__

5. __control__

6. __monster__

7. __inspect__

8. __district__

Definitions Write the list word that means the same thing as the word or phrase.

9. one more than ninety-nine

10. many boys and girls

11. entire

12. material

13. difference

14. moment of time

15. numbers that tell where you live

9. __hundred__

10. __children__

11. __complete__

12. __substance__

13. __contrast__

14. __instant__

15. __address__

Home Activity Your child spelled words with VCCCV (vowel-consonant-consonant-consonant-vowel) syllable patterns. Ask your child to spell the words one syllable at a time.

Scoring Rubric: Writing for Tests: Summary

	4	3	2	1
Focus/Ideas	Strong summary; only uses important information	Good summary; mostly uses important information	Summary has some main ideas and too many details	Does not understand summary form
Organization	Important ideas are in correct sequence	Sequence of events is generally correct	Sequence of events isn't always clear	No clear sequence of events
Voice	Shows understanding of the main ideas	Shows understanding of topic	Lacks understanding of topic	Does not understand topic
Word Choice	Uses strong action verbs and time-order words	Uses some strong action verbs and time-order words	Few or no strong verbs or time-order words	Poor word choice
Sentences	Clear sentences of different lengths and types	Sentences of a few lengths and types	Sentences of similar length and type	No variety of sentence length and type
Conventions	Few, if any, errors; correct use of prepositions	Several small errors; use of prepositions	Many errors; weak use of prepositions	Many serious errors; incorrect or no use of prepositions

Vocabulary • Unknown Words

You can use a glossary or a dictionary to find the meaning, syllabication, and pronunciation of **unknown words**.

---

clutch (kluch) *v.* to grasp something tightly **clutch • es, clutched, clutch • ing**

ech • o (ek′ ō) *v.* to be heard again and again **ech • oes, ech • oed, ech • o • ing**

reed (rēd) *n.* a kind of tall grass that grows in wet places *plural* **reeds**

scram • ble (skram′ bəl) *v.* to make your way, especially by climbing or crawling quickly **scram • bles, scram • bled, scram • bling**

val • ley (val′ ē) *n.* a region of low land that lies between hills or mountains *plural* **val • leys**

Directions Read the passage. Use the glossary entries to answer the questions.

On his first nature hike, Mike stumbled upon an interesting scene. Sloppy looking twig nests perched shakily in the tops of lofty trees. The raspy squawk of a great blue heron echoed around the valley. A few of the tall, gray birds were wading among the reeds in the pond. Mike clutched his binoculars and scrambled down toward the water. He hoped to get a closer look at these strange birds.

1. What does the word *echoed* mean?

was heard again and again

2. Would you go up or down to get to a valley?

down

3. What are reeds?

tall grasses

4. How many syllables are in the word *clutched?*

1

5. Which syllable should you stress when you say *scrambled?*

the first; scram

Home Activity Your child used a glossary to understand meanings, syllabication, and pronunciation of words from *Fly, Eagle, Fly!* Read an article about nature with your child. Encourage your child to use a dictionary to find the meanings and pronunciations of unknown words.

Outlining and Summarizing

Summarizing refers to finding the most important ideas about a topic or text. You can summarize what you read or what you learn in class. One way to summarize is by making an **outline.** An outline shows a main idea and details, as in the one shown below.

An Endangered Animal—The African Elephant	

I. Size
  A. Weight
    1. 7,000 to 15,000 pounds
    2. Males larger
  B. Height and Length
    1. 10 to 13 ft high
    2. 20 to 24 ft long
	II. Diet—Vegetation
	  A. Grasses
	  B. Leaves
	  C. Fruit
	
	III. Habitat—Africa
	  A. Forest
	  B. Grassland

Directions Write the words from the box in the outline. Use the outline above as a guide.

> **Habitat**   **Deer**   **45 to 80 pounds**   **Rabbits**   **Wetlands**

The Red Wolf	

I. Size
  A. 4 1/2 to 5 1/2 ft long
  B. Weight
    1. **45 to 80 pounds**
    2. Males larger
II. **Habitat**
  A. Forests
  B. Mountains
  C. **Wetlands**
	III. Diet
	  A. Mainly small animals
	    1. Rodents
	    2. **Rabbits**
	  B. Others
	    1. Insects
	    2. Berries
	    3. **Deer**

Home Activity Your child learned how to make an outline to summarize ideas. Give your child information about a familiar topic. Include at least three main ideas and several details about the main ideas. Help him or her organize these ideas in an outline.

Syllables VCCCV

Spelling Words				
monster	surprise	hundred	complete	control
sample	instant	inspect	pilgrim	contrast
explode	district	address	substance	children

Proofread a Paragraph James wrote about stamp collecting. Circle four words that are spelled incorrectly. Cross out the extra word in the first sentence.

Some (childrn) try to collect a sample of each stamp pictured over in a stamp album. I tried that, but I thought I'd never get a complete collection. Most of my pages were empty. Now I collect only (Chrismas) stamps. I have almost two (hunderd) stamps. Does that (surpris) you?

Frequently Misspelled Words

Christmas
went

1. __children__   2. __Christmas__

3. __hundred__   4. __surprise__

Proofread Words Fill in a circle to show which word is spelled correctly. Write the word.

5. In the dark, the tree looked like a _____ .
   ○ monstor   ● monster   ○ montser

6. They gave me a free _____ at the grocery store.
   ● sample   ○ saple   ○ slampe

7. What is your _____ ?
   ○ adress   ○ addres   ● address

8. I ate so much, I thought I would _____ !
   ○ explod   ○ esplode   ● explode

5. __monster__

6. __sample__

7. __address__

8. __explode__

Home Activity Your child spelled words with VCCCV (vowel-consonant-consonant-consonant-vowel) syllable patterns. Have your child circle the three consecutive consonants in a list word and underline the vowels on either side.

© Pearson Education, Inc., 3

Prepositions

Directions Read the selection. Then read each question that follows the selection. Decide which is the best answer to each question. Mark the space for the answer you have chosen.

Eagles

(1) Eagles live throughout the world. (2) They build their nests on treetops. (3) Eagles hunt during the day. (4) They spot prey from the air. (5) Eagles rest at night.

1 What is the preposition in sentence 1?
- ⬤ throughout
- ◯ eagles
- ◯ world
- ◯ live

2 What is the preposition in sentence 2?
- ◯ their
- ◯ they
- ⬤ on
- ◯ nests

3 What is the preposition in sentence 3?
- ◯ hunt
- ⬤ during
- ◯ the
- ◯ day

4 What is the prepositional phrase in sentence 4?
- ◯ the air
- ◯ They spot
- ◯ They spot prey
- ⬤ from the air

5 What is the prepositional phrase in sentence 5?
- ⬤ at night
- ◯ Eagles rest
- ◯ rest at night
- ◯ Eagles rest at

Home Activity Your child prepared for taking tests on prepositions. Look through a cookbook with your child. Ask him or her to find three prepositional phrases in a recipe and identify the preposition in each one.

Irregular Plurals

Spelling Words				
wolves	knives	feet	men	children
women	sheep	heroes	scarves	mice
geese	cuffs	elves	banjos	halves

Word Meanings Write the list word for each meaning clue.

1. animals that give wool   `s h e e p`

2. more than one mouse   `m i c e`

3. stringed instruments   `b a n j o s`

4. brave people   `h e r o e s`

5. two equal parts of a whole   `h a l v e s`

6. more than one man   `m e n`

7. small make-believe people   `e l v e s`

Complete the Sentence Write the letters from the shaded boxes to finish the sentence.

8. People wear ____scarves____ around their necks.

Proofreading Draw a line through the misspelled word in each sentence. Write the word correctly.

9. The ~~childrun~~ learned spelling words. ___children___

10. The ~~wolfs~~ howled at the moon. ___wolves___

11. A baby has small ~~foots~~. ___feet___

12. A flock of ~~gooses~~ flew over us. ___geese___

13. I got mustard on my shirt ~~cuffes~~. ___cuffs___

14. These ~~knifes~~ are very sharp. ___knives___

15. Three ~~womin~~ painted the room. ___women___

© Pearson Education, Inc., 3

School + Home **Home Activity** Your child is learning to spell irregular plurals. Say the singular form of a list word (*mouse*). Ask your child to spell the plural (*mice*). Continue until all the words have been spelled.

Singular and Plural Pronouns

Directions Write the pronoun in each sentence.

1. Have you seen people play basketball?   you

2. They can have a lot of fun.   They

3. We have a basketball team.   We

4. Troy can dribble the ball and shoot it.   it

5. He is the best player on this team.   He

6. Maya is not tall, but she is fast.   she

7. We were watching another team.   We

8. They were a very talented bunch.   They

9. Maya wanted to challenge them.   them

10. Thanks to Maya, we won the game.   we

Directions Write *S* if the underlined pronoun is singular. Write *P* if it is plural.

11. Some people like sports, and they join a team.   P

12. Fans watch them from the bleachers.   P

13. Janet jumps, and she glides through the air.   S

14. All of us watch Janet play basketball.   P

15. I guess people will invent even more games to play.   S

16. Maybe we can think of a new game.   P

17. Dan has an idea, and I like it.   S

18. He plays on several sports teams.   S

19. Janet asked me to play ball with her.   S

20. Dan wants me to play a game with him.   S

Name _____

Vowels: *r*-Controlled

Spelling Words				
third	early	world	certain	dirty
herself	earth	word	perfect	verb
nerve	worm	thirsty	workout	earn

Classifying Write the list word that belongs in each group.

1. first, second, ___
2. yourself, himself, ___
3. letter, syllable, ___
4. unclean, messy, ___
5. positive, sure, ___
6. correct, all right, ___
7. noun, adjective, ___

1. **third**
2. **herself**
3. **word**
4. **dirty**
5. **certain**
6. **perfect**
7. **verb**

Scrambled Words Unscramble the list words. Write them correctly.

8. lyear
9. enrve
10. hirstyt
11. touwkor
12. nrea
13. threa
14. rowld
15. rowm

8. __e__ __a__ __r__ __l__ __y__
9. __n__ __e__ __r__ __v__ __e__
10. __t__ __h__ __i__ __r__ __s__ __t__ __y__
11. __w__ __o__ __r__ __k__ __o__ __u__ __t__
12. __e__ __a__ __r__ __n__
13. __e__ __a__ __r__ __t__ __h__
14. __w__ __o__ __r__ __l__ __d__
15. __w__ __o__ __r__ __m__

© Pearson Education, Inc., 3

Proverb Write the words you wrote for number 8 and for number 15. You will read some famous words of wisdom.

The ___**early**___ bird catches the ___**worm**___ .

        8   15

Home Activity Your child practiced spelling words with *er*, *ir*, *or*, and *ear*. Ask your child to write the words and to circle the letters for the *r*-vowel sounds. Then read the words together. When you come to circled letters, exaggerate the vowel sound by stretching it out.

Subject and Object Pronouns

Directions Write *SP* if the underlined pronoun is a subject pronoun. Write *OP* if it is an object pronoun.

1. <u>I</u> visited one of the hottest places in the world. __SP__

2. <u>We</u> went to Death Valley in the summer. __SP__

3. The hot sun dazzled <u>us</u>. __OP__

4. We took plenty of water for Robert and <u>them</u>. __OP__

5. <u>They</u> took pictures of the desert plants. __SP__

Directions Choose the correct pronoun to complete each sentence. Write the sentence.

6. My family and (me, I) visited the Grand Canyon.

   My family and I visited the Grand Canyon.

7. (We, Us) looked down one mile at the canyon's bottom.

   We looked down one mile at the canyon's bottom.

8. The canyon's colors surprised Jack and (me, I).

   The canyon's colors surprised Jack and me.

9. Dad and (he, him) rafted on the river at the bottom of the canyon.

   Dad and he rafted on the river at the bottom of the canyon.

10. Later (they, them) hiked in the park.

    Later they hiked in the park.

Prefixes

Opposites Write the list word that is opposite
in meaning to the given word or phrase.

1. indoors   **outdoors**
2. suffix   **prefix**
3. noon   **midnight**
4. on time   **overdue**
5. posttest   **pretest**
6. infield   **outfield**
7. Mideast   **Midwest**
8. inside   **outside**

Spelling Words
prepaid
midnight
overflow
outdoors
outline
overgrown
prefix
Midwest
pretest
midpoint
outgoing
overtime
overdue
outside
outfield

Word Search Circle the list words in the puzzle.
Look across and down. Write the words you find.

```
m o u t g o i n g a c
i v o v e r g r o w n
d e v f g m s w u g l
p r e p a i d t t p s
o f v m u n y r l w a
i l t o v e r t i m e
n o q b f v p c n l b
t w s k i z g v e u m
```

9. **outgoing**   12. **overtime**   14. **overflow**
10. **overgrown**   13. **midpoint**   15. **outline**
11. **prepaid**

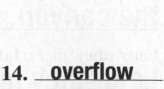 **Home Activity** Your child learned to spell words with the prefixes *pre-*, *mid-*, *over-*, and *out-*.
Make two sets of cards with list words on them. Play Concentration. When a match is made, the
person must spell the word correctly to keep the cards.

© Pearson Education, Inc., 3

Possessive Pronouns

Directions Write the possessive pronouns in the sentences.

1. Uncle Rick has valuable rocks on his ranch. ___his___

2. Aunt Julie makes her jewelry with the stones. ___her___

3. She likes their blue color. ___their___

4. Our gifts were made from her purple stones. ___Our, her___

5. Mine is a necklace, and hers is a pin. ___Mine, hers___

Directions Choose the possessive pronoun in ( ) that could replace the underlined words in each sentence. Write the sentence.

6. I bought a ring, and the ring's stones are green. (their, its)

   I bought a ring, and its stones are green.

7. The artists showed us the artists' best jewelry. (his, their)

   The artists showed us their best jewelry.

8. The green stones are the color of Laura's eyes. (hers, her)

   The green stones are the color of her eyes.

9. Are these earrings the earrings you own? (his, yours)

   Are these earrings yours?

10. My necklace is ruby, and Jen's necklace is turquoise. (hers, yours)

    My necklace is ruby, and hers is turquoise.

Suffixes

Spelling Words				
dentist	editor	artist	hostess	actress
swimmer	seller	tutor	tourist	organist
lioness	shipper	chemist	investor	conductor

Adding Suffixes Add a suffix to the base word. Write the list word you make in the chart.

base	-er	-or	-ess	-ist
1. invest		**investor**		
2. tour				**tourist**
3. sell	**seller**			
4. lion			**lioness**	
5. art				**artist**
6. edit		**editor**		
7. host			**hostess**	
8. organ				**organist**
9. conduct		**conductor**		

Proofreading Circle the correctly spelled word. Write the word.

10. dentalist (dentist)   11. __**dentist**__

11. actess (actress)   11. __**actress**__

12. (shipper) shiper   12. __**shipper**__

13. (tutor) tuter   13. __**tutor**__

14. swimer (swimmer)   14. __**swimmer**__

15. (chemist) chemest   15. __**chemist**__

© Pearson Education, Inc., 3

School + Home

Home Activity Your child practiced spelling words with the suffixes -er, -or, -ess, and -ist. To practice together, choose a word. Draw blanks for each letter, then write in the suffix. Let your child guess the word and fill in the remaining blanks. Then have him or her write the whole word.

Contractions

Directions Write the contraction in each sentence. Then write the word or words that make up the contraction.

1. You can't win the race without training.

 can't; cannot _____

2. These are Olympic athletes, and they're training many hours each week.

 they're; they are _____

3. She's a great swimmer.

 She's; She is _____

4. She didn't know swimming was so challenging.

 didn't; did not _____

5. Maybe you'll become a swimmer too.

 you'll; you will _____

Directions Write the contraction for the underlined words.

6. You <u>will not</u> believe Gertrude Ederle's strength and will power.

 won't _____

7. She <u>could not</u> have crossed the English Channel without them.

 couldn't _____

8. The Channel is wide, and <u>it is</u> stormy.

 it's _____

9. Many swimmers have tried to swim the Channel, and <u>they have</u> given up.

 they've _____

10. Gertrude Ederle was a great swimmer, and <u>she is</u> my role model.

 she's _____

Syllables VCCCV

Spelling Words				
monster	surprise	hundred	complete	control
sample	instant	inspect	pilgrim	contrast
explode	district	address	substance	children

Analogies Write the list word that completes each comparison.

1. Adult is to **adults** as **child** is to ___children___ .

2. Begin is to **end** as **unfinished** is to ___complete___ .

3. 1,000 is to **thousand** as **100** is to ___hundred___ .

4. Check is to **examine** as **examine** is to ___inspect___ .

5. Light is to **dark** as **compare** is to ___contrast___ .

6. Quick is to **fast** as **immediate** is to ___instant___ .

7. Explorer is to **pioneer** as **traveler** is to ___pilgrim___ .

8. Real is to **person** as **make-believe** is to ___monster___ .

Finding Syllables Decide where to divide each word into syllables. Write each syllable. Remember that for VCCCV words, you divide after the first consonant.

hundred = hun dred

9. surprise	___sur___	___prise___	
10. control	___con___	___trol___	
11. sample	___sam___	___ple___	
12. substance	___sub___	___stance___	
13. address	___ad___	___dress___	
14. district	___dis___	___trict___	
15. explode	___ex___	___plode___	

© Pearson Education, Inc., 3

Home Activity Your child is learning spelling words with the VCCCV (vowel-consonant-consonant-consonant-vowel) syllable pattern. Ask your child to write each word and to circle in crayon the three consonants that come together.

Prepositions

Directions Write the preposition in each sentence.

1. The eagle held a fish in its feet.

2. The fish was for the baby eagles.

3. The eagle's nest was high above the lake.

4. The baby eagles' cries filled the air of the forest.

5. The mother eagle landed on the big nest.

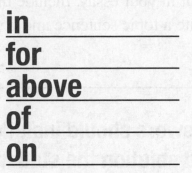

in _____

for _____

above _____

of _____

on _____

Directions Write the prepositional phrase in each sentence. Underline the preposition.

6. These eagles live in Florida.

in Florida

7. They make their homes along the marshes.

along the marshes

8. They lay their eggs during the winter.

during the winter

9. The mother bird stays with the eggs.

with the eggs

10. The father bird gets food from the water.

from the water

11. He drops it into the babies' mouths.

into the babies' mouths

12. The babies will leave the nest before summer.

before summer

Problem-Solution Chart

Directions Fill in the chart with notes on the problem and solution you are going to write about in your essay. Include the facts and details you will use to support your ideas. Write a topic sentence and concluding statement for your essay.

Topic Sentence

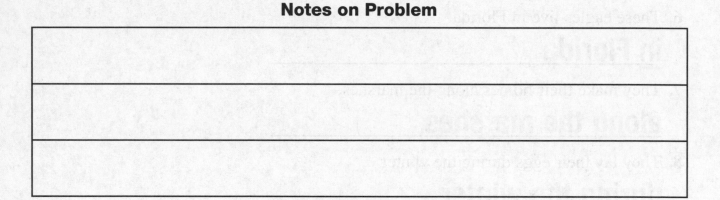

Answers should include facts and details about the problem and solution the student has chosen to write about.

Notes on Problem

Notes on Solution

Concluding Statement

Concluding Statements

Directions Underline the sentence that is the best concluding statement for each paragraph.

1. There's a dog that talks and a man whose wig keeps falling off. Sometimes I laugh so hard that I begin to cry.

   Concluding Statements

   In one episode, a car drove into a garage and out the other side.

   <u>This is by far the funniest show on television.</u>

   Sometimes my dad watches the show with me.

2. By the end of the day, we had walked thirteen miles. We had climbed three mountains and crossed two rivers. All I'd had to eat was a peanut butter sandwich.

   Concluding Statements

   There wasn't even any jelly for the sandwich.

   The views from the mountain tops were beautiful.

   <u>I slept very, very well that night.</u>

Directions Write a concluding statement for each paragraph. **Possible answers**

3. Cape Cod has long, sandy beaches. There are miles of bike trails and beautiful lakes and forests. The nights are cool, and the days are warm and sunny.

   <u>**There's no place like Cape Cod for a summer vacation.**</u>

   _____

4. My brother Bob helps me with my homework and makes sure I'm ready for school each morning. He takes me fishing, plays ball with me, and reads to me at night.

   <u>**Bob is my hero.**</u>

   _____

Prepositional Phrases

Make your writing more specific by using prepositional phrases to add details.

General	We swept up trash.
More Specific	We swept up trash on the playground.

Directions Read each sentence and the three prepositional phrases below it. Circle the prepositional phrase that can be used to add specific details to the sentence. Add the prepositional phrase and write the new sentence.

1. Parents and kids can help clean up DeSoto Park.

   Prepositional Phrases   in the trash   (from the community)   through the river

   Parents and kids from the community can help clean up DeSoto Park.

2. We hauled away a pile.

   Prepositional Phrases   (of old newspapers)   at our meeting   into the woods

   We hauled away a pile of old newspapers.

3. Students met in the park.

   Prepositional Phrases   under the water   for my mom   (at ten in the morning)

   Students met in the park at ten in the morning.

4. We threw all the litter.

   Prepositional Phrases   for a safe park   (into a dumpster)   by hard work

   We threw all the litter into a dumpster.

Peer and Teacher Conferencing Problem-Solution Essay

Directions Read your partner's essay. Refer to the Revising Checklist as you write your comments or questions. Offer compliments as well as revision suggestions. Then take turns talking about each other's draft. Give your partner your notes. After you and your teacher talk about your essay, add your teacher's comments to the notes.

Revising Checklist

Focus/Ideas

☐ Is the problem-solution essay focused on one problem in the school or community?

☐ Does the writer offer a logical method of solving the problem?

Organization

☐ Is there a clear topic sentence and concluding statement?

☐ Are details of the problem and solution organized in separate paragraphs?

Voice

☐ Does the writer show care and understanding of the problem?

Word Choice

☐ Are time-order words used effectively in the solution?

Sentences

☐ Do prepositional phrases add details to the essay?

☐ Are sentences clear, varied, and logical?

Things I Thought Were Good _____

_____

Things I Thought Could Be Improved _____

_____

Teacher's Comments _____

_____

Syllable Pattern CV/VC

Directions Circle the word with two vowels together where each vowel has a separate vowel sound. Then underline the letters that stand for the two different vowel sounds.

1. clean   paint   (pat<u>io</u>)
2. (<u>au</u>dio)   faith   search
3. greed   journal   (rod<u>eo</u>)
4. either   (med<u>iu</u>m)   southern
5. beach   pound   (p<u>io</u>neer)
6. (d<u>uo</u>)   poison   waiter
7. grain   group   (stad<u>iu</u>m)
8. mean   freeze   (vid<u>eo</u>)

Directions Read the paragraph. Circle all the underlined words with two vowels together where each vowel has a separate vowel sound. Write the words on the lines below.

> Marie was eager to (create) a new song. She thought she had an (idea) for a tune. She tried it on the (piano.) Then she wrote a part for the (violin.) She liked the way it sounded. Marie invited three friends to go to the (studio) with her. Her friends were singers. Marie explained the music. The (trio) made a (stereo) recording. Someday you might even hear it on the (radio.)

9. **create**
10. **idea**
11. **piano**
12. **violin**
13. **studio**
14. **trio**
15. **stereo**
16. **radio**

© Pearson Education, Inc., 3

Home Activity Your child identified and wrote words in which two vowels together each stand for a separate vowel sound, as in *stereo* and *stadium*. Ask your child to read the words aloud from the page above. Have your child name the long vowel sounds in each word.

Name _____

Compare and Contrast

- When you **compare and contrast** two or more things, you tell how they are alike and different.
- Some clue words that signal that things might be the same are *like, same, both, also,* and *as well as.*
- Some clue words that signal that things might be different are *but, however, different,* and *instead.*

Directions Read the following passage.

Fong and his family traveled to Senegal for the summer. On their first night, they ate dinner at a friend's house. Instead of tables and chairs, everyone sat on the floor around a big blanket. Out came a large bowl of food.

Fong watched as the dinner guests ate from the bowl of food with their hands. Rather than taking food onto a plate as they did at home, the guests ate from the part of the bowl that faced them. Just like at home, the food was delicious.

Directions Fill in the Venn diagram to compare and contrast two styles of dining.

Fong's Family

Sits on chairs around a table.

Eats from separate plates.

Both

Delicious food

Senegalese Family

Sits on the floor around a big blanket.

Eats from the same bowl.

Home Activity Your child compared and contrasted dining customs in two different cultures. Talk with your child about customs you grew up with and compare and contrast them with customs today.

© Pearson Education, Inc., 3

Writing • Letter to the Editor

Key Features of a Letter to the Editor

• includes the features of a letter: date, salutation, body, closing, and signature

• written to bring attention to an issue or problem

• often tries to be persuasive

＊January 5, 2009

＊Dear Editor,

＊At Smith School, we have a terrible playground. We have rusty monkey bars and a slide that is not slippery. We don't have a jungle gym or a merry-go-round like Jones School. The ground is cement. If people fall, they might get hurt. This playground is no fun. It's also dangerous.

Students need a good playground. I sit all day in my classroom. I work hard learning and taking tests, so recess is important to me. I want to have fun at recess. The students at Smith School have voted for a new playground. It will have a jungle gym and a merry-go-round. It will have a floor made of recycled tires, so if people fall, they won't get hurt.

We will pay for the new playground by raising money. We are holding a bake sale in the school gym on January 17 and 18. On February 7 and 8, we will collect glass and aluminum in the school parking lot to recycle. We hope people will come to these events to help us earn our new playground.

＊Sincerely,
＊Cassie Taff

---

1. Draw a star next to the date, salutation, body, closing, and signature of the letter to the editor. What is the salutation for a letter to the editor? **Dear Editor,**

   What is the name of the student who wrote this letter? **Cassie Taff**

2. Underline the issue or problem the student brings up in her letter.
   List three details that support the student's opinion. **Possible answers: We have rusty monkey bars and a slide that is not slippery; We don't have a jungle gym or a merry-go-round; The ground is cement.**

3. What does this student want the readers of the newspaper to do?

   Come to the school's bake sale and recycling drive.

   Draw a box around three words or phrases that persuade the reader to help.

   Possible answers: dangerous; need; I work hard; voted; We hope; earn

Vocabulary

Directions Write the word on the line that fits the meaning of the sentence.

Check the Words You Know
___festival   ___rhythm
___paces   ___graceful
___pale   ___cotton
___handkerchief ___snug

1. Every New Year, my neighborhood has a _____**festival**_____ with fireworks.

2. One song had a great _____**rhythm**_____, so everyone danced.

3. The dancer moved her arms in _____**graceful**_____ curves.

4. I pull the covers up to my chin, and then I feel _____**snug**_____ in bed.

5. In summer, I wear cool _____**cotton**_____ T-shirts.

Directions Match the word with its meaning. Draw a line from the word to its definition.

6. paces — piece of cloth for wiping one's nose or face

7. pale — wrapped up; warm and cozy

8. handkerchief — walks; steps

9. cotton — having very little color

10. snug — material made from a plant

Write a Description

On a separate sheet of paper, describe a costume that you would like to wear on a special occasion. Use as many vocabulary words as possible.

Students' writing should incorporate the vocabulary in a description of a costume they would like to wear.

Home Activity Your child identified and used words from *Suki's Kimono*. Read a story about Japan together. Encourage your child to discuss the article or story using this week's vocabulary words.

Adjectives and Articles

An **adjective** is a word that describes a person, place, or thing. Adjectives tell more about nouns. *A*, *an*, and *the* are special kinds of adjectives called **articles.**

| Adjectives | <u>Some</u> girls wore <u>long</u>, <u>bright</u> skirts. |
| Articles | <u>A</u> boy wore <u>an</u> awesome shirt to <u>the</u> party. |

- The articles *a* and *an* are used only with singular nouns. *A* is used before a word that begins with a consonant sound: *a jacket, a full cup. An* is used before a word that begins with a vowel sound: *an eagle, an orange jacket, an empty cup.*
- Use *the* before singular or plural nouns: *the shoe, the shoes.*

Directions Write the adjective that describes each underlined noun.

1. Many countries have colorful <u>clothing</u> for celebrations. **colorful**

2. Indian women wear silk <u>dresses</u>. **silk**

3. Many Scottish men have plaid <u>kilts</u> for special occasions. **plaid**

4. In Russia, men put on long <u>coats</u>. **long**

5. Japanese kimonos are made in many <u>colors</u>. **many**

Directions Circle the article in ( ) that correctly completes each sentence.

6. The American Indian wore (**a**, an) jacket with colorful beads.

7. (A, **The**) short pants that that man is wearing are German.

8. The African man wore (a, **an**) orange robe.

9. (**The**, A) Mexican musicians had big hats.

10. The woman from Chile wore (a, **an**) outfit with a long, white skirt.

School + Home **Home Activity** Your child learned about adjectives and articles. On a walk, ask your child to use adjectives to describe various objects, such as a house, a tree, and a dog.

© Pearson Education, Inc., 3

Syllable Pattern CV/VC

Spelling Words				
create	medium	piano	idea	radio
video	studio	violin	duo	patio
rodeo	pioneer	trio	stadium	audio

Connections Connect the first and last parts of the word.
Write the word.

vide-   -oneer   1. __video__

vi-   -o   2. __violin__

pi-   -um   3. __pioneer__

stadi-   -a   4. __stadium__

ide-   -olin   5. __idea__

Seeing Relationships Read the first word pair. Write a list word to
complete the second word pair.

6. see and television, hear and ____   6. __radio__

7. farmer and field, artist and ____   7. __studio__

8. huge and large, middle-sized and ____   8. __medium__

9. ceiling and dining room, sky and ____   9. __patio__

10. three and trio, two and ____   10. __duo__

11. wreck and fix, destroy and ____   11. __create__

12. sight and video, sound and ____   12. __audio__

13. clang and bell, music and ____   13. __piano__

14. twin and duo, triplet and ____   14. __trio__

15. clown and circus, cowboy and ____   15. __rodeo__

 Home Activity Your child spelled words with CV/VC (consonant-vowel-vowel-consonant) syllable
pattern. Discuss any list words that may be unfamiliar to your child.

Main Idea

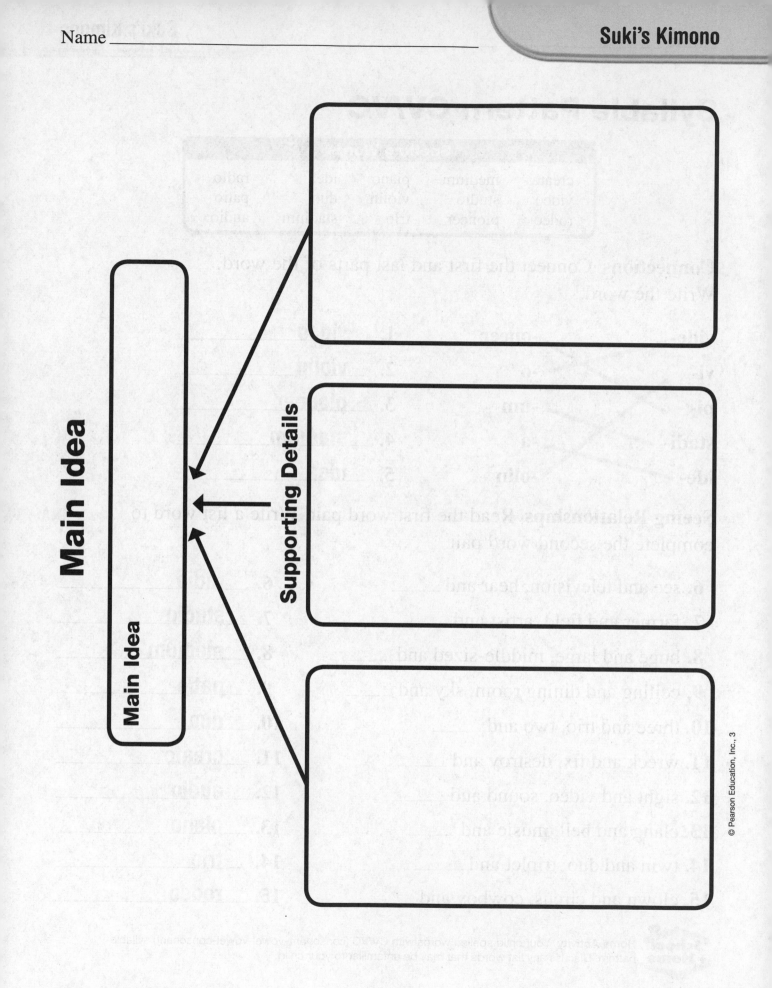

Main Idea

Supporting Details

Main Idea

Vocabulary • Synonyms

- Sometimes you may come across a word you don't know. There may be another word in the sentence that has the same meaning. These words are called **synonyms**, and they can help you figure out the meaning of a word.
- Look for **synonyms** to help you figure out the meaning of unfamiliar words.

Directions Circle the synonym for the underlined word. Then write the meaning of the underlined word on the line.

1. The <u>festival</u> was held as a (celebration) of the city's anniversary.

   a day or special time of rejoicing or feasting

2. You (grab) the baseball, and I'll <u>snatch</u> the glove from my locker.

   to seize something suddenly

3. José walked three <u>paces</u> in front of me, but Jim walked several (steps) behind.

   forward movements by lifting and placing feet one after the other

4. I feel so (warm) and <u>snug</u> inside my sleeping bag.

   giving comfort; sheltered

5. I am (happy) to tell you that I'm <u>pleased</u> with your schoolwork.

   to be satisfied with

6. The flag <u>flutters</u> and (waves) in the wind.

   moves back and forth lightly; flaps

7. It is not kind to (laugh) at people, so please stop <u>giggling</u>.

   silly and uncontrolled laughing

8. If it is <u>chilly</u> outside, wear a hat so you won't get (cold.)

   unpleasantly cool

© Pearson Education, Inc., 3

Home Activity Your child used synonyms and context clues to find the meaning of unfamiliar words. Read a story or folktale with your child. Encourage your child to identify unfamiliar words by looking for synonyms within the text.

Newsletter

- A **newsletter** is just what its name sounds like. It is a letter that contains news. Many groups publish newsletters. These groups include clubs, associations, labor unions, and political parties. Newsletters usually contain announcements of upcoming events, information about membership, articles about recent events, and descriptions of the group's goals.

- Newsletters are usually published weekly or monthly. They are usually only a few pages long.

Directions Read the newsletter and answer the questions that follow.

✤ Li'l Theater Alliance Rag ✤

Fall Issue

AUDITIONS

September 1, 9 A.M.—5 P.M.
Walnut Street Theater, Studio 5

The Sound of Music. We need two boys and five girls, ages 5–16. Singing and some dancing.

Miss Saigon. We need two boys, ages 3–5, to play Tam. Asian Americans encouraged to audition. Tam is a silent role; acting experience a plus.

ON STAGE THIS FALL

A Little Night Music. September 12–October 31. Barrymore Theater.

Macbeth. September 19–October 10. The Little Shakespeare Company That Could.

The Cherry Orchard. September 1–30. Chekhov Repertory Theater.

Edwin Booth Awards

This year the Booth Awards for Excellence in Theater, sponsored by the Li'l Theater Alliance, will be presented in the Verdi Theater. The November 1 award ceremony will begin promptly at 7 P.M. For the list of nominees, see page 6.

BENEFIT

The local theater community was shocked to hear of the fire that destroyed the Phoenix Theater. We are pleased to announce that several Alliance theaters have agreed to donate a portion of the ticket sales for the week of October 1–7 to the Phoenix.

1. Who might be interested in reading this newsletter?

   People who work in theater or who attend stage performances

2. What are the Edwin Booth Awards?

   They are awards for excellence in theater.

3. When can you see a performance of *The Cherry Orchard*?

   between September 1 and 30

4. How often is the newsletter issued? **four times a year**

 Home Activity Your child read a newsletter and answered questions about the information. Share with your child a newsletter that you receive at home. Discuss the different kinds of listings and articles in the newsletter with your child.

Syllable Pattern CV/VC

Proofread a Menu Circle four misspelled words in the menu specials. Write them correctly. Write an adjective that could have been used instead of *nice*.

Spelling Words

Pioneer Cáfe

Specials
Lunch duo.......1/2 sandwich, soup of the day
Lunch (treo)......1/2 sandwich, soup of the day,
         salad

Our favorite float: a (meduim) cola with berry
         ice cream
You won't (beleive) how good it is!
Or, (creat) your own nice float flavor.

Spelling Words

create
medium
piano
idea
radio
video
studio
violin
duo
patio
rodeo
pioneer
trio
stadium
audio

1. __trio__   2. __medium__

3. __believe__   4. __create__

5. __Answers will vary.__

Frequently Misspelled Words

cousin
believe

Proofread Words Circle the word that is spelled correctly.
Write it on the line.

6. Did you see the new (stadium) staduim?   6. __stadium__

7. We watched a vidio (video) last night.   7. __video__

8. Tara plays the paino (piano.)   8. __piano__

9. Your idia (idea) is fantastic!   9. __idea__

10. I like that (radio) radioe station!   10. __radio__

© Pearson Education, Inc., 3

School + Home **Home Activity** Your child spelled words with CVVC (consonant-vowel-vowel-consonant) and CVV (consonant-vowel-vowel) syllable patterns. Have your child divide the list words into syllables.

Adjectives and Articles

Directions Read the selection. Then read each question that follows the selection. Decide which is the best answer to each question. Mark the space for the answer you have chosen.

American Clothing Traditions

(1) America is not known for its clothing traditions. (2) However, many Americans dress up for special occasions or events. (3) _____ wedding is sure to have tuxedos and fancy dresses. (4) Sports fans wear colorful clothes at games. (5) Some fans even paint their faces bright colors. (6) Another place to see different clothes is at a costume party. (7) You may see scary monsters or a big star.

1 What adjective describes *occasions* in sentence 2?
- ⬭ dress
- ⬭ up
- ⬛ special
- ⬭ events

2 What article could you use at the beginning of sentence 3?
- ⬭ An
- ⬭ The
- ⬛ A
- ⬭ Big

3 What adjective is used in sentence 5?
- ⬛ bright
- ⬭ paint
- ⬭ faces
- ⬭ colors

4 What article is used in sentence 6?
- ⬭ at
- ⬛ a
- ⬭ Another
- ⬭ to

5 What two adjectives are used in sentence 7?
- ⬭ monsters, star
- ⬭ You, see
- ⬭ scary, star
- ⬛ scary, big

© Pearson Education, Inc., 3

Home Activity Your child prepared for taking tests on adjectives and articles. Circle a paragraph in a newspaper or magazine article. Ask your child to count the articles in the paragraph.

Homophones

Directions Choose the word that best matches each definition. Write the word on the line.

__cell_____ **1.** a small room in a prison   sell   cell

__write_____ **2.** to record on paper   right   write

__hour_____ **3.** 60 minutes   hour   our

__weak_____ **4.** not strong   weak   week

__night_____ **5.** a period of darkness   knight   night

__ate_____ **6.** swallowed   ate   eight

__tale_____ **7.** a story   tail   tale

__too_____ **8.** also   to   too

Directions Choose the best word to complete each sentence. Write the word on the line.

__sent_____ **9.** My aunt (cent/sent) us a letter.

__hear_____ **10.** I did not (hear/here) you.

__meet_____ **11.** The letter said my aunt would (meat/meet) us at the airport.

__plane_____ **12.** Our (plain/plane) arrived late.

__see_____ **13.** We looked everywhere and did not (sea/see) my aunt.

__I_____ **14.** Finally (eye/I) spotted her near the baggage claim area.

__knew_____ **15.** Then we (knew/new) everything would be fine in our new country.

Home Activity Your child identified and wrote homophones—words that sound the same but have different meanings and spellings. Work with your child to make a list of other homophones, such as *for/four, heard/herd, sail/sale,* and *one/won.* Take turns writing sentences that correctly use each homophone.

Main Idea and Details

- The **topic** is what a piece of writing is about.
- The **main idea** is the most important idea about a topic.
- **Supporting details** are small pieces of information that tell more about the main idea.

Directions Read the following passage.

If you're going to eat cookies, you should eat homemade cookies. When you make your own cookies, you can make cookies that are as good for you as possible. My grandmother and I often make cookies together. We always use the freshest ingredients. We look for recipes that don't use much sugar. We put in healthy foods, such as nuts and raisins, to give our cookies their special flavor. Nothing tastes better than a warm cookie right out of the oven!

Directions Fill in the graphic organizer to show the topic, main idea, and details of the passage.

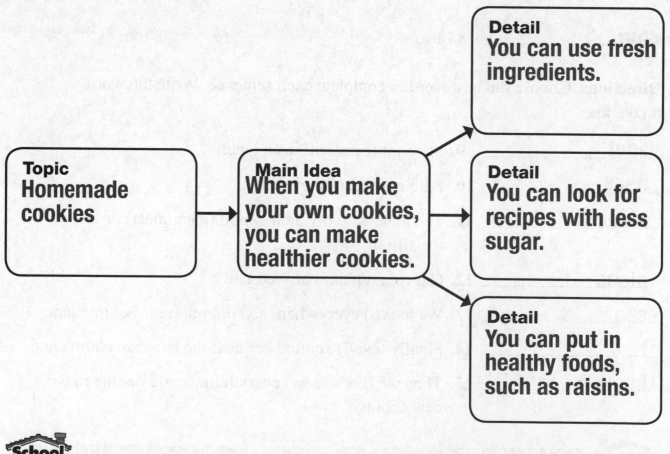

Topic
Homemade cookies

Main Idea
When you make your own cookies, you can make healthier cookies.

Detail
You can use fresh ingredients.

Detail
You can look for recipes with less sugar.

Detail
You can put in healthy foods, such as raisins.

© Pearson Education, Inc., 3

School + Home **Home Activity** Your child identified the main idea and supporting details in a passage. Read a realistic story with your child. Then ask him or her to identify the topic, main idea, and the supporting details.

328 **Comprehension**

Writing • Personal Narrative

Key Feature of a Personal Narrative

- tells about a personal experience
- written in the first person
- usually written in the order in which the events happened

Costume Party

My name is Tony. I'm the odd person in my family. That's because I'm the only boy. I have two older sisters and two younger ones. I'm right in the middle.

Last year, a friend of ours was having a costume party. We all wanted to go. Mom said we had to clean our bedrooms before we went to the party.

I made a deal with my sisters. If they would clean my room, I would let them choose my costume. After we made the deal, my sisters cleaned my room. I thought that was pretty cool.

When it was time to get dressed for the party, my sisters decided on a costume for me. They dressed me up like a rabbit and painted my face! I was kind of mad at first. Then Mom said it was the funniest thing she had seen in a long time. I had to smile. I did look pretty funny. We all had a good laugh.

1. How can you tell this narrative is written in first person?

   It uses the pronoun "I."

2. What words does the author use to tell you how long ago the events in this narrative happened?

   "Last year"

3. What words does the author use to show the order of events in the narrative?

   after, when, then

Vocabulary

Directions Choose a vocabulary word from the box and write it next to its meaning.

_____**soars**_____ **1.** flies at a great height

_____**bouquet**_____ **2.** bunch of flowers

_____**difficult**_____ **3.** hard to do or understand

_____**nibbling**_____ **4.** eating with short, quick bites

_____**pier**_____ **5.** walk or dock built out over water

> **Check the Words You Know**
> ___bouquet
> ___circus
> ___difficult
> ___nibbling
> ___pier
> ___soars
> ___swallow

Directions Choose a word from the box that fits the meaning of the sentence and write it on the line.

6. The _____**circus**_____ performers included clowns, tumblers, trapeze artists, and trained lions and tigers.

7. My throat hurt too much to _____**swallow**_____ anything except ice-cold drinks.

8. I like to watch the squirrels _____**nibbling**_____ the scraps of food we toss into the garden.

9. Abuelito's kite _____**soars**_____ high above the others because he has great skill.

10. I would not have found the exam so _____**difficult**_____ if I'd only studied harder.

Write a Story

On a separate sheet of paper, write a short story about a fun day you once spent with a parent or grandparent. Use as many vocabulary words as you can in your writing.
Students' writing should incorporate the lesson vocabulary words in a story about a fun day spent with a parent or grandparent.

Home Activity Your child identified and used vocabulary words from *I Love Saturdays y domingos*. Read an article about circus animals with your child. Use this week's vocabulary words to talk about the article.

© Pearson Education, Inc., 3

Comparative and Superlative Adjectives

Adjectives are often used to make comparisons. To compare two people, places, or things, you usually add *-er* to an adjective to make a comparative adjective. To compare three or more people, places, or things, you usually add *-est* to an adjective to make a superlative adjective.

Sometimes you must change the spelling of an adjective when you write the *-er* or *-est* form.

Drop final *e*	fine	finer	finest
Change *y* to *i*	easy	easier	easiest
Double final consonant	big	bigger	biggest

Chicago is a <u>bigger</u> city than Baltimore.
New York is the <u>biggest</u> city in the United States.

Directions Underline the adjective that compares in each sentence.

1. Abuelito goes to the seashore on the <u>sunniest</u> day of the week.

2. This fish is <u>smaller</u> than that one.

3. Abuelito makes the <u>prettiest</u> kite of all.

4. Abuelito has the <u>cleanest</u> aquarium in town.

5. Some fish in the aquarium are <u>bigger</u> than others.

Directions Write *C* if the underlined adjective is a comparative adjective. Write *S* if it is a superlative adjective.

6. Grandpa had a <u>harder</u> childhood than his granddaughter. __**C**__

7. Grandma's grandmother had the <u>longest</u> trip to California. __**S**__

8. The <u>roughest</u> ride was in a covered wagon. __**S**__

9. Was Grandpa's trip from Europe <u>easier</u>? __**C**__

10. Abuelita is the <u>proudest</u> grandparent. __**S**__

Home Activity Your child learned about adjectives that compare. Ask your child to describe some television programs using adjectives that compare.

© Pearson Education, Inc., 3

Homophones

Spelling Words				
to	too	two	week	weak
road	rode	stair	stare	bear
bare	write	right	new	knew

Context Clues Write the missing words. Use all the words in each homophone group in one sentence.

Do you (1) ____ with your (2) ____ hand?

1. __write__   2. __right__

The (3) ____ dogs want (4) ____ eat (5) ____ .

3. __two__   4. __to__   5. __too__

Sam (6) ____ he'd get a (7) ____ bike.

6. __knew__   7. __new__

We (8) ____ on the bumpy (9) ____ .

8. __rode__   9. __road__

He's felt (10) ____ all (11) ____ .

10. __weak__   11. __week__

The dancing (12) ____ danced in its (13) ____ feet.

12. __bear__   13. __bare__

The cats just (14) ____ at the (15) ____ .

14. __stare__   15. __stair__

School + Home **Home Activity** Your child wrote homophones. Point to a list word. Have your child use the word in a sentence.

© Pearson Education, Inc., 3

Scoring Rubric: Writing for Tests: Personal Narrative

	4	**3**	**2**	**1**
Focus/Ideas	Focuses on specific, real memory; told from writer's point of view	Includes events from writer's memory; told from writer's point of view	Includes some events from writer's memory; mostly told from writer's point of view	Narrative does not focus on real events from writer's memory
Organization	Clear order of events	Can follow order of events	Unclear order of events	No order of events
Voice	Writer shows personal emotions and thoughts	Writer shows some personal emotions and thoughts	Writer shows few personal emotions and thoughts	Writer makes no effort to show personal emotions and thoughts
Word Choice	Strong use of verbs and adjectives to bring the story to life	Good try at using verbs and adjectives	Poor use of verbs and adjectives; story lacks description	No effort made to use verbs and adjectives
Sentences	Clear sentences of different lengths and types	Sentences of a few lengths and types	Sentences of similar length and type	No variety of sentence length and type
Conventions	Few, if any, errors; correct use of verbs and adjectives	Several small errors; use of verbs and adjectives	Many errors; weak use of verbs and adjectives	Many serious errors; incorrect or no use of verbs and adjectives

Vocabulary • Homophones

- A **cygnet** is a baby swan and a **signet** is a heavy gold ring. The two words sound exactly alike, but they look different and they mean different things. Words that sound alike but look different and have different meanings are called **homophones**.
- You can use **context clues** to figure out the correct homophone to use in a sentence.

Directions Next to each word below, write its homophone.

1. brake **break** 　　　　　　2. waist **waste**

3. pane **pain** 　　　　　　4. pause **paws**

5. soar **sore** 　　　　　　6. rap **wrap**

7. suite **sweet** 　　　　　　8. reed **read**

Directions Each sentence below has a pair of homophones in ( ). Use context clues to choose the correct homophone and underline it.

9. The bald eagle and the stars and stripes are (cymbals, <u>symbols</u>) of the U.S.A.

10. The driver slammed his foot on the (<u>brake</u>, break) when he saw the deer.

11. Someday I hope to (right, <u>write</u>) a play as famous as *Macbeth*.

12. The squirrel (<u>hoards</u>, hordes) acorns all fall so she can eat during the winter.

13. The crowds cheered for the speaker until they were (<u>hoarse</u>, horse).

14. Don't forget to (ring, <u>wring</u>) out the dishcloth after you clean the sink.

15. The streets of San Francisco are often hidden in the morning (missed, <u>mist</u>).

16. The long, hot August afternoon had left me feeling (board, <u>bored</u>) and restless.

17. A (bare, <u>bear</u>) got into our kitchen and ate all our food while we were on vacation.

18. It would take two weeks for the catcher's injured shoulder to (<u>heal</u>, heel).

Home Activity Your child identified and compared homophones. Read a short story with your child. Point to words that have homophones, such as *stare*. Take turns with your child defining the word in the story, then spelling and defining its homophone (i.e., *stair*).

Maps

Maps are drawings of places that show cities, states, and countries. Some maps show roads. Other maps show hills, mountains, and bodies of water. **Symbols** show the location of different places.

Directions Look at the map of Florida. Then answer the questions.

1. Florida is located between which two bodies of water?

   Gulf of Mexico and Atlantic Ocean

2. What is the state capital of Florida? What number and letter tell the location of the capital?

   Tallahassee, A2

3. Which two states border Florida?

   Georgia, Alabama

4. What river is shown on the map?

   Suwanee River

5. Would you use this map to find the road routes you would follow to drive from Tampa to Orlando? Explain.

   No, it shows the two cities, but it does not show any roads.

Home Activity Your child answered questions about a simple state map. Look at a map of your own state with your child. Locate places you have visited. Point out major rivers, lakes, mountains, or any appropriate landform. If possible, identify the bordering states.

Homophones

Spelling Words				
to	too	two	week	weak
road	rode	stair	stare	bear
bare	write	right	new	knew

Proofread Directions Becky wrote directions to her house. Circle four misspelled words. Write them correctly. What word should Becky have used instead of **shortest**? Write it.

- Start on Sunshine (Rode)
- Go to the flower shop.
- Turn (write) after two blocks.
- It's across from the (knew) park.
- There are (too) yellow houses. It's the shortest one.

1. __Road__
2. __right__
3. __new__
4. __two__
5. __shorter__

Frequently Misspelled Words
too
two

Meaning Connections Write a list word to complete the sentence.

6. I'm the art helper this _____ .

7. It's a grizzly _____ !

8. Mom _____ the train to work.

9. We just _____ the boat would sink.

10. The box is on the top _____ .

11. Tie the leash _____ the post.

12. Don't use _____ much flour in the cake.

6. __week__

7. __bear__

8. __rode__

9. __knew__

10. __stair__

11. __to__

12. __too__

© Pearson Education, Inc., 3

School + Home

Home Activity Your child identified misspelled homophones. Ask your child to spell and define three groups of homophones.

Comparative and Superlative Adjectives

Directions Read the selection. Then read each question that follows the selection. Decide which is the best answer to each question. Mark the space for the answer you have chosen.

A Fun Day with Grandparents

(1) Of all the people in her family, Ana's grandparents are more happy about her visit. (2) At breakfast, Grandma makes a bigger breakfast than Ana's mother usually makes. (3) Her pancakes with honey are sweeter than eggs. (4) They have a party that is lively than a regular day. (5) A piñata is the most great part of the party. (6) Grandma gives Ana a necklace as a gift. (7) Her grandparents are the nicest grandparents in the world.

1 What change, if any, should be made to sentence 1?

- ⬭ Change *more happy* to **more happier**
- ⬭ Change *more happy* to **happiest**
- ⬭ Change *more happy* to **most happy**
- ⬭ Make no change

2 What change, if any, should be made to sentence 3?

- ⬭ Change *sweeter* to **sweetest**
- ⬭ Change *sweeter* to **more sweet**
- ⬭ Change *sweeter* to **most sweeter**
- ⬛ Make no change

3 What change, if any, should be made to sentence 4?

- ⬛ Change *lively* to **livelier**
- ⬭ Change *lively* to **most lively**
- ⬭ Change *lively* to **more liveliest**
- ⬭ Make no change

4 What change, if any, should be made to sentence 5?

- ⬭ Change *most great* to **greater**
- ⬭ Change *most great* to **most greatest**
- ⬛ Change *most great* to **greatest**
- ⬭ Make no change

5 What change, if any, should be made to sentence 6?

- ⬭ Change *large* to **larger**
- ⬭ Change *large* to **largest**
- ⬭ Change *large* to **more larger**
- ⬛ Make no change

Home Activity Your child prepared for taking tests on adjectives that compare. Have your child find two adjectives that compare in a letter or an e-mail from a friend or family member.

Vowel Patterns *a, au, aw, al, augh, ough*

Directions Choose the word with the vowel sound in **ball**. Write the word on the line.

because   1. We moved (because/when) we wanted to live near family.

small   2. Now we live in a (little/small) apartment.

lawn   3. Mom works hard so that someday we can buy a house with a (lawn/yard).

talk   4. Sometimes we (speak/talk) about our old home.

palm   5. We think about the beautiful land and the (banana/palm) trees that grew everywhere.

caught   6. We (caught/found) fish in the ocean every day.

always   7. We miss some things, but we (always/still) agree that we are glad we came to this country.

sought   8. In this country, we found what we (needed/sought).

Directions Write **a, au, aw, al, augh** or **ough** to complete each word. Use the word box to help you. Write the whole word on the line before the sentence.

| cough   automobile   sausage   shawl   taught   walk   walnut |

shawl   9. I picture my grandmother in her rocker, wearing a purple sh **aw** l around her shoulders.

walnut   10. I remember the scent of warm w **a** lnut rolls.

sausage   11. I miss the s **au** sage she cooked for our dinner.

cough   12. It was so good and spicy that it made me c **ough** .

taught   13. But it was my grandmother who t **augh** t us to enjoy what we have now.

walk   14. We can w **al** k around freely wherever we want.

automobile   15. We even have our own **au** tomobile.

 Home Activity Your child identified and wrote words with the vowel sound in *ball* as in *small, because, lawn, talk, taught,* and *cough*. Work together to write a list of words that rhyme with these words. Then have your child write sentences that include words on the list.

© Pearson Education, Inc., 3

Name _____

Sequence

- To tell the **sequence** in a story, tell the important events in the order in which they happened.
- Clue words such as *first, next, then,* and *finally* are often used to sequence in a story. Dates, days, and times can also be clues.

Directions Read the following passage.

The first clue that a big change was coming happened at dinner on Monday. Mom and Dad started talking about travel. They said travel would be a good experience for my sister and me. On Tuesday, Dad told us he would be working overseas for a year and the whole family would go along. From Wednesday to Friday we packed. Finally, the big day came. We flew for hours and hours on Saturday. We stepped out of the plane and into a new adventure.

Directions Fill in the graphic organizer to show the important story events in the correct sequence. Then answer the question.

Monday	Tuesday	Wednesday	Saturday
1. Mom and Dad talked about travel.	2. Dad told about living overseas.	3. The family packed.	4. The family flew to a new home.

5. How did clue words help you fill in the organizer above?

The clue words are the names of the days. They tell what
happened on each day. The clue word "finally" tells what
happened last.

School + Home **Home Activity** Your child identified the sequence in a realistic story. Talk with your child about a day or activity you shared. Then ask your child to use clue words to tell the events in sequence.

Writing • Free Verse Poetry

Key Features of Free Verse Poetry

- words arranged in lines
- no fixed rhyme schemes
- may or may not have stanzas
- may include little or no punctuation

music class

steady *thump thump thump* CLASH
drums and cymbals
make me jerk stiffly
on the hard seat
where I was told to sit

a long screech
like a mad barn cat
I press my hands hard against my ears
until they hurt like the sound
made by that violin

tinkling sounds
made by fingers running up
running quickly down
the piano keys
two and three and four struck together
make chords
that my stretching fingers can't quite reach

then the soothing flow
of a mellow tone
like melting dark chocolate
sending warm waves down my back
filling my middle with comfort

my first day of music class
and I chose
the cello.

1. Circle the last word of each line in the first stanza. Do these words rhyme?

   no

2. How are the line lengths in the second stanza different?

   some are longer and some are shorter

3. Write the words in the third stanza that create a mental picture of hands playing the piano.

   fingers, running, piano keys, stretching fingers

Vocabulary

Check the Words You Know

___homesick   ___described   ___curious
___raindrops   ___airport   ___delicious
___farewell   ___memories   ___cellar

Directions Draw a line from the word to its definition.

1. homesick   parting

2. farewell   told what something looked like

3. memories   longing for home

4. delicious   things you remember

5. described   tasting very good

6. cellar   an underground room

Directions Write a word from the box that fits the meaning of the sentence.

7. I opened my umbrella when I felt _____**raindrops**_____ falling on my head.

8. At the _____**airport**_____ I wait to board the plane.

9. I enjoy social studies because I am _____**curious**_____ about the world.

10. I have many happy _____**memories**_____ of my summer vacation.

11. This Chinese restaurant has _____**delicious**_____ food.

Write a Journal Entry

On a separate sheet of paper, write a journal entry about a happy memory you have.
Use as many vocabulary words as possible.

Students' writing should incorporate the lesson vocabulary words in a journal entry about a memory.

© Pearson Education, Inc., 3

Home Activity Your child identified and used words from *Good-Bye, 382 Shin Dang Dong*. Read a story or poem that tells about feelings. Discuss the story or poem using this week's vocabulary words.

Name _____

Adverbs

An **adverb** is a word that can tell when, where, or how something happens.

Now the movers pack the furniture. (when)
They carry the furniture outside. (where)
They carefully load the van. (how)

- Adverbs can come before or after the verbs they describe.
- Adverbs that tell how something happens often end in *-ly*.

Directions Underline the adverbs in the sentences.

1. Kim's mother often cooks Korean dishes.

2. She chops cabbage carefully.

3. She gently mixes more vegetables.

4. She quickly cooks the mixture on the stove.

Directions Choose the correct word in ( ) to write each new sentence.

5. Everyone (usual, usually) wears costumes to the school party.

Everyone usually wears costumes to the school party.

6. Kim (happily, happy) wears her Korean outfit.

Kim happily wears her Korean outfit.

7. The jacket fits (tight, tightly) around her shoulders.

The jacket fits tightly around her shoulders.

8. The skirt falls (loosely, loose) around her feet.

The skirt falls loosely around her feet.

© Pearson Education, Inc., 3

Home Activity Your child learned about adverbs. Ask your child to describe something he or she did today using one or more adverbs.

Vowel Patterns *au, augh, ou, ough*

Spelling Words				
because	though	taught	bought	touch
would	author	could	enough	sausage
fought	should	faucet	daughter	brought

Definitions Write the list word that fits the clue.

1. gave instructions   1. **taught**
2. battled for something   2. **fought**
3. writer of articles or stories   3. **author**
4. opposite of the word *son*   4. **daughter**
5. paid for something   5. **bought**

Word Meanings Write the missing list word to complete each sentence.

6. Anjay likes cheese and _____ on his crackers.   6. **sausage**
7. We _____ not swim after eating.   7. **should**
8. My mom made _____ salad for ten people.   8. **enough**
9. We won the game _____ of good defense.   9. **because**
10. Andrea got water from the _____.   10. **faucet**
11. On Fitness Day, I _____ a jump rope to school.   11. **brought**
12. The blanket is soft to _____.   12. **touch**
13. If we practice, we _____ be great.   13. **could**
14. We need the key to get inside, _____.   14. **though**
15. I _____ love to watch that program!   15. **would**

© Pearson Education, Inc., 3

School + Home
Home Activity Your child wrote words with *au, augh, ou,* and *ough* that make different vowel sounds. Have your child pronounce each word to make sure they are saying the vowel sound correctly.

Spelling Vowel Patterns *au, augh, ou, ough*   **343**

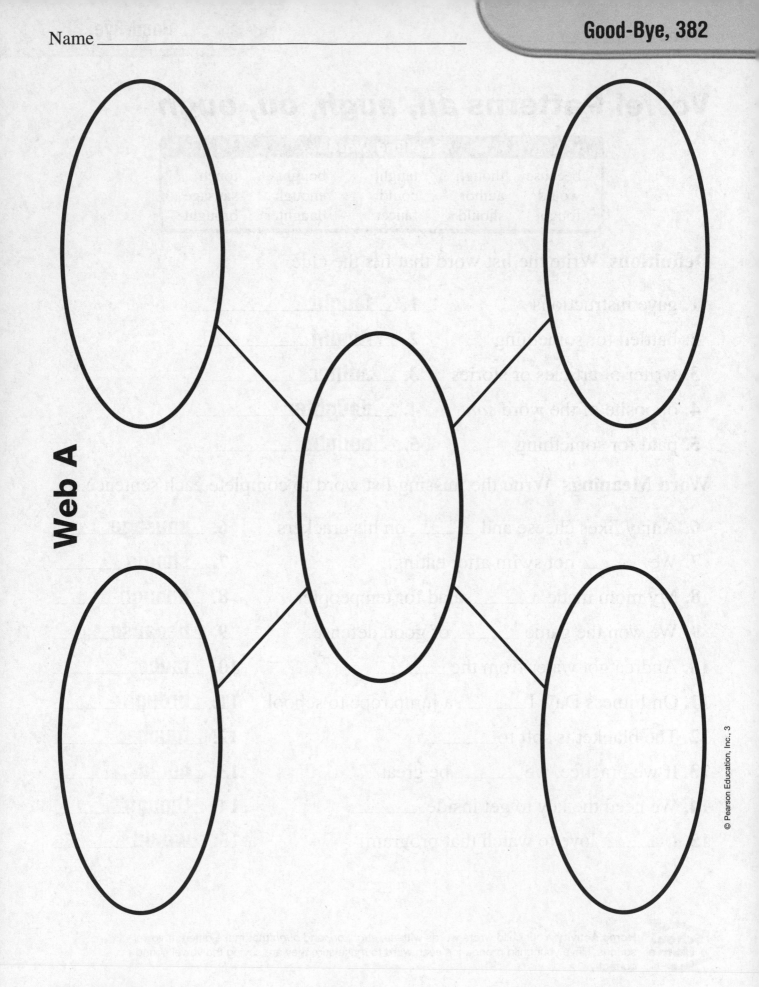

Web A

Vocabulary • Word Structure

- A **compound word** is a word made up of two or more smaller words.
- You can often figure out the meaning of an unfamiliar compound word if you know the meanings of the smaller words. Sometimes the meanings of the smaller words do not help with meaning but do help you recognize the compound word.

Directions Read the following passage about a boy who returned to his birthplace. Then answer the questions below. Look for compound words as you read.

> Haresh had moved away from India when he was a baby. He couldn't remember his birthplace at all, so he was glad when his grandparents asked him to visit them in India. Haresh had a great time. He ran through the raindrops with cousins he had just met. He saw many new sights. But Haresh was a little homesick. When it was time to say farewell and report to the airport, he was ready. Haresh looked forward to returning to India next summer, though.

1. What are the two parts of *birthplace*?

birth and *place*

2. How do the two parts of *raindrops* help you figure out the word's meaning?

Rain is water, and *drops* are things that fall. *Raindrops* means "water falling from the sky."

3. If you are homesick, what do you want to do?

go home

4. What two smaller words make up the compound word *farewell*?

fare and *well*

5. Which word is compound—*report* or *airport*? How do you know?

airport; The two words that make up the compound—*air* and *port*—are both complete words on their own.

© Pearson Education, Inc., 3

Home Activity Your child identified and used compound words. With your child, see how many compound words you can think of that include the word *over*. Make a list of the words.

Atlas

An **atlas** is a book of maps. **CD-ROM atlases** contain maps too. CD-ROMs can store a large amount of information on a small disk. On one CD-ROM, you can find a collection of maps of countries, states, cities, as well as road maps.

Directions Look at the map of Massachusetts. Then answer the questions below.

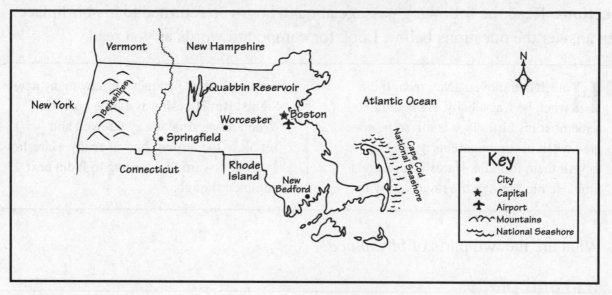

1. What are the names of two cities in Massachusetts?

   Possible responses: Boston, New Bedford, Worcester, Springfield

2. The airport is located near which city and which body of water?

   Boston; Atlantic Ocean

3. Which two states border Massachusetts on the north?

   New Hampshire and Vermont

4. What are the Berkshires?

   mountains

5. How would you describe the location of the Quabbin Reservoir in the state?

   Possible response: close to the center of the state

Home Activity Your child answered questions about a map. Look at an atlas with your child. Look through the different maps and discuss all of the different features that are shown.

Vowel Patterns *au, augh, ou, ough*

Spelling Words				
because	though	taught	bought	touch
would	author	could	enough	sausage
fought	should	faucet	daughter	brought

Proofread a List Ella wrote about her day in class. Circle the four spelling mistakes. Write the words correctly. Write the word Ella should have used in the last sentence instead of better.

Class was very interesting becauze we had a guest speaker. She was an author. She brout her book with her. The book was about goals. She said we shoold always have goals. She tawt us to aim high and be the better we can be.

1. **because**

2. **brought**

3. **should**

4. **taught**

5. **best**

Frequently Misspelled Words
because
caught
thought

Proofread Words Fill in a circle to show which word is spelled correctly. Write the word.

6. ○ fout ○ fawt ● fought **fought**

7. ● faucet ○ fawcet ○ foucet **faucet**

8. ○ tuch ● touch ○ toucgh **touch**

9. ○ enuff ○ enouh ● enough **enough**

10. ○ woud ● would ○ woughd **would**

11. ● could ○ cood ○ coud **could**

12. ○ thogh ○ thow ● though **though**

School + Home **Home Activity** Your child wrote words with *au, augh, ou,* and *ough* that make different vowel sounds. Ask your child to circle the four hardest words for him or her to spell and then write them.

© Pearson Education, Inc., 3

Adverbs

Directions Read the selection. Then read each question that follows the selection. Decide which is the best answer to each question. Mark the space for the answer you have chosen.

Korea

(1) It rains heavily in Korea in winter. (2) After the rains, the rice grows quickly in the wet fields. (3) Farmers soon plant some vegetables. (4) Fishermen work there on the coasts. (5) They catch many kinds of fish easily. (6) Some farmers grow oranges yearly. (7) Today Korea produces much food.

1 Which word is an adverb in sentence 1?
- ⬭ rains
- ⬭ in
- ⬛ heavily
- ⬭ winter

2 Which word is an adverb in sentence 3?
- ⬭ plant
- ⬭ some
- ⬭ Farmers
- ⬛ soon

3 Which word is an adverb in sentence 4?
- ⬭ on
- ⬭ the
- ⬛ there
- ⬭ They

4 Which word is an adverb in sentence 5?
- ⬛ easily
- ⬭ many
- ⬭ catch
- ⬭ They

5 Which word is an adverb in sentence 7?
- ⬭ Korea
- ⬛ Today
- ⬭ much
- ⬭ produces

© Pearson Education, Inc., 3

 Home Activity Your child prepared for taking tests on adverbs. While reading a book with your child, have him or her describe the actions in a picture using two adverbs in the description. Then have your child explain what might happen next.

Vowel Patterns *ei, eigh*

Directions Read each sentence. Underline the word that has *ei* or *eigh*. Write *long a*, *long e*, or *long i* on the line to tell what sound the vowel pattern stands for.

long *a*	1. We enjoy shopping at our <u>neighborhood</u> bakery.
long *e*	2. We always go on <u>either</u> Friday or Saturday.
long *e*	3. Shelves of baked goods reach from floor to <u>ceiling</u>.
long *i*	4. I'm not the right <u>height</u> yet to reach the top shelf.
long *a*	5. That shelf must be <u>eight</u> feet high!
long *a*	6. We <u>weigh</u> all our choices and make up our minds.
long *e*	7. We smile when we <u>receive</u> our package from the salesclerk.

Directions Choose a word from the box to match each clue. Write the word on the line.

rein	8. a strap used to control a horse
seize	9. to grab an object
leisure	10. free time
neighbor	11. a person who lives nearby
height	12. the space between something's lowest and highest point
freight	13. cargo carried from one place to another by truck, ship, or other vehicle
deceive	14. not tell the truth
vein	15. a blood vessel in a living creature's body

> deceive
> freight
> height
> leisure
> neighbor
> rein
> seize
> vein

© Pearson Education, Inc., 3

Home Activity Your child identified and used words with the long *a, e,* or *i* sound spelled *ei* or *eigh*. Work together to make a crossword puzzle, beginning with words and definitions from this page.

Draw Conclusions

- A **conclusion** is a decision or opinion that makes sense based on facts and details.
- You can also use what you **already know** to draw a conclusion.

Directions Read the following passage and use the information to complete the chart below.

My dad is a baker. He works right around the corner from our house. He leaves our house in the morning, when it is still very, very dark out. He has to start early so people can have fresh baked goods when the bakery opens.

Dad doesn't mind getting up so early. He says it's really quiet outside when he goes to work. And he especially likes the smiles on people's faces when they bite into something good that he has made.

Directions Write a fact from the story in boxes 1–3. Write something you know about that relates to the story in box 4. Then write a conclusion in box 5.

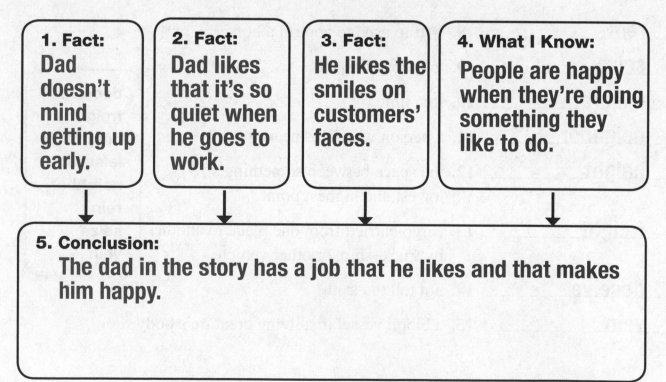

1. Fact:
Dad doesn't mind getting up early.

2. Fact:
Dad likes that it's so quiet when he goes to work.

3. Fact:
He likes the smiles on customers' faces.

4. What I Know:
People are happy when they're doing something they like to do.

5. Conclusion:
The dad in the story has a job that he likes and that makes him happy.

© Pearson Education, Inc., 3

Home Activity Your child learned about drawing conclusions. Tell your child about something that you did today. Ask him or her to draw a conclusion based on what you've said and what he or she already knows about you or the thing you did.

Name _____

Writing • Invitation

Key Features of an Invitation

- gives the reason for the invitation
- provides a date, time, and location
- includes contact information if a reply is needed
- often uses creative pictures or drawings

Monday Night Party!

What: You are warmly invited to join my family for a night of pizza, pasta, and football. Help us <u>cheer on our favorite team</u> as they fearlessly clash with their opponents. It is shaping up to be the most <u>thrilling game</u> of the season! We will have plenty of pizza, pasta, and snacks to munch on as <u>football history</u> is made.

When: Monday, January 6 at 5:30 PM

Where: Lila's apartment
2846 N. Marina St., #304
Seattle, WA 98000

R.S.V.P. Please call Lila at 200-525-5543 to let me know if you can make it!

---

1. Underline the words that tell why Lila is having a pizza party.

2. Draw a circle around each of the following: date, time, and location.

3. Draw a box around the contact information.

Vocabulary

Directions Write the word from the box that fits the meaning of each sentence.

> ### Check the Words You Know
> ___bakery   ___dough
> ___batch   ___braided
> ___mixture   ___boils
> ___ingredients

1. I walked to the _____**bakery**_____ to buy bread.

2. Mom and I made a _____**batch**_____ of 24 muffins for the bake sale.

3. Flour is one of the main _____**ingredients**_____ in baking.

4. My father _____**boils**_____ water when he makes tea.

Directions Read the definition. Write **true** next to the word with that meaning. Write **false** next to the word that does not have that meaning.

5. several things blended together

   _____**true**_____ mixture   _____**false**_____ braided

6. a place where breads are made and sold.

   _____**false**_____ batch   _____**true**_____ bakery

7. made into a twisted shape

   _____**true**_____ braided   _____**false**_____ boiled

8. a mix of flour and other ingredients that you bake

   _____**false**_____ bakery   _____**true**_____ dough

Write a Menu

On a separate sheet of paper, create a menu for a restaurant. Your menu may include foods for breakfast, lunch, or dinner. Use as many vocabulary words as possible. **Students' writing should incorporate this lesson's vocabulary words in a menu written for breakfast, lunch, or dinner.**

Home Activity Your child identified and used words from *Jalapeño Bagels*. Read a recipe or magazine article about food. Discuss the recipe or article using the vocabulary words.

Comparative and Superlative Adverbs

You can use **adverbs** to compare actions. The *-er* form of an adverb compares two actions. This is a **comparative adverb.** The *-est* form of an adverb compares three or more actions. This is a **superlative adverb.**

    Jeremy works <u>hard</u>.
    Jeremy works <u>harder</u> than Tom does.
    Jeremy works <u>hardest</u> of all the students.

Most adverbs that end in *-ly* use *more* and *most* to make comparisons.
    The truck moved <u>slowly</u>.
    The truck moved <u>more slowly</u> than the car.
    The truck moved <u>most slowly</u> of all.

Directions Underline the adverb that compares in each sentence.

1. Mrs. Alvarez sings the <u>loudest</u> of all the employees at the bakery.

2. She bakes <u>faster</u> than Mr. Lane does.

3. The bread dough rises <u>most quickly</u> of all.

4. You must knead bread dough <u>more carefully</u> than other kinds of dough.

5. Mrs. Alvarez has been baking <u>longer</u> than you have.

Directions Circle the correct word in ( ) to complete each sentence.

6. The muffins bake (slower, slowest) than the cinnamon rolls.

7. Mr. Costa works the (faster, fastest) of all the bakers.

8. Of all the workers, Tony sings (more cheerfully, most cheerfully).

9. Mr. Costa mixes sweet roll dough (most rapidly, more rapidly) than Tony.

10. The sweet rolls are done (sooner, soonest) of all.

Home Activity Your child learned about adverbs that compare. Ask your child to compare how he or she rides a bicycle to the way a friend rides, using an adverb that compares.

Vowel Patterns *ei, eigh*

Spelling Words				
ceiling	neighbor	either	eighteen	height
neither	weight	leisure	protein	freight
receive	weigh	deceive	sleigh	conceited

Finish the Sentence Write a list word to complete the sentence.

1. How much does the bag _____?   1. __weigh__

2. I want to go for a _____ ride.   2. __sleigh__

3. My _____ is moving soon.   3. __neighbor__

4. Meat is a good source of _____.   4. __protein__

5. I want _____ soup or salad.   5. __either__

6. My cousin is _____ years old.   6. __eighteen__

7. The _____ of the bridge is 150 feet.   7. __height__

8. The train was loaded with _____.   8. __freight__

9. The _____ was too heavy for me to lift.   9. __weight__

Definitions Write the list word that fits the clue.

10. time to rest and play   10. __leisure__

11. opposite of the word *give*   11. __receive__

12. rhymes with the word *greeted*   12. __conceited__

13. to try to trick   13. __deceive__

14. rhymes with the word *either*   14. __neither__

15. opposite of the word *floor*   15. __ceiling__

| neither |
| leisure |
| ceiling |
| receive |
| deceive |
| conceited |

© Pearson Education, Inc., 3

Home Activity Your child wrote words with the vowel pattern *ei* and *eigh*. Read a sentence on this page. Ask your child to spell the list word.

Four-Column Chart

Vocabulary • Unfamiliar Words

- Sometimes you come across words you don't know. You can use the words and sentences around the **unfamiliar word** to help you figure out its meaning.
- Look for context clues around unfamiliar words to help you figure out what they mean.

Directions Read each sentence. Use context clues to figure out the meaning of the underlined word. Write the meaning on the line.

1. After dinner my brother likes ice cream, but I like cake for <u>dessert</u>.

food that you eat after dinner

2. Our cat likes milk, but he <u>especially</u> loves cream.

most of all

3. This cake is made with only four <u>ingredients</u>, but it still tastes delicious.

things that go together to make a kind of food

4. My mom cooks many <u>international</u> foods, such as those from China and Spain.

from many different countries

5. Would you like to work in a <u>bakery</u>, where they make cakes and cookies?

place that makes and sells baked goods

6. If you follow this <u>recipe</u>, you will make a delicious cornbread.

directions for making a kind of food

7. Pancakes are a <u>mixture</u> of flour, eggs, and milk.

a group of things mixed together to make something

8. I would like a <u>piece</u> of cherry pie.

part of something

© Pearson Education, Inc., 3

Home Activity Your child used context clues to find the meaning of unfamiliar words. Read a story or advertisement about a bakery. Encourage your child to look for context clues to figure out the meaning of unfamiliar words.

356 Vocabulary

Outlining

Summarizing is finding the most important ideas about a topic. You can summarize when you read sources during research. One way to summarize is by making an outline. An **outline** shows a main idea and details, like the one shown below.

Favorite Mexican Dishes

I. Meat
  A. Beef
    1. Dried beef
    2. Grilled beef steak
  B. Poultry
    1. Chicken
    2. Chicken enchiladas

II. Vegetables
  A. Beet salad
  B. Zucchini with corn

III. Fruit
  A. Grapefruit salad
  B. Mango salsa

Directions Write the words from the box in the outline. Use the outline above as a guide.

> Shrimp   Peppers   Spaghetti   Parmesan   Vegetables

Common Italian Ingredients

I. Cheese
  A. Mozzarella
  B. **Parmesan**

II. **Vegetables**
  A. Mushrooms
  B. Onions
  C. **Peppers**

III. Pasta
  A. Rigatoni
  B. **Spaghetti**

IV. Fish
  A. Salmon
  B. Sea bass
  C. **Shrimp**

© Pearson Education, Inc., 3

Home Activity Your child learned how to make an outline to summarize ideas. Write the names of several different foods. Ask your child to organize the food names in an outline by food groups.

Vowel Patterns *ei, eigh*

Spelling Words

ceiling	neighbor	either	eighteen	height
neither	weight	leisure	protein	freight
receive	weigh	deceive	sleigh	conceited

Proofread a Paragraph Jay wrote his opinion about the best breed of dog. Circle the four misspelled words. Write them correctly. Then rewrite the run-on sentence as two separate sentences.

I think the labrador is the best dog. They are (eether) black, chocolate, or yellow. They are very friendly with family, (naybors) and even the mailman! They (wiegh) a lot, so you have to make sure they don't sit on you, if they do you might get licked. There is (allmost) nothing you can't do with a labrador!

Frequently Misspelled Words

believe
friend

1. __either__   2. __neighbors__

3. __weigh__   4. __almost__

5. __They weigh a lot, so you have to make sure they don't sit on you. If they do, you might get licked.__

Proofread Words Circle the word that is spelled correctly. Write it.

6. (ceiling)   cieling   6. __ceiling__

7. neether   (neither)   7. __neither__

8. eightteen   (eighteen)   8. __eighteen__

9. (height)   hight   9. __height__

10. (protein)   proteine   10. __protein__

11. (sleigh)   sleiy   11. __sleigh__

12. (decieve)   deceive   12. __deceive__

School + Home **Home Activity** Your child identified misspelled words with the vowel pattern *ei* and *eigh*. Have your child pronounce each spelling word and underline the vowel patterns.

Name _____

Comparative and Superlative Adverbs

Directions Read the selection. Then read each question that follows the selection. Decide which is the best answer to each question. Mark the space for the answer you have chosen.

International Day at My School

(1) Tomorrow is International Day at my school. (2) My class works _____ of all the classes. (3) We prepare _____ than anyone. (4) My group is in charge of the food fair. (5) Allison, a girl in my group, said she will get there the _____ . (6) The food fair will last _____ this year than last year. (7) But we are ready to work hard. (8) Our teacher said if we do, this year will go _____ than ever.

1 What superlative adverb can you use in sentence 2?

- ⬭ hard
- ⬭ harder
- ⬛ hardest
- ⬭ most hard

2 What comparative adverb can you use in sentence 3?

- ⬭ frequentest
- ⬭ frequenter
- ⬭ most frequently
- ⬛ more frequently

3 What superlative adverb can you use in sentence 5?

- ⬭ earlier
- ⬭ more early
- ⬛ earliest
- ⬭ most earliest

4 What comparative adverb can you use in sentence 6?

- ⬭ longest
- ⬛ longer
- ⬭ more long
- ⬭ most long

5 What comparative adverb can you use in sentence 8?

- ⬛ more smoothly
- ⬭ most smoothly
- ⬭ smoothest
- ⬭ most smooth

Home Activity Your child prepared for taking tests on adverbs that compare. While working in the kitchen with your child, ask him or her to make up a sentence about cooking that includes an adverb that compares.

© Pearson Education, Inc., 3

Name_____

Suffixes -y, -ish, -hood, -ment

Directions Combine the base word and suffix. Write the new word on the line.

1. pay + -ment = **payment**_____

2. cloud + -y = **cloudy**_____

3. self + -ish = **selfish**_____

4. boy + -hood = **boyhood**_____

5. storm + -y = **stormy**_____

6. excite + -ment = **excitement**_____

7. false + -hood = **falsehood**_____

8. baby + -ish = **babyish**_____

Directions Add **-y, -ish, -hood,** or **-ment** to the base word in ( ) to best complete each sentence. Use the word box for help. Write the new word on the line.

childhood	entertainment	foolish	frosty
movement	neighborhood	snowy	

childhood_____ 9. During my (child) we moved often.

neighborhood_____ 10. We moved to a (neighbor) with woods and a pond nearby.

entertainment_____ 11. Playing outdoors provided plenty of (entertain).

snowy_____ 12. One (snow) day, my brother and I decided to go skating.

movement_____ 13. We were scared by (move) along the edge of the pond.

foolish_____ 14. How (fool) we felt when we saw it was Ben, our new neighbor.

frosty_____ 15. We thought it was a (frost) snowman come to life.

© Pearson Education, Inc., 3

Home Activity Your child added the suffixes *-y, -ish, -hood,* and *-ment* to base words to form new words. Work together to form other words with these suffixes, such as *thirsty, childish,* and *shipment.* Have your child write sentences using the new words.

Author's Purpose

- The **author's purpose** is the author's reason for writing.
- An author usually writes to inform, to persuade, to entertain, or to express an opinion.

Directions Read the following passage.

Philadelphia is a wonderful place to visit. It is a beautiful city with lots of history. The Declaration of Independence and the U.S. Constitution were signed in Philadelphia. You can tour Independence Hall, where these documents were written.

The downtown area has several beautiful parks. You can sit in a park and hear live music while you eat ice cream and watch people.

Philadelphia has theaters, concert halls, great restaurants, and stores. You can always find something interesting to do in Philadelphia.

Directions Fill in the graphic organizer to tell the author's purpose and support your response. Then answer the question.

Author's Purpose
to persuade readers to
visit Philadelphia

Fact from article
Visitors can visit historic sites.

Fact from article
Visitors can relax in the beautiful parks.

Fact from article
Visitors can go to theaters, concerts, restaurants, and stores.

Do you think the author accomplished his or her purpose? Why or why not?

Responses will vary. Students should support their answers with facts from the passage.

School + Home **Home Activity** Your child identified an author's purpose for writing. Read a story or article together. Talk about why the author might have written it.

Writing • Book Review

Key Features of a Book Review

- tells the name of the book and what the book is about

- gives an opinion about the story or subject

- often urges others to read, or avoid, the book

- demonstrates an understanding of the text

Name: Rita Pein

Book Review: My Colors, My World/Mis colores, mi mundo

Everyone will love the amazing colors in My Colors, My World/Mis colores, mi mundo. The book is about a young girl who lives in a desert area. When people think about deserts, they usually think of different shades of brown. The desert can seem very plain. But the desert in this book is filled with beautiful pinks, oranges, and greens.

This book is fun to read for many reasons. The illustrations are lively and beautiful to behold. The colors seem to jump off the pages. The narrator tells how the colors relate to the world around her. She shows examples of where they each appear.

The best part about this book is that it's written in both English and Spanish. If you can read Spanish, you can read the Spanish side. If you can read English, you can read the English side. If you want to learn one of these languages, you can read both sides to learn new words. In conclusion, this book has so much to offer—vibrant colors and beautiful words. You will love it!

---

1. Circle the title of the book that appears in the review.

2. Write one sentence summarizing the book.

The book tells about the colors of the girl's world in both Spanish and English.

3. Does the writer think readers will like the book? How do you know?

The writer says that everyone will love the beautiful colors and words.

Vocabulary

Directions Underline the word that completes each sentence. Write the word on the line.

> ### Check the Words You Know
> ___flights   ___fierce   ___stoops   ___treasure
> ___pitcher   ___feast   ___ruined   ___cardboard

1. Our team's _____**pitcher**_____ struck everyone out.
   <u>pitcher</u>   treasure

2. My neighbors' _____**stoops**_____ needed repairs to the broken stairs.
   fierce   <u>stoops</u>

3. After my aunt discovered the chest in the attic, she found a _____**treasure**_____.
   feast   <u>treasure</u>

4. My grandmother made us a special _____**feast**_____ for the holiday.
   flights   <u>feast</u>

5. I walked up three _____**flights**_____ of stairs.
   treasure   <u>flights</u>

Directions Write the word from the box that completes each sentence.

6. The lion looked very _____**fierce**_____ when it growled.

7. We packed the books in a _____**cardboard**_____ box.

8. I ate so much at the _____**feast**_____ that I'm not hungry now.

9. The cake was _____**ruined**_____ when she dropped it on the floor.

10. The ring from my grandfather is something to keep as a _____**treasure**_____.

Write a Thank-You Note

On a separate sheet of paper, write a thank-you note that James might write to Uncle Romie after his visit. Use as many vocabulary words as possible.

Students should use vocabulary in a thank-you note from James to his Uncle Romie.

Home Activity Your child has identified and used the vocabulary words from *Me and Uncle Romie*. Read a story about a family together. Have a conversation with your child about your family, using some of the vocabulary words in this lesson.

Conjunctions

A **conjunction** is a word that connects words or groups of words.

- To add information, use the conjunction *and*. To show a choice, use the conjunction *or*. To show a difference, use the conjunction *but*.

    James went to the park <u>and</u> a ball game.
    James had never been to New York City, <u>but</u> he liked it.
    James could stay in the city <u>or</u> go back home.

- You can use a conjunction to combine two sentences into a compound sentence. Add a comma before the conjunction in a compound sentence.

    James went to a ball game. Then he went home.
    James went to a ball game, and then he went home.

Directions Write the conjunction in each sentence.

1. Railroads were built in the 1800s, and Americans soon depended on them. **and**

2. Americans could travel by stagecoach, but trains were much faster. **but**

3. People could go 20 miles or all the way across country. **or**

4. Today Americans travel by airplanes, cars, and trains. **and**

5. You can take a train within a city or between cities. **or**

Directions Circle the conjunction in ( ) that best completes each sentence.

6. Daniel saw the Statue of Liberty (but, (and)) the Empire State Building.

7. Was the Statue of Liberty dedicated in 1884 ((or) but) 1886?

8. It was sent to the United States in 1884, (or, (but)) it was dedicated in 1886.

9. Is the statue made of copper (but, (or)) marble?

10. The statue was cleaned (but, (and)) restored in the 1980s.

 Home Activity Your child learned about conjunctions. Ask your child to name his or her favorite things to do after school, using one or more conjunctions.

Suffixes

Spelling Words				
rocky	foolish	rainy	childhood	selfish
treatment	movement	neighborhood	childish	parenthood
crunchy	bumpy	payment	sleepy	shipment

Opposites Write the missing list word. It will be the **opposite** of the underlined word.

1. This lizard's skin is <u>smooth</u>.

2. Do you think tomorrow will be <u>sunny</u>?

3. I was <u>alert</u> the entire trip.

4. The salesman was <u>generous</u> with his time.

5. There's a lot of <u>stillness</u> in the wasp nest.

6. Our guide seemed <u>wise</u> to me.

7. My brother acts pretty <u>grown up</u>.

8. Dad collected coins throughout his <u>adulthood</u>.

1. **bumpy**

2. **rainy**

3. **sleepy**

4. **selfish**

5. **movement**

6. **foolish**

7. **childish**

8. **childhood**

Context Clues A word is missing from each of the opinions below. Write the missing word.

9. Jelly with **crunchy** peanut butter tastes best.

10. Anyone would like to get a **shipment** of gifts.

11. I should get a **payment** for washing dishes.

12. My **neighborhood** is the friendliest.

13. A **rocky** beach is not much fun.

14. There's nothing easy about **parenthood**.

15. The best **treatment** for a cold is to rest.

Home Activity Your child spelled words with the suffixes -y, -ish, -hood, and -ment. Have your child try spelling the base word and the suffix separately.

© Pearson Education, Inc., 3

Critique/Book Review

Title _____

Author _____

Illustrator _____

Plot or Nonfiction Topic _____

My Opinion _____

Additional Notes:

Vocabulary • Context Clues

- Homonyms are words that are spelled and pronounced the same way but have different meanings.
- Use **context clues,** or the words around a homonym, to figure out what the word means.

Directions Read the following passage. Then answer the questions below. Look for context clues that show the meanings of homonyms as you read.

> In the city, I go to big league baseball games. When I visited the country, I went to a minor league game. I didn't think I'd like that kind of baseball, but I was wrong. In the city, we have to climb several flights to get to our seats. At the small, minor league stadium, we sat down close to the field and saw the pitcher clearly. It was easy to see everything on the field. The food was good, too. We gobbled up as much as we could. I didn't miss my big league team at all.

1. In this passage, does *kind* mean "nice and generous" or "type or sort"?

type or sort

2. What are *flights*? What word is a clue to the meaning?

sets of steps; *Climb* is a context clue.

3. How do you know that *pitcher* means "the player who throws the ball to a batter"?

The passage is all about baseball.

4. Does *gobbled* mean "made a sound like a turkey" or "ate quickly"? How do you know?

ate quickly; The sentence about food is the clue.

5. Does *miss* mean "to feel the absence of" or "a title for a girl"?

to feel the absence of

Home Activity Your child used context clues to understand homonyms. Say sentences with homonyms such as *squash* (to crush/a vegetable) or *mine* (belonging to me/to take coal or other minerals from the ground). Ask your child to use context clues to determine the meaning of each word.

Name _____

Electronic Text

- A **search engine** can help you find online resources on a topic. To use a search engine, type in a **keyword** or phrase. In a few seconds, the search engine will pull up a list of Internet sites that contain the word or phrase.

- Sometimes the list contains hundreds or thousands of results. You can narrow your search by using the "Advanced Search" feature. This feature allows you to describe your topic more specifically.

Directions To complete this worksheet, you need a computer. Follow the instructions below and fill in the answers as you go.

Answers will vary. Sample answers shown.

1. Choose a topic for a class presentation. Write the topic here.

   New York City

2. Type in the URL www.kidsclick.org and hit Enter/Return.

3. Click on the major category where you think you will find information on your topic. Write the name of the category here.

   Geography/History/Biography

4. Now you see a list of narrower topics. Click on a narrower category. Write its name here.

   Cities: New York City

5. Now you see a list of Web sites with descriptions of the information you can find there. Choose a Web site that may have information for your presentation. Explain why you chose this resource.

   I choose www.nationalgeographic.com/nyunderground/docs/ nymain.html because I want to learn more about the New York City subway system.

6. Click on the link (the underlined word or phrase) to explore the Web site you chose. Discuss the experience of doing online research with a partner.

Home Activity Your child read about search engines and used a child-appropriate search engine to research a topic. Try another online search with your child. Work together to choose a topic, narrow it, and find appropriate Web sites with information on your topic.

Name _____

Suffixes

Spelling Words				
rocky	foolish	rainy	childhood	selfish
treatment	movement	neighborhood	childish	parenthood
crunchy	bumpy	payment	sleepy	shipment

Proofread an Order Form Greg is selling snack bars for his team. Circle four spelling errors and one capitalization error. Write the words correctly.

Order Form		
Item	**How Many?**	**Cost**
rocky road bars	3	$ 3.00
crunchie bars	2	$ 2.00
	Total:	$ 5.00

Deliver to: 1413 Sleepy Hollow Road

Notes: Deliver on saturday.
Leave the box on the vary top step unless it is rainey.
The paymant has been made.

Frequently Misspelled Words

different
very

1. __crunchy__ 2. __very__ 3. __rainy__

4. __payment__ 5. __Saturday__

Proofread Words Circle the word that is spelled correctly.

6. The **shipmint** (**shipment**) should arrive soon.

7. This ride is (**bumpy**) **bumpie**.

8. Don't be **selfist** (**selfish**) with the markers.

9. We are having a **nieghborhood** (**neighborhood**) picnic.

10. He spent his (**childhood**) **childood** in Cleveland.

Home Activity Your child identified misspelled words with the suffixes -y, -ish, -hood, and -ment. Have your child underline the suffixes in the list words.

© Pearson Education, Inc., 3

Conjunctions

Directions Read the selection. Then read each question that follows the selection. Decide which is the best answer to each question. Mark the space for the answer you have chosen.

My Birthday Party

(1) I had a big birthday party this year, with lots of friends _____ family. (2) Aunt Laurie did not make it, _____ Uncle Hal did. (3) I got both books _____ games for presents. (4) My mother set up a net in the backyard. (5) People could either play volleyball _____ badminton. (6) Some people stayed late. (7) We played board games.

1 What conjunction can you use to complete sentence 1?
- ⬭ but
- ⬬ and
- ⬭ or
- ⬭ to

2 What conjunction can you use to complete sentence 2?
- ⬬ but
- ⬭ and
- ⬭ or
- ⬭ from

3 What conjunction can you use to complete sentence 3?
- ⬭ but
- ⬭ to
- ⬬ and
- ⬭ or

4 What conjunction can you use to complete sentence 5?
- ⬭ but
- ⬭ and
- ⬭ some
- ⬬ or

5 Which answer best combines sentences 6 and 7 using a conjunction?
- ⬭ Some people stayed late, but we played board games.
- ⬬ Some people stayed late, and we played board games.
- ⬭ Some people stayed, late but we played board games.
- ⬭ Some people stayed, late and we played board games.

© Pearson Education, Inc., 3

Home Activity Your child prepared for taking tests on conjunctions. Read a short newspaper article with your child and have him or her point out conjunctions.

Syllable Pattern CV/VC

Spelling Words				
create	medium	piano	idea	radio
video	studio	violin	duo	patio
rodeo	pioneer	trio	stadium	audio

Hidden Words Circle the list word hidden in each puzzle. Write the word.

1. m b c r e a t e t c   **create**
2. c p i o n e e r d g   **pioneer**
3. b n k m e d i u m   **medium**
4. f o i d e a j d c a   **idea**
5. o l s t a d i u m   **stadium**
6. u v i o l i n l m p   **violin**

Meaning Clues Circle the word that fits the meaning clue. Write it.

7. moving pictures   video or audio   **video**
8. outdoor space   piano or patio   **patio**
9. pair   duo or radio   **duo**
10. artist's workplace   rodeo or studio   **studio**
11. sound   audio or duo   **audio**
12. group of three   trio or duo   **trio**
13. hear music and news here   patio or radio   **radio**
14. instrument with keys   piano or radio   **piano**
15. place where cowboys compete   radio or rodeo   **rodeo**

Summarizing Look at the words you wrote for numbers 7–15. Write a sentence that tells how they are all alike.

They all end in *o*.

© Pearson Education, Inc., 3

Home Activity Your child spelled words with the CVVC (consonant-vowel-vowel-consonant) and CVV (consonant-vowel-vowel) syllable patterns. Together, write the words on a calendar page. Fill the calendar. Take turns choosing a date and spelling the word on that date.

Adjectives and Articles

Directions Circle each article. Underline each adjective.

1. Once, (the) word *kimono* referred to <u>all</u> clothes in Japan.

2. Then (a) <u>new</u> piece of clothing was invented.

3. People called (the) <u>loose</u> outfit (a) kimono.

4. They loved (the) <u>bright</u>, <u>colorful</u> kimonos.

5. (A) kimono was (an) outfit for <u>both</u> men and women.

Directions Choose the article in ( ) that correctly completes each sentence. Write the sentence.

6. Kimonos had (a, an) advantage over other clothes.

   Kimonos had an advantage over other clothes.

7. On (a, an) winter day, people could wear many layers of kimonos.

   On a winter day, people could wear many layers of kimonos.

8. Around 1900, (a, the) people of Japan began wearing styles from Europe and America.

   Around 1900, the people of Japan began wearing styles from Europe and America.

9. Now, people might wear kimonos for (a, the) wedding.

   Now, people might wear kimonos for a wedding.

10. Kimonos are (a, an) enchanting sight at parties and festivals.

    Kimonos are an enchanting sight at parties and festivals.

Homophones

Spelling Words				
to	too	two	week	weak
road	rode	stair	stare	bear
bare	write	right	new	knew

Complete the Sentences Write the list word that completes each sentence.

1. Jason has (to, two) bikes.   **two**

2. Next (week, weak) is my eighth birthday.   **week**

3. Can you (write, right) neatly with a pen?   **write**

4. Do not (stair, stare) at people on the street.   **stare**

5. Maya wants to go to the party (two, too).   **too**

6. Which (road, rode) goes to the park?   **road**

7. Maya had no shoes, so her feet were (bear, bare).   **bare**

8. Who (new, knew) the answer to the problem?   **knew**

9. I tripped on a (stair, stare) and fell.   **stair**

Mixed-up Homophones Cross out two incorrectly used list words in each sentence. Write the correct words.

A ~~knew~~ baby kitten is very ~~week~~.

10. ___**new**___   11. ___**weak**___

We ~~road~~ ~~too~~ the show in a big car.

12. ___**rode**___   13. ___**to**___

Is the ~~bare~~ in the ~~write~~ cage?

14. ___**bear**___   15. ___**right**___

Home Activity Your child is learning to spell homophones—words with the same pronunciation but different spellings and meanings. Ask your child to point to a list word, spell it, and use it in a sentence. Continue until all words have been used.

Comparative and Superlative Adjectives

Directions Underline the adjectives that compare in the sentences.

1. I have the <u>friendliest</u> grandparents in the world.

2. Grandpa is the <u>busiest</u> man in town.

3. He is <u>older</u> than many of his neighbors.

4. No one is <u>nicer</u> than Grandma.

5. I have the <u>tastiest</u> meals at her house.

Directions Choose the adjective in ( ) that correctly completes each sentence. Write the sentence.

6. Abuelito's life was (easier, easiest) in Texas than in Mexico.

   Abuelito's life was easier in Texas than in Mexico.

7. Grandpa's stories are (longer, longest) than Abuelito's.

   Grandpa's stories are longer than Abuelito's.

8. The family sailed on the (bigger, biggest) ship in Europe.

   The family sailed on the biggest ship in Europe.

9. It was (safer, safest) than a trip in a covered wagon.

   It was safer than a trip in a covered wagon.

10. My grandparents tell the (finer, finest) stories in the world.

    My grandparents tell the finest stories in the world.

Vowel Patterns *au, augh, ou, ough*

Spelling Words				
because	though	taught	bought	touch
would	author	could	enough	sausage
fought	should	faucet	daughter	brought

Synonyms Write the list word for each synonym or synonym phrase. The answer to the riddle will be in the shaded boxes.

What is a skunk worth?

1. writer | a | u | t | h | o | r |

2. meat | s | a | u | s | a | g | e |

3. able to | c | o | u | l | d |

4. female child | d | a | u | g | h | t | e | r |

5. all that was needed | e | n | o | u | g | h |

6. water tap | f | a | u | c | e | t |

Before and After Write the list word that begins and ends with the same letters as each word shown.

7. bright   __**brought**__

8. bone   __**because**__

9. world   __**would**__

10. said   __**should**__

11. trench   __**touch**__

12. alter   __**author**__

© Pearson Education, Inc., 3

Home Activity Your child is learning to spell words with *au, augh, ou,* and *ough*. Ask your child to circle these letters in each word and say the vowel sound that each makes.

Adverbs

Directions Underline the adverbs in the sentences.

1. Luis's family <u>recently</u> moved to a new place.

2. Luis <u>excitedly</u> moved his things into his new room.

3. <u>Next</u> he went to meet his new neighbors.

4. <u>Yesterday</u> Luis saw his new school.

5. He <u>soon</u> got to know the new neighborhood.

Directions Choose the correct word in ( ) to complete each new sentence. Write the new sentence.

6. Maria (sudden, suddenly) felt homesick for her old school.
Maria suddenly felt homesick for her old school.

7. (Usual, Usually), Maria enjoyed meeting new people.
Usually, Maria enjoyed meeting new people.

8. She sat (quietly, quiet) in class all day.
She sat quietly in class all day.

9. Some girls (cheerful, cheerfully) asked Maria to play.
Some girls cheerfully asked Maria to play.

10. She (quick, quickly) felt better.
She quickly felt better.

Vowel Patterns *ei, eigh*

Spelling Words				
ceiling	neighbor	either	eighteen	height
neither	weight	leisure	protein	freight
receive	weigh	deceive	sleigh	conceited

Crossword Puzzle Write the list word that could be used in an answer to each question.

Across

2. the top of a room
5. how tall something is
6. cargo
7. trick

Down

1. to get
2. overly proud
3. not either
4. carriage used on snow

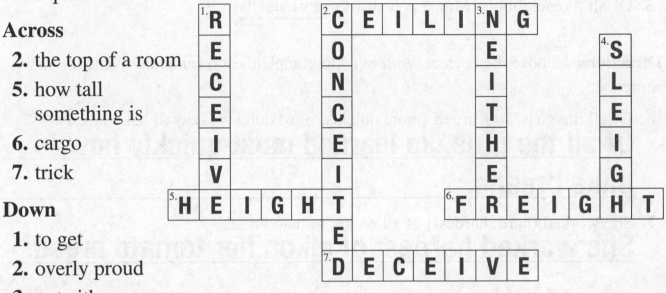

Alphabetizing Write each group of words in ABC order.

neighbor
protein
either

9. __either__
10. __neighbor__
11. __protein__

weight
leisure
eighteen

12. __eighteen__
13. __leisure__
14. __weight__

© Pearson Education, Inc., 3

School + Home **Home Activity** Your child learned spelling words with the vowel pattern *ei* and *eigh*. Together, divide the words into two groups based on their vowel pattern. Ask your child to choose words from each group to spell to you.

Comparative and Superlative Adverbs

Directions Underline the adverb that compares in each sentence.

1. Bread bakes <u>longer</u> than biscuits do.

2. The big oven heats <u>more quickly</u> than the other ovens.

3. Of all the breads, the banana bread will be done <u>soonest</u>.

4. Mrs. Stone kneads dough <u>harder</u> than Kelly does.

5. Of all the neighbors, Mrs. Lopez works <u>most slowly</u>.

Directions Choose the correct word in ( ) to complete each sentence. Write the new sentence.

6. Of all the girls, Jo learned (more quickly, most quickly) how to bake breads.
Of all the girls, Jo learned most quickly how to bake breads.

7. She worked (hard, hardest) of all on her tomato bread.
She worked hardest of all on her tomato bread.

8. Everyone eats her pumpkin bread (faster, fastest) than any other bread.
Everyone eats her pumpkin bread faster than any other bread.

9. Uncle Dan compliments Jo (more frequently, most frequently) than I do.
Uncle Dan compliments Jo more frequently than I do.

10. Jo stays in the kitchen (longer, longest) than Mom.
Jo stays in the kitchen longer than Mom.

Suffixes

Spelling Words				
rocky	foolish	rainy	childhood	selfish
treatment	movement	neighborhood	childish	parenthood
crunchy	bumpy	payment	sleepy	shipment

Suffix Story Read the story. Circle each list word where the writer forgot to use a suffix. Write the word with its suffix.

One (rain) day a (fool) king went for a ride.

1. __rainy__   2. __foolish__

The road was (bump) and (rock.)

3. __bumpy__   4. __rocky__

The king wanted to get a (ship) of (crunch) cereal.

5. __shipment__   6. __crunchy__

The (move) of the coach made the king feel (sleep.)

7. __movement__   8. __sleepy__

In the right (neighbor) the king made a (pay) for the cereal.

9. __neighborhood__   10. __payment__

The (self) king was very (child) and gobbled up all the cereal with both hands.

11. __selfish__   12. __childish__

This was his (treat) of cereal ever since (child.)

13. __treatment__   14. __childhood__

(Parent) should help him know better.

15. __Parenthood__

School + Home Home Activity Your child spelled words with the suffixes -y, -ish, -hood, and -ment. Have your child read the story on the page, using the words he or she wrote as answers.

Conjunctions

Directions Write the conjunction in each sentence.

1. Would you rather visit the city or the country on your trip? **or** _____
2. You can ride horses and have picnics in the country. **and** _____
3. The country is quiet, but it is interesting. **but** _____
4. In the city, you can go to museums and cafés. **and** _____
5. You can ride in buses, trains, or taxis. **or** _____

Directions Choose the conjunction in ( ) that best completes each sentence. Write the sentence.

6. We went to the museum (but, and) saw all kinds of art.

We went to the museum and saw all kinds of art.

_____

7. We saw paintings of people (and, but) buildings.

We saw paintings of people and buildings.

_____

8. Most sculptures stand on the floor, (or, but) some hang from the ceiling.

Most sculptures stand on the floor, but some hang from the ceiling.

9. Did you like the paintings (but, or) the sculptures better?

Did you like the paintings or the sculptures better?

10. My trip to the museum was educational (but, or) tiring.

My trip to the museum was educational but tiring.

Persuasion Chart

Directions Fill in the graphic organizer with ideas for the introduction, supporting reasons, and conclusion in your persuasive essay. **Answers will vary.**

Introduction: State your position.

↓

First reason

↓

Second reason

↓

Third reason (most important)

↓

Conclusion

Use Persuasive Words

Persuasive words convince readers to take an action or agree with the writer's position. Here are some different kinds of persuasive words:

Words that state that an action is necessary: *should, must, important*

Words that compare: *best, most delicious, most important*

Words that describe positive traits: *educational, healthful, safe, effective*

Directions Write sentences for your persuasive essay. Use the kind of persuasive word shown. Underline your persuasive words.

1. Word that states that an action is necessary

_____

_____

2. Word that compares

_____

_____

3. Word that describes positive traits

_____

_____

4. Any kind of persuasive word

<u>Answers should be based on the provided hints and should be complete sentences</u> with appropriate capitalization and punctuation.

Add Adverbs

You have learned that adverbs tell about verbs. They can tell **when** (*soon, often*), **where** (*outside, here*), or **how** (*excitedly, carefully, hungrily*) something happens. You can use adverbs to make your essay more specific and persuasive.

General	She looked at the photographs of Puerto Rico.
More Specific	She looked closely at the photographs of Puerto Rico.

Directions Add an adverb to each sentence to make it more specific. Write the new sentence. **Possible answers:**

1. Japanese people ____ wear kimonos for special occasions.

Japanese people often wear kimonos for special occasions.

2. Sam ate the big plate of spaghetti ____.

Sam ate the big plate of spaghetti today.

3. Tourists in China ____ walk on the Great Wall.

Tourists in China eagerly walk on the Great Wall.

4. You must wrap those Mexican vases ____.

You must wrap those Mexican vases carefully.

Editing 3

Directions This is part of a persuasive essay. Edit the paragraph. Look for errors in spelling, grammar, and mechanics. Use proofreading marks to show the corrections.

Proofreading Marks	
Delete (Take out)	⌒
Add	∧
Spelling	◯
Uppercase letter	≡
Lowercase letter	/

        learning

After ~~learned~~ about the culture of Japan, I want to make a Japanese meal. This

    an   **experience**

will be a interesting way to ◯experence◯ Japans customs and recipes right at home.

   want

I really ~~wants~~ to make Japanese noodles, sushi, and green tea cake. Ill find these

         s **J**   **ingredients**

delicious recipe in a japanese cookbook and help shop for the ◯engredients◯. I will

                   cleaning   **through**

assist in preparing the meal and ~~cleaned~~ up the kitchen when we are ◯throu◯. The

                                      W

meal will be a tasty treat for our entire family. we may even like these recipes so

           want

much that we ~~wanted~~ to try more foods from Japan or other countries. Best of all,

the food~~s~~ we will be preparing are nutritious because we will be cooking with

vegetables

◯vegtables◯ rice, meat, and noodles.

Now you'll edit the draft of your persuasive essay. Next you'll use your revised and edited draft to make a final copy of your essay. Finally, you'll share your written work with your audience.

Vowel Sounds in *moon* and *foot*

Directions Circle each word with the vowel sound in **moon** or the vowel sound in **foot**. Then write each word in the correct column.

1. Our (school) (took) us on a field trip to an art museum.

2. We spent a (full) day studying famous paintings and (statues).

3. We (looked) at works by some of the art world's (true) masters.

4. After we returned to class, our teacher asked us to make a (new) drawing in our (notebooks).

5. I sketched a picture of President Lincoln wearing a black (wool) (suit) and a very tall hat.

vowel sound in moon

6. school

7. statues

8. true

9. new

10. suit

vowel sound in foot

11. took

12. full

13. looked

14. notebooks

15. wool

Directions Cross out the one word in each line that does **not** have the vowel sound in **moon** or the vowel sound in **foot**.

16. ~~build~~   cushion   glue

17. bushel   ~~rocket~~   smooth

18. ~~button~~   bookstore   juice

19. football   stew   ~~story~~

20. balloon   pudding   ~~throat~~

Home Activity Your child identified and wrote words with the vowel sounds in *moon* (as in *school*, *new*, *glue*, and *fruit*) and *foot* (as in *cookie* and *cushion*). Have your child write riddles using words with the vowel sounds in *moon* and *foot*. Try to guess the answer after your child reads each riddle to you.

Fact and Opinion

- A **statement of fact** tells something that can be proved true or false. You can prove it by reading or asking an expert.

- A **statement of opinion** tells someone's ideas or feelings. Words that tell feelings, such as *should* or *best,* are clues to opinions.

Directions Read the following passage.

A symbol is something that stands for something else. There are many symbols that stand for the United States. The bald eagle is the national bird of the United States. The cartoon-like character, Uncle Sam, also stands for our country. But the best symbol of all is the red, white, and blue United States flag. We should always show respect for our country's flag.

Directions Complete each chart by writing one more fact and one more opinion from the passage above. Then answer the question.

Fact	How to Prove
A symbol is something that stands for something else.	Look up the word *symbol* in the dictionary.
1. **Possible response: The bald eagle is the national bird of the United States.**	2. **Look up *bald eagle* in an encyclopedia.**

Opinion	Clue Words
But the best symbol of all is the red, white, and blue United States flag.	best
3. **We should always show respect for our country's flag.**	4. **should**

5. What supports the statement, *There are many symbols that stand for the United States.*

The list of symbols: bald eagle, Uncle Sam, the United States flag

Home Activity Your child identified facts and opinions in a passage. Read an article about the United States. Find a statement of fact. Then find a statement of opinion. Have your child explain the difference.

© Pearson Education, Inc., 3

Writing • Notes

Key Features of Notes

- used to capture important ideas
- often help with a future writing task
- may include abbreviations, short sentences, and sentence fragments

Notes on *The Story of the Statue of Liberty*
(pages 378 and 379)

- Bartholdi wanted the S. of L. to be so large people could climb up inside it
- Other people gave him ideas about how to build it
- First—a large steel skeleton
- People worked on the head and crown
- others worked on the torch—held in right hand
- In left hand—tablet with July 4, 1776, Declaration of Independence
- Torch arm sent to Philadelphia in 1876, then to NYC
- Head shown in Paris to raise money

1. Circle all the proper nouns that are capitalized, including abbreviations.

2. What does the abbreviation "S. of L." stand for in these notes?

The abbreviation "S. of L." stands for Statue of Liberty.

3. Why was the statue's head shown in Paris?

The statue's head was shown in Paris in order to raise money.

Vocabulary

Directions Solve each riddle with a word from the box. Write the word on the line.

1. I describe something that you will always remember.
   What am I? **unforgettable**

2. People who live in a free country have me.
   What am I? **liberty**

3. Kings and queens wear me on their heads.
   What am I? **crown**

4. I am another word for uncovered.
   What am I? **unveiled**

5. I am a light that helps people see in dark caves.
   What am I? **torch**

> **Check the Words You Know**
>
> ___ liberty
> ___ crown
> ___ tablet
> ___ symbol
> ___ unveiled
> ___ torch
> ___ models
> ___ unforgettable

Directions Write the word from the box that best completes each sentence below.

6. The wood carver made two _____ of an airplane.   **models**

7. At night we lit a _____ to help us see our campsite.   **torch**

8. A flag is a _____ of a country.   **symbol**

9. A _____ is a stone that has writing cut into it.   **tablet**

Write an Editorial

On a separate sheet of paper, write an editorial about the first time the Statue of Liberty was seen in New York. Write as if you worked for a newspaper. Tell readers how you felt when you first saw the new statue. Use as many vocabulary words as possible.

Students' writing should use vocabulary to describe the unveiling of the Statue of Liberty and express their feelings about it.

Home Activity Your child has identified and used vocabulary from *The Story of the Statue of Liberty*. Read a story together about this or another historical monument. Have a conversation about the monument and its meaning. Encourage your child to use vocabulary words.

Capital Letters

> Use **capital letters** for proper nouns. Proper nouns include days of the week, months of the year, and holidays. Titles for people should be capitalized when they are used with a person's name. Do not capitalize titles when they are used by themselves.
>
> **Incorrect**   Last october aunt Rosie and my Uncle gave a party for halloween.
> **Correct**   Last October Aunt Rosie and my uncle gave a party for Halloween.
> **Incorrect**   Does mother's day come earlier than memorial day?
> **Correct**   Does Mother's Day come earlier than Memorial Day?

Directions Write the words that should have capital letters correctly.

1. Last may Mara saw some wonderful sights.

May

2. Mara's mom and aunt lucy took her to the Statue of Liberty.

Aunt Lucy

3. They saw the Liberty Bell in philadelphia on memorial day.

Philadelphia; Memorial Day

Directions Write the sentences. Use capital letters correctly.

4. Bartholdi hoped the statue would be finished by july 4, 1876.

Bartholdi hoped the statue would be finished by July 4, 1876.

5. Only the statue's arm and torch were ready by the fourth of july.

Only the statue's arm and torch were ready by the Fourth of July.

Home Activity Your child learned about capital letters. While looking at a magazine, ask your child to point out three capital letters used for days of the week, months of the year, or holidays.

Vowel Sounds in *moon* and *foot*

Spelling Words				
few	school	true	goose	fruit
cookie	cushion	noodle	bookmark	balloon
suit	chew	glue	Tuesday	bushel

Names Write list words to name the pictures.

1. __suit__   2. __fruit__   3. __bookmark__

Categorizing Add a list word to each group.

4. duck, chicken, ___   4. __goose__

5. cake, pie, ___   5. __cookie__

6. paste, tape, ___   6. __glue__

7. Sunday, Thursday, ___   7. __Tuesday__

8. pillow, pad, ___   8. __cushion__

9. liter, quart, ___   9. __bushel__

Rhyming Words Complete each sentence with a list word that rhymes with the underlined word.

10. We <u>grew</u> a __few__ different kinds of vegetables.

11. It's __true__ that <u>blue</u> is my favorite color.

12. I will blow up your __balloon__ <u>soon</u>.

13. The meat in this <u>stew</u> is hard to __chew__ .

14. That <u>doodle</u> you drew looks like a __noodle__ .

15. The __school__ building seems <u>cool</u> today.

Home Activity Your child wrote words with the vowel sound in *moon* (spelled *oo*, *ew*, *ue*, *ui*) and the vowel sound in *foot* (spelled *oo*, *u*). Have your child pronounce and spell the words with *oo*.

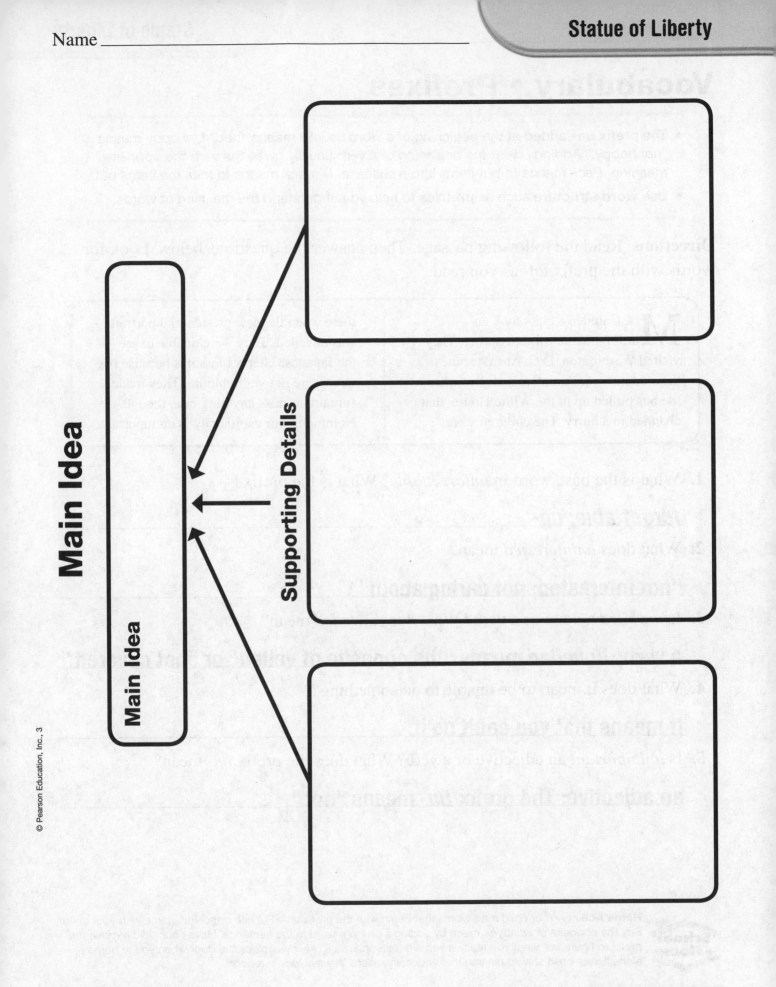

Main Idea

Main Idea

Supporting Details

Vocabulary • Prefixes

- The **prefix *un-*** added at the beginning of a word usually means "not." *Unhappy* means "not happy." Adding *un-* at the beginning of a verb usually gives the verb the opposite meaning. *Pack* means to put items into a suitcase. *Unpack* means to take the items out.

- Use **word structure** such as **prefixes** to help you understand the meaning of words.

Directions Read the following passage. Then answer the questions below. Look for words with the prefix *un-* as you read.

Mrs. Camden's class took an unforgettable trip last spring. They visited Washington, D.C. At first some of the students were uninterested. But when the bus pulled up to the White House, that changed in a hurry. The children were there when the new presidential portrait was unveiled. They were unable to see the Japanese cherry blossoms because the trees were not yet in bloom. They made sure not to miss anything else, though. Nothing in our capital city is unimportant.

1. What is the base word in *unforgettable*? What is the prefix?

   forgettable; un-

2. What does *uninterested* mean?

   "not interested; not caring about"

3. Is *unveiled* a noun or a verb? What does *unveiled* mean?

   a verb; *Unveiled* means "the opposite of veiled" or "not covered."

4. What does it mean to be unable to do something?

   It means that you can't do it.

5. Is *unimportant* an adjective or a verb? What does the prefix *un-* mean?

   an adjective; The prefix *un-* means "not."

© Pearson Education, Inc., 3

Home Activity Your child read words that begin with the prefix *un-*. Play an opposites game with your child. Say the opposite of what you mean by adding a *un-* to a word in the sentence. Have your child remove the prefix to figure out what you really mean. For example, say, "Always unlock the door when you're home alone." Your child should tell you that you really mean, "Always lock the door."

Time Line

A **time line** shows events in the order that they happened or will happen. It can show days, weeks, months, and years.

Directions Look at the time line. Use the time line to answer the questions.

1885   1903   1924   1956   1986
1886

1885 Statue parts arrive in New York in June.
1886 President Grover Cleveland officially accepts statue on October 28.
1903 Poem by Emma Lazarus is added to the base.
1924 Statue becomes a national monument.
1956 Island is renamed Liberty Island.
1986 Centennial celebration honors statue's 100th year.

1. What is the first year shown on the time line?

   1885

2. In which year was a poem added to the statue?

   1903

3. When did the statue parts arrive in New York? When did President Cleveland accept the statue? About how much time passed between these two events?

   1885; 1886; a little more than a year

4. What major events happened between 1920 and 1960?

   statue became a national monument; island was renamed

5. Why was 1986 an important year for the Statue of Liberty?

   The Statue of Liberty turned 100 years old.

Home Activity Your child read information on a time line and answered questions about it. Help your child list the dates of some important family events. Ask him or her to make a time line with these events.

Vowel Sounds in *moon* and *foot*

Spelling Words				
few	school	true	goose	fruit
cookie	cushion	noodle	bookmark	balloon
suit	chew	glue	Tuesday	bushel

Proofread a Schedule Kelsey made a schedule. Circle four spelling errors on this week's page. Write the words correctly. Then circle five words that need capital letters.

(monday)	no school—(cuold) go to Gym for Kids
(tuesday)	fruit and (cooky) sale
(wednesday)	blow up (ballons) for party
(thursday)	Jena's birthday party
(friday)	Jena's (tru) birthday

Frequently Misspelled Words

through
took
would
could

1. **could**   2. **cookie**

3. **balloons**   4. **true**

Proofread Words Fill in a circle to show which word is spelled correctly. Write it.

5. ○ noddle   ● noodle   ○ noodel   5. **noodle**

6. ● bookmark   ○ bukmark   ○ book mark   6. **bookmark**

7. ○ cushon   ● cushion   ○ cooshion   7. **cushion**

8. ○ ballewn   ○ ballon   ● balloon   8. **balloon**

9. ○ glew   ○ gleu   ● glue   9. **glue**

10. ○ friut   ● fruit   ○ froot   10. **fruit**

© Pearson Education, Inc., 3

School + Home

Home Activity Your child identified misspelled words with the vowel sound in *moon* (spelled *oo, ew, ue, ui*) and the vowel sound in *foot* (spelled *oo, u*). Ask your child to write a sentence containing two or more list words.

Capital Letters

Directions Read the selection. Then read each question that follows the selection. Decide which is the best answer to each question. Mark the space for the answer you have chosen.

A New Home

(1) The family sailed across the ocean in february. (2) On friday, the ship arrived in a new country. (3) The next day Aunt Sue took her guests to the city.

(4) Their aunt told the family about holidays in america. (5) She said people enjoy fireworks on Independence Day. (6) Americans remember explorers on columbus day. (7) I hope Grandpa visits us at Hanukkah.

1 What change, if any, should be made to sentence 1?

- ⬤ Change *february* to **February**
- ◯ Change *family* to **Family**
- ◯ Change *ocean* to **Ocean**
- ◯ Make no change

2 What change, if any, should be made to sentence 2?

- ◯ Change *country* to **Country**
- ◯ Change *ship* to **Ship**
- ⬤ Change *friday* to **Friday**
- ◯ Make no change

3 What change, if any, should be made to sentence 3?

- ◯ Change *took* to **Took**
- ◯ Change *guests* to **Guests**
- ◯ Change *city* to **City**
- ⬤ Make no change

4 What change, if any, should be made to sentence 4?

- ◯ Change *holidays* to **Holidays**
- ⬤ Change *america* to **America**
- ◯ Change *aunt* to **Aunt**
- ◯ Make no change

5 What change, if any, should be made to sentence 6?

- ◯ Change *explorers* to **Explorers**
- ⬤ Change *columbus day* to **Columbus Day**
- ◯ Change *remember* to **Remember**
- ◯ Make no change

© Pearson Education, Inc., 3

Home Activity Your child prepared for taking tests on capital letters. Look at a calendar with your child and have him or her point out capital letters and explain the reasons for their use.

Schwa spelled with an *a, e, i, o, u,* and *y*

Directions Choose the word with a vowel that has the same sound as the underlined vowels in **ab̲out, tak̲en, penci̲l, lem̲on, circu̲s,** and **Sibyl̲** to complete each sentence. Write the word on the line to the left.

afraid

1. Susan was (afraid/scared) to walk her dog without a leash.

rascal

2. Every time she opened the front door, the little (pooch/ rascal) ran off.

local

3. One time she took her dog to a (local/nearby) park.

animals

4. All the (animals/doggies) were fetching or chasing.

vinyl

5. Susan removed her puppy's (vinyl/nylon) leash and let the dog run freely.

paper

6. When her dog ran off, Susan opened a (paper/plastic) bag and pulled out a treat.

traveled

7. Susan's dog quickly (traveled/bounded) back.

morsel

8. Now anytime Susan offers her dog a tasty (biscuit/ morsel), it comes racing to her.

Directions Circle the letter in each word that stands for the same sound as the underlined vowels in **ab̲out, tak̲en, penci̲l, lem̲on, circu̲s,** and **Sibyl̲.**

9. kitch(e)n

10. riv(e)r

11. s(u)rprise

12. fam(i)ly

13. mel(o)n

14. sug(a)r

15. vin(y)l

16. doll(a)r

17. nick(e)l

18. (a)go

19. op(e)n

20. cany(o)n

Home Activity Your child identified and wrote words that contain the vowel sound called schwa, heard in words with unaccented syllables such as *about, taken, pencil, lemon, circus,* and *Sibyl.* Help your child write sentences with words that have this sound. Ask your child to read each sentence and identify the letter that stands for the schwa sound.

Cause and Effect

- An **effect** is something that happens.
- A **cause** tells why that thing happens.
- An effect may have more than one cause.

Directions: Read the following passage.

No matter where you live, English sparrows probably live nearby. Like most of us, the ancestors of today's English sparrows were immigrants. The first family members came from England. They were set free in New York in the 1800s. Over the years, sparrows have moved to all parts of our country.

Americans have a love-hate relationship with sparrows. Some people dislike them because, they say, the sparrows push aside native birds and because they are messy.

Many people enjoy sparrows. They like them because they think they're cute and because sparrows eat harmful worms and insects.

Directions: Fill in the chart to identify cause and effect.

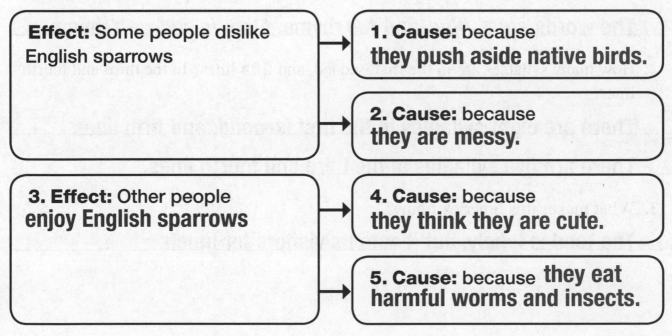

Effect: Some people dislike English sparrows

1. Cause: because **they push aside native birds.**

2. Cause: because **they are messy.**

3. Effect: Other people **enjoy English sparrows**

4. Cause: because **they think they are cute.**

5. Cause: because **they eat harmful worms and insects.**

Home Activity Your child identified cause and effect. With your child, talk about a wild bird or animal that lives near your home. Talk about causes and effects related to having the bird or animal nearby.

© Pearson Education, Inc., 3

Comprehension 397

Writing • Limerick

Key Features of Limericks

- a form of poetry
- made up of five lines and a specific rhyme scheme (*aabba*)
- sometimes humorous or witty

The Toad in the Shoe

1 A hungry toad lived in a shoe;

2 alone, he was always so blue.

3 A friend would fly in,

4 the toad, he would grin,

5 and then he would eat his lunch, too.

---

1. Which words in the poem rhyme?

   The words *shoe, blue,* and *too* rhyme. Also, *in* and *grin* rhyme.

2. How many syllables are in the first, second, and fifth lines? In the third and fourth lines?

   There are eight syllables in the first, second, and fifth lines.

   There are five syllables in the third and fourth lines.

3. What makes this limerick funny?

   The toad is lonely, but it eats its visitors for lunch.

Vocabulary

Directions Match each word with its meaning. Draw a line to connect them.

Check the Words You Know

___narrow   ___foolish
___perches   ___bows
___recipe   ___chilly
___foreign

1. foolish   cool
2. recipe   from a different country
3. narrow   silly
4. chilly   directions for cooking food
5. foreign   skinny

Directions Write the word from the box that best completes each sentence below.

6. Watch the red bird as it _____ on the branch.   **perches**

7. After he sings, he _____ to the audience.   **bows**

8. The gap was too _____ for me to squeeze through.   **narrow**

9. He moved here from a _____ country called Sudan.   **foreign**

10. My stepmother wrote that _____ for beef stew.   **recipe**

Write a Recipe

On a separate sheet of paper, write a recipe for something you like to eat or drink. It can be something simple, like chocolate milk or a sandwich. Use as many vocabulary words as possible. **Students' writing should use vocabulary in a simple recipe for a food they like.**

School + Home **Home Activity** Your child identified and used vocabulary words from *Happy Birthday Mr. Kang.* Have your child plan a menu for dinner or help you prepare food from a written recipe. Encourage your child to use vocabulary words in conversations.

Abbreviations

An **abbreviation** is a shortened form of a word. Many abbreviations begin with a capital letter and end with a period.

- Some titles used for names of people are abbreviations. For example, *Dr.* is the abbreviation for *Doctor*. The title *Miss* is not abbreviated.

  Mr. Don Lee Chang   Ms. Lucy Ruiz   Mrs. Maya Levin

- An **initial** is the first letter of a name. It is written with a capital letter and is followed by a period.

  Mr. Don L. Chang   L. T. Ruiz   M. E. Levin

- The names of days and months can be abbreviated. *May, June,* and *July* are not abbreviated.

  Days of the Week
  Sun.   Mon.   Tues.   Wed.   Thurs.   Fri.   Sat.
  Months of the Year
  Jan.   Feb.   Mar.   Apr.   Aug.   Sept.   Oct.   Nov.   Dec.

Directions Write each abbreviation. Be sure to capitalize letters and use periods correctly.

1. Mrs W. Wenders   **Mrs. W. Wenders**

2. j r Burton   **J. R. Burton**

3. sat, aug 4   **Sat., Aug. 4**

4. ms T j. Matthews   **Ms. T. J. Matthews**

Directions Some abbreviations can be used in sentences. Find the word that can be abbreviated in the sentence below. Write the sentence with the abbreviation.

5. Mister Alexis got a pet bird when he moved to this country.

Mr. Alexis got a pet bird when he moved to this country.

Home Activity Your child learned about abbreviations. Look through the mail with your child. Have him or her identify abbreviations used for people's names and titles.

© Pearson Education, Inc., 3

Schwa

Spelling Words				
above	another	upon	animal	paper
open	family	travel	afraid	nickel
sugar	circus	item	gallon	melon

Context Clues Write the missing spelling word.

1. May I have _____ piece of pizza?

2. I have three dimes and one _____ in my bank.

3. He was eating a slice of _____.

4. I wrote a letter on a sheet of green _____.

5. My _____ likes to watch football Sunday afternoons.

6. Please get a _____ of milk.

7. The _____ had clowns and acrobats.

8. Is the _____ bowl empty?

9. Each _____ on the list must be done by noon.

10. Once _____ a time, there was a handsome prince.

11. My favorite _____ is the giraffe.

1. __**another**__

2. __**nickel**__

3. __**melon**__

4. __**paper**__

5. __**family**__

6. __**gallon**__

7. __**circus**__

8. __**sugar**__

9. __**item**__

10. __**upon**__

11. __**animal**__

Opposites Write the spelling word that means the opposite.

12. shut   __**open**__

13. brave   __**afraid**__

14. stay home __**travel**__

15. below   __**above**__

afraid
travel
above
open

Home Activity Your child spelled words with the schwa sound (an unstressed vowel sound such as the *a* in *above*). Have your child pick a number between 1 and 15. Read the list word with that number and ask your child to spell it.

Name _____

Name _____   **Mr. Kang**

T-Chart

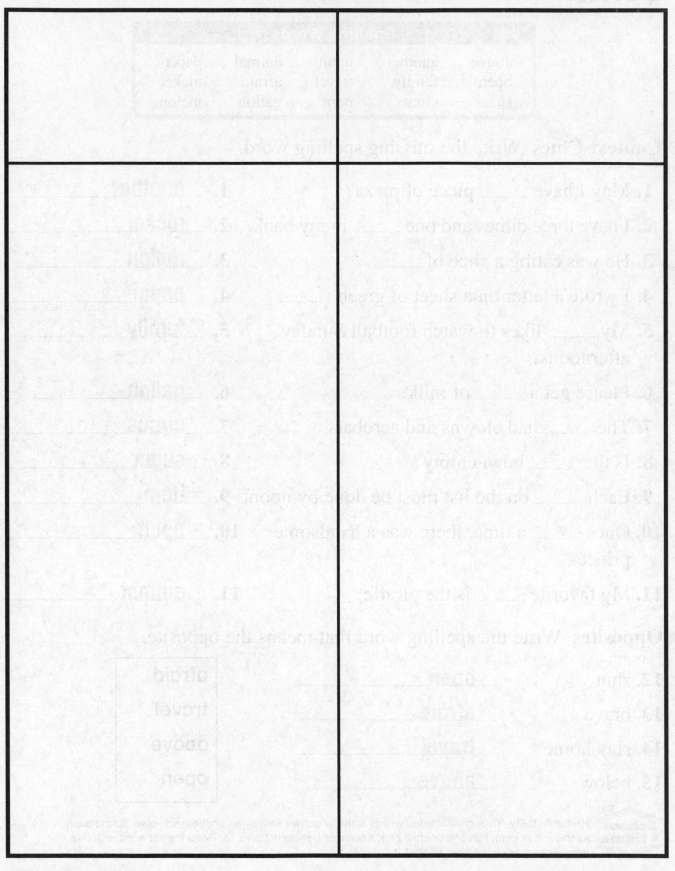

© Pearson Education, Inc., 3

402 **Writing** Plan

Vocabulary • Antonyms

- Sometimes when you read you see unfamiliar words. The **context**, or words around it, may help you figure out the meaning.
- Look to see if the author used an **antonym**, a word with the opposite meaning, and use that word to help you with the meaning of the unfamiliar word.

Directions Read the paragraph. Then answer the questions below.

My family wanted to eat at a Chinese food restaurant instead of the usual burger place. We had never been to a Chinese restaurant before and were excited to learn about a different culture. We walked in through a narrow hallway that didn't seem wide enough for us to fit.

We drank hot tea with dinner, which was perfect because I was chilly. I tried to eat with chopsticks, but felt foolish because I seemed clumsy with them. I thought it was sensible to ask for a fork! After this restaurant becomes an old favorite, maybe my family will again try something new—maybe Brazilian food!

1. What does the word *usual* mean in the passage? What context clue helps?

   regular; different

2. What does the word *narrow* mean in the passage? What context clue helps?

   thin; wide

3. What does the word *chilly* mean in the passage? What context clue helps?

   cold; hot

4. What does the word *foolish* mean in the passage? What context clue helps?

   silly; sensible

5. What does the word *old* mean in the passage? What context clue helps?

   familiar; new

 Home Activity Your child has identified and used context clues to understand new words. Read a story with your child and encourage looking for context clues to help her or him understand the meaning of unfamiliar words.

Maps

Maps are drawings of places that show cities, states, and countries. Maps can show the location of landforms, bodies of water, and other important places.

Directions Look at the map of China. Then answer the questions.

China

Mongolia
Harbin
Inner Mongolia
Yellow River
Beijing
Korea
Pacific Ocean
Tibet
Yangtze River
Nepal
Bhutan
Shanghai
India
Pearl River
Taiwan
Myanmar
Laos
Vietnam

Key
∿∿ River
⊓⊔ Great Wall
• City
★ Capital
— Country Border

1. What are two countries that border China?

   Possible response: India and Nepal

2. Which river is located in southern China?

   Pearl River

3. The Great Wall runs along the border of which region?

   Inner Mongolia

4. The capital of China is located close to which body of water?

   Pacific Ocean

5. Is Mongolia a country, or is it part of China? How can you tell?

   A country. There is a country border symbol all around it.

School + Home

Home Activity Your child answered questions about a map of China. Together, look at maps of different countries. Find countries that are divided into states, provinces, regions, and so on. Look for each country's landforms, bodies of water, cities, and the capital.

© Pearson Education, Inc., 3

Schwa

Spelling Words				
above	another	upon	animal	paper
open	family	travel	afraid	nickel
sugar	circus	item	gallon	melon

Proofread a Description Jake wrote about an imaginary animal. Circle four words that are spelled incorrectly and two words that should be combined into one compound word. Write the words correctly.

My (anamal) looks like a lizard with (opun) wings. It has (beutiful) colors. It lives above the (tree tops). For food it breaks open a (mellon.) It is not afraid of (any thing.)

Frequently Misspelled Words

upon
again
beautiful

1. __animal__   2. __open__   3. __beautiful__

4. __melon__   5. __treetops__   6. __anything__

Proofread Words Fill in a circle to show which word is spelled correctly. Write the word.

7. There was an ____ in the paper about our class.

○ itam   ○ itum   ● item

7. __item__

8. Are you ____ you might get lost on the subway?

● afraid   ○ ifraid   ○ afriad

8. __afraid__

9. There are five people in my ____ .

● family   ○ famaly   ○ familie

9. __family__

10. The candy cost a ____ each.

○ nicle   ○ nickle   ● nickel

10. __nickel__

Home Activity Your child identified misspelled words with the schwa sound (an unstressed vowel sound such as the *a* in *above*). Give clues about a list word. Ask your child to guess and spell the word.

© Pearson Education, Inc., 3

Abbreviations

Directions Read the selection. Then read each question that follows the selection. Decide which is the best answer to each question. Mark the space for the answer you have chosen.

A Birthday Party

(1) I went to a friend's birthday party last April. (2) The party was on a Monday. (3) It was held at Mister Edwards' house. (4) On the Wednesday before the party, I got a present for my friend. (5) My friend's name is Richard James Edwards. (6) I will have a party for my own birthday in October.

1 How would you abbreviate the word "April" in sentence 1?

- ⬭ Ap.
- ⬛ Apr.
- ⬭ App.
- ⬭ Apar.

2 How would you abbreviate the word "Monday" in sentence 2?

- ⬭ Moon.
- ⬭ Nov.
- ⬭ Mo.
- ⬛ Mon.

3 Which word can you abbreviate in sentence 3?

- ⬭ Edwards'
- ⬭ held
- ⬛ Mister
- ⬭ house

4 How could you abbreviate "Richard James Edwards" in sentence 5?

- ⬛ R. J. Edwards
- ⬭ Richard J. E.
- ⬭ Richard James E.
- ⬭ R. James E.

5 Which word can you abbreviate in sentence 6?

- ⬭ party
- ⬛ October
- ⬭ birthday
- ⬭ own

 Home Activity Your child prepared for taking tests on abbreviations. Have your child write the days of the week, using abbreviations correctly.

Final Syllables *-tion, -ion, -ture, -ive, -ize*

Directions Circle the correctly spelled word in each pair.

1. commosion — **(commotion)**
2. **(invasion)** — invation
3. generasion — **(generation)**
4. posision — **(position)**
5. relaxasion — **(relaxation)**
6. **(division)** — divition
7. vacasion — **(vacation)**
8. explotion — **(explosion)**

Directions Add **-ture, -ive,** or **-ize** to complete each word below. Write the complete word on the line. (HINT: there is only one correct choice for each word.)

9. pas _____**pasture**_____
10. act _____**active**_____
11. rup _____**rupture**_____
12. mass _____**massive**_____

13. maxim _____**maximize**_____
14. real _____**realize**_____
15. cap _____**capture**_____
16. adven _____**adventure**_____

Directions Choose four words from the above list and write a sentence for each word.

17. **Sentences will vary.** _____

18. _____

19. _____

20. _____

Home Activity Your child identified and wrote words that end with the syllables *-tion, -ion, -ture, -ive,* and *-ize.* Work together to write sentences using the words from the page above. Ask your child to underline the final syllable in the words used from this page.

Graphic Sources

- **Graphic sources** are ways of showing information visually, or in a way you can see.
- Charts, diagrams, maps, and graphs are examples of graphic sources.

Directions Read the following passage.

The principal made an exciting announcement. Students would be allowed to draw on the walls! But they couldn't just scribble any old thing. Each class would submit a plan for a mural that would express school pride.

Mrs. Maki's students held a meeting to decide what to show on their mural. The students suggested a school sports team in action, students working in the media center, or students participating in activities such as drama, choir, or band. After listing the possibilities, the class took a vote. Which idea do you think won?

Directions: Use information from the passage to create a graphic source that shows the information in a visual way. Then use the information in your graphic source to help explain the passage.

Possible response: a tally chart which includes all the topics from the paragraph and a vote tally beside each choice.

School + Home **Home Activity** Your child created a graphic source to show information from a passage visually. Read a newspaper or magazine article with your child. Ask your child to make a graphic source that shows information from the passage at a glance.

Writing • Description

Key Features of a Description

- explanation of something using sensory details
- is a written "picture" for the reader
- includes careful word choice

Description of "Girl with a Pearl Earring"

At a museum, I saw the painting "Girl with a Pearl Earring" by Johannes Vermeer. The painting is so ancient that when I studied it closely, I could see many tiny cracks in the canvas. In the painting, a girl looks over her left shoulder. Her skin is pale. Her dark eyes seemed to follow me when I moved. Over her hair she wears a soft blue scarf. The only other bright color in the painting is the girl's mouth, which is red like an apple. A lot of the painting is dark as night. It has a black background, and the girl's back and the side of her face are in shadow. A white earring gleams in her left ear like a star.

The painting makes me wonder what it was like to live a long time ago. It also makes me feel kind of gloomy, because the girl looks a little sad. Her mouth is open a little, as if she wants to say something. I wonder what she would say if she could talk?

---

1. Find the topic of this description and circle it.

2. Underline the sensory details that help you imagine what this painting looks like. Remember, sensory details appeal to taste, touch, sound, smell, and sight.

3. Draw a box around other strong details that show careful word choice.

Vocabulary

Directions Match each word with its meaning. Draw a line to connect them.

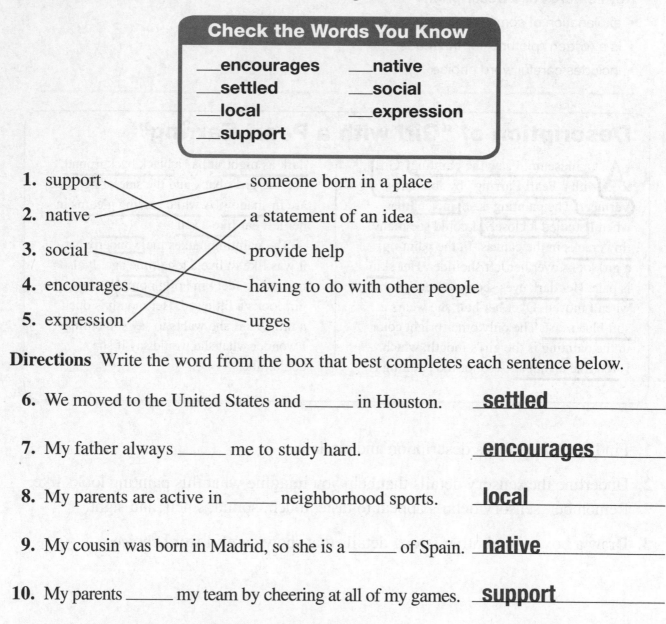

Check the Words You Know

___encourages   ___native
___settled   ___social
___local   ___expression
___support

1. support — someone born in a place
2. native — a statement of an idea
3. social — provide help
4. encourages — having to do with other people
5. expression — urges

Directions Write the word from the box that best completes each sentence below.

6. We moved to the United States and _____ in Houston.   **settled**

7. My father always _____ me to study hard.   **encourages**

8. My parents are active in _____ neighborhood sports.   **local**

9. My cousin was born in Madrid, so she is a _____ of Spain.   **native**

10. My parents _____ my team by cheering at all of my games.   **support**

Write a Description

On a separate sheet of paper describe a painting that you think would look good on the wall of a building in your neighborhood. Use as many vocabulary words as possible. **Students' writing should use vocabulary in a description of wall paintings they would like to see.**

School + Home   **Home Activity** Your child has identified and used vocabulary words from *Talking Walls: Art for the People.* Take a walking tour of your neighborhood. Encourage your child to use this week's vocabulary words as you talk about what you see.

Combining Sentences

When you **combine sentences,** you join two sentences that are about the same topic. You make them into one sentence.

- You can join two simple sentences and make a compound sentence. Add a comma and a conjunction such as *and, but,* or *or.*

  Jen drew a tree. I drew a bird. Jen drew a tree, and I drew a bird.

- You can combine two sentences that have the same subject.

  Jen got blue paint. Jen painted the sky. Jen got blue paint and painted the sky.

- You can combine two sentences that have the same predicate.

  Jen painted. I painted. Jen and I painted.

- You can combine two sentences by using an appositive.

  We made a mural. A mural is a wall painting. We made a mural, a wall painting.

- You can combine two sentences by using adjectives or adverbs.

  That mural is big. Our mural is bigger. Our mural is bigger than that mural.
  We painted the mural. We painted it quickly. We painted the mural quickly.

- You can combine two sentences by using prepositional phrases.

  They saw the mural. It was on Main Street. They saw the mural on Main Street.

Directions Combine each pair of sentences into a compound sentence. Use a comma and the conjunction in ( ).

1. Some murals show famous people. Our mural shows ordinary people. (but)

   Some murals show famous people, but our mural shows ordinary people.

2. I will show you the mural. You can find it yourself. (or)

   I will show you the mural, or you can find it yourself.

Directions Combine the sentences. Use the underlined words only once in the new sentence.

3. Diego Rivera came from Mexico. Diego Rivera painted murals in America.

   Diego Rivera came from Mexico and (*or* but) painted murals in America.

Home Activity Your child learned about combining sentences. Point out two short related sentences in a book you are reading with your child. Have your child combine the sentences.

Final Syllables

Spelling Words				
question	creature	furniture	division	collision
action	direction	culture	vacation	mansion
fiction	feature	sculpture	vision	celebration

Opposites Write the missing list word. It will be the opposite of the underlined word.

1. The hero in this book lives in a <u>shack</u>.

1. **mansion**

2. At first, I had trouble with <u>multiplication</u>.

2. **division**

3. Let me interrupt with a <u>statement</u> about wind power.

3. **question**

4. Jed left for his <u>usual job</u>.

4. **vacation**

5. This story is <u>true</u>.

5. **fiction**

Context Clues Write the last word of the sentence.

6. The situation called for quick **action** .

7. The school nurse tested everyone's **vision** .

8. Her cheery smile is her best **feature** .

9. In art class, Tami made a plaster **sculpture** .

10. Please come to my birthday **celebration** .

11. We bought some used **furniture** .

12. An armadillo is an odd **creature** .

13. We walked in the wrong **direction** .

14. The toy robots had a **collision** .

15. Nature was important in the Aztec **culture** .

Home Activity Your child wrote words that end with *-tion*, *-sion*, and *-ture*. Have your child underline these endings in the list words.

© Pearson Education, Inc., 3

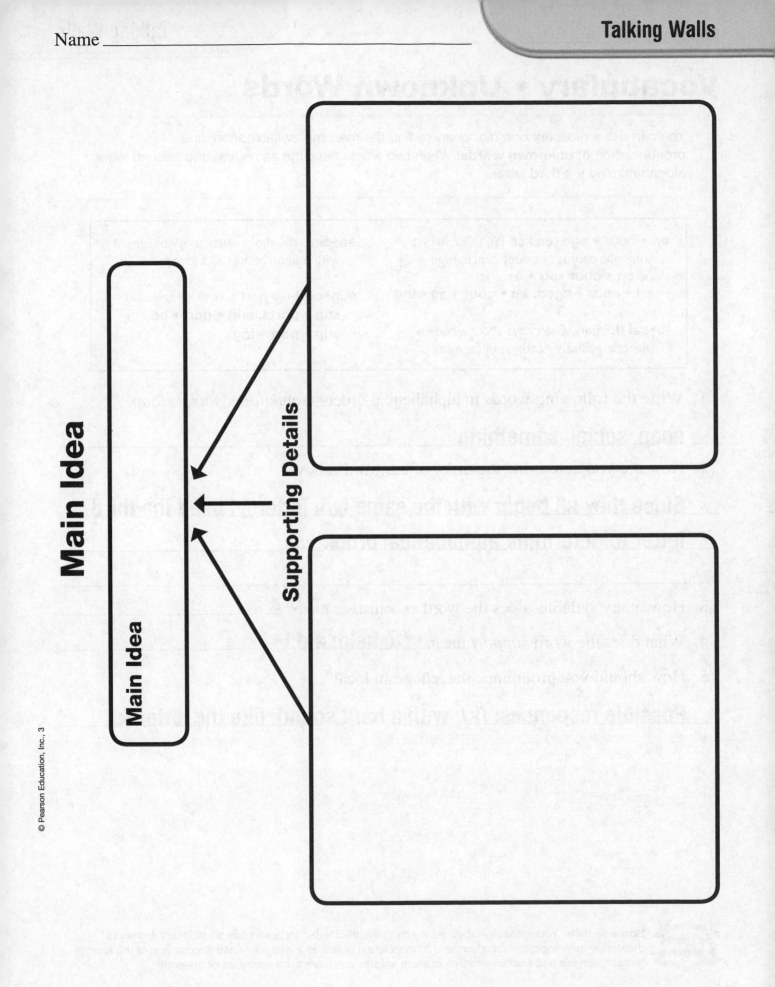

Main Idea

Supporting Details

Main Idea

Vocabulary • Unknown Words

You can use a glossary or a dictionary to find the meaning, syllabication, and pronunciation of **unknown words.** When two words have the same first and second letter, alphabetize by the third letter.

---

en • cour • age (en kȧr' ij), *VERB.* to give
someone courage or confidence; urge
on **en • cour •ag • es,**
en • cour • aged, en • cour • ag • ing

lo•cal (lō' kəl), *ADJECTIVE.* about a certain
place, especially nearby, not far away

so•cial (sō' shəl), *ADJECTIVE.* concerned
with human beings as a group

sup•port (sə port'), *VERB.* to help; aid
sup • ports, sup • port • ed,
sup • port • ing

---

1. Write the following words in alphabetical order—*something, social, soap.*

soap, social, something

2. How did you determine the order of the words above?

**Since they all begin with the same two letters, I used the third
letter to determine alphabetical order.**

3. How many syllables does the word *encourages* have? **4**

4. What does the word *support* mean? **"to help; aid"**

5. How should you pronounce the letter *c* in local?

Possible responses: /k/; with a hard sound; like the letter *k*

Home Activity Your child alphabetized words to the third letter and used sample glossary entries to determine meanings, syllabication, and pronunciation of words. Have your child choose one of the sample glossary entries and explain what information readers can learn from each part of the entry.

Alphabetical Order

Entries or subjects in encyclopedias, dictionaries, and indexes are listed in **alphabetical order,** so you can find information quickly and easily. When two entries have the same first letter, alphabetize by the second letter. If the second letters are also the same, alphabetize by the third letter, and so on.

Directions Circle each list of words that is in alphabetical order.

1. care   drag
   family   dance
   mail   finger
   master   water
   plow   work

2. must   astronaut
   really   driver
   treat   drop
   table   event
   under   sleepy

Directions Look at the spines on this set of encyclopedias. Then look at the article topics listed below. Write the letter(s) of the volume in which you would find an article on that topic.

3. Architecture   **A**

4. Russia   **Q–R**

5. Snow and Snowflakes   **Sh–Sz**

6. Seashells   **S–Sg**

7. Xylophones   **W–Z**

8. Dance   **D**

9. Giraffes   **G–H**

10. Boats   **Ba–Bq**

Volume 1 | Volume 2 | Volume 3 | Volume 4 | Volume 5 | Volume 6 | Volume 7 | Volume 8
A | Ba-Bq | Br-C | D | E-F | G-H | I-J | K-L

Volume 9 | Volume 10 | Volume 11 | Volume 12 | Volume 13 | Volume 14 | Volume 15 | Volume 16
M-N | O-P | Q-R | S-Sg | Sh-Sz | T | U-V | W-Z

Home Activity Your child recognized words that were in alphabetical order and used alphabetical order to find articles on topics for research. Use the illustration of the encyclopedias on this page. Name other topics of interest such as dogs, computers, and games and have your child tell in which volume he or she would find an article on that topic.

Final Syllables

Spelling Words				
question	creature	furniture	division	collision
action	direction	culture	vacation	mansion
fiction	feature	sculpture	vision	celebration

Proofread a Description Gina's class is studying local history. Circle four spelling errors. Write the words correctly. Then write the two incomplete sentences as one sentence.

Mr. and Mrs. Hill (we're) very important in the history of our town. They built the Hill (manshun) in 1880. It still has the original (furnichure.) Many people tour the house when they are on (vacasion.) My favorite feature. Is the dolphin sculpture.

Frequently Misspelled Words

we're
were

1. __were__   2. __mansion__

3. __furniture__   4. __vacation__

5. __My favorite feature is the dolphin sculpture.__

Proofread Words Circle the word that is spelled correctly. Write it.

6. I have a (question) quesion.   6. __question__

7. It's fun to learn about a new   calture (culture.)   7. __culture__

8. An eagle has excellent   vishun (vision.)   8. __vision__

9. We had a big (celebration) celebrasion.   9. __celebration__

10. Which (direction) direcsion   is the library?   10. __direction__

School + Home **Home Activity** Your child identified misspelled words that end with *-tion*, *-sion*, and *-ture*. Give clues about a list word. Ask your child to guess and spell the word.

Combining Sentences

Directions Read the selection. Then read each question that follows the selection. Decide which is the best answer to each question. Mark the space for the answer you have chosen.

Diego Rivera: Muralist

(1) Diego Rivera is a famous Mexican painter. (2) He painted murals. (3) He used bold colors. (4) He used bright colors. (5) Rivera's colors reflected a style. (6) Aztec art had a similar style. (7) The murals often showed Mexico's history. (8) They also showed politics. (9) Sometimes Rivera's murals would upset people. (10) Many people loved them.

1 Which answer best combines sentence 1 and sentence 2?

- ⬭ Diego Rivera is a famous Mexican painter, he painted murals.
- ⬤ Diego Rivera is a famous Mexican painter of murals.
- ⬭ Diego River is a famous Mexican painter, and he painted murals.
- ⬭ Diego Rivera is a famous Mexican painter and, he painted murals.

2 Which answer best combines sentence 3 and sentence 4?

- ⬤ He used bold, bright colors.
- ⬭ He used bold, or bright colors.
- ⬭ He used bold colors, bright colors.
- ⬭ He used bold colors, but he used bright colors.

3 Read this combination of sentence 5 and sentence 6: *Rivera's colors reflected a style similar _____ Aztec art.* Which word completes the sentence?

- ⬭ in
- ⬭ for
- ⬭ of
- ⬤ to

4 Which answer best combines sentence 7 and sentence 8?

- ⬭ The murals often showed Mexico's history, politics.
- ⬭ The murals often showed Mexico's history, or showed politics.
- ⬤ The murals often showed Mexico's history and politics.
- ⬭ The murals often showed Mexico's historical politics.

5 Read this combination of sentence 9 and sentence 10: *Sometimes Rivera's murals would upset people _____ many people loved them.* Which answer completes the sentence?

- ⬤ , but
- ⬭ but,
- ⬭ , and
- ⬭ or

© Pearson Education, Inc., 3

 Home Activity Your child learned about combining sentences. Point out two short related sentences in a book you are reading with your child. Have your child combine the sentences.

Prefixes *im-, in-*

Directions For each definition, write a word on the line that beings with **im-** or **in-**.

1. not mature   <u>**immature**</u>

2. not efficient   <u>**inefficient**</u>

3. not sincere   <u>**insincere**</u>

4. not polite   <u>**impolite**</u>

5. not perfect   <u>**imperfect**</u>

6. not mortal   <u>**immortal**</u>

7. not adequate   <u>**inadequate**</u>

8. not capable   <u>**incapable**</u>

9. not partial   <u>**impartial**</u>

10. not possible   <u>**impossible**</u>

11. not correct   <u>**incorrect**</u>

12. not direct   <u>**indirect**</u>

13. not practical   <u>**impractical**</u>

14. not probable   <u>**improbable**</u>

15. not pure   <u>**impure**</u>

Directions Now write three sentences of your own. In each sentence include at least one of the **im-** or **in-** words from above.

16. <u>**Sentences will vary.**</u> _____

17. _____

18. _____

Home Activity Your child used words with the prefixes *im-* and *in-*, which mean "not." Read a newspaper or magazine article with your child. Point out words with the prefixes *im-* and *in-* and have your child explain what they mean.

© Pearson Education, Inc., 3

Name _____

Literary Elements • Plot and Theme

- The important events in a story make up the **plot** with a beginning, middle, and end.
- The "big idea" of the story is called the **theme**. It can be stated in a single sentence.

Directions Read the following story. Then fill in the chart below.

The ants felt sorry for the grasshopper. He'd saved no food and was starving. So they shared what they had. The grasshopper swore he'd remember their kindness and repay them someday. When summer came, the ants were playing outside and accidentally hurt themselves.

How would they gather their food? Just then the grasshopper stopped by. When he heard what happened, he told the ants to climb on his back. The ants told the grasshopper where to go and what to gather. Soon the trio had all the food they needed for the winter ahead.

What happened at the beginning of the story?

1. **The ants shared their food with the grasshopper.**

⬇

What happened in the middle of the story?

2. **The ants hurt themselves and couldn't gather food.**

⬇

What happened at the end of the story?

3. **The grasshopper helped the ants gather food.**

4. What is the "big idea" of this story? **Responses may vary.**

Help others because one day you might need someone to help you.

© Pearson Education, Inc., 3

 Home Activity Your child identified the plot and theme of a story. Read a favorite story together. Ask your child to retell the beginning, middle, and end of the story and to say one sentence that tells the "big idea."

Comprehension 419

Writing • Comic Book

Key Features of a Comic Book

- tells a story using a series of drawings
- characters' dialogue is part of the drawing
- sometimes uses narration

The Crystal Palace Giant

I'm tired of working all day to keep the Queen happy.

Me too! Let's go back to that palace with the crystals. We can live there.

Home at last!

The ants make their living arrangements and settle in for the night.

Did you hear something?

You mean that awful thunder?

What could it be?

Aaagh!!!

It's a giant!

Where have you been, my little ones?

To a place we will never, ever go again!

1. How many panels are used to tell the story?

six

2. Draw a circle around the same dialogue that is spoken by more than one character
Students should circle dialogue from the 2nd, 5th, and 6th panels.
3. Draw a box around any narration.
Students should draw a box around the narration in the 3rd panel.
Tell how you knew this line was narration and not dialogue.

It is told from a third-person point of view; it does not appear in

a word bubble.

Vocabulary

Directions Read each sentence. Write the meaning of the underlined word.

> ## Check the Words You Know
> ___goal   ___discovery
> ___scoop   ___crystal
> ___journey   ___joyful
> ___disappeared   ___unaware

1. They used a <u>scoop</u> to pour the birdseed into the feeder. **tool like a shovel**

2. The hikers were on a <u>journey</u> over the mountain. **a trip**

3. My <u>goal</u> this summer is to learn how to swim. **something desired**

4. I saw the ant carry a <u>crystal</u> of salt. **solid naturally formed substance**

5. The chipmunk <u>disappeared</u> among the rocks. **vanished from view**

Directions Match each word on the left with its meaning. Draw a line from the word to its definition.

6. discovery   not noticing

7. joyful   something new you find

8. unaware   full of happiness

9. disappeared   was no longer seen

Write a Narrative

On a separate sheet of paper, write a narrative about visiting another planet. Write about being very small compared with other things on the planet. Use as many vocabulary words as possible. **Narrative should use vocabulary words to tell about visiting another planet.**

© Pearson Education, Inc., 3

Home Activity Your child identified and used vocabulary from *Two Bad Ants*. Read a story about insects to your child. Then discuss the story using this week's vocabulary words.

Name _____

Commas

> Use a **comma** and a conjunction to join two sentences.
>
>   There was a crumb on the table, and the ant crawled toward it.
>
> Use **commas** to separate words in a series.
>
>   We had sandwiches, cookies, and fruit at the picnic.
>
> Use a **comma** after the greeting and the closing of a friendly letter.
>
>   Dear Jake,
>   Your friend,
>
> Use a **comma** between the name of a city and a state in an address.
>
>   Chico, CA 95926   Berea, Kentucky
>
> Use a **comma** to separate the month and day from the year.
>
>   July 21, 2006

Directions Write *C* if commas are used correctly in the sentence. Write *NC* if commas are not used correctly.

1. Some kinds of ants are army ants, honey ants, and dairying ants.   **C**

2. Army ants travel in lines and they hunt other insects.   **NC**

3. Dear Amy   **NC**

Directions Write each sentence. Add commas where they are needed.

4. Some ants eat other insects but many do not.

   Some ants eat other insects, but many do not.

   _____

5. The newspaper had an article about ants on November 14 2005.

   The newspaper had an article about ants on November 14, 2005.

© Pearson Education, Inc., 3

Home Activity Your child learned about commas. Have your child point out five commas in a book that you are reading together.

Multisyllabic Words

Spelling Words				
leadership	gracefully	refreshment	uncomfortable	overdoing
remarkable	carefully	unbearably	ownership	unacceptable
impossibly	reappeared	unprepared	oncoming	misbehaving

Missing Syllables Add the missing syllables and write the list words.

1. The deer moved grace_____.   1. __gracefully__
2. He was ___bear___ rude.   2. __unbearably__
3. Watch out for ___com___ cars.   3. __oncoming__
4. That is a ___mark___ carving!   4. __remarkable__
5. Juice is my favorite ___fresh___.   5. __refreshment__
6. Sam is ___fort___ in crowds.   6. __uncomfortable__
7. Do the addition care_____.   7. __carefully__
8. He took a lead_____ position.   8. __leadership__
9. She gets tired from ___do___.   9. __overdoing__
10. Sue was ___pos___ stubborn.   10. __impossibly__

Definitions Write the list word with the same meaning as the underlined words.

11. He was <u>not prepared</u> for the test.   11. __unprepared__
12. The sun <u>appeared again</u> from behind the clouds. 12. __reappeared__
13. The puppy kept <u>behaving badly</u>.   13. __misbehaving__
14. My score on the test was <u>not acceptable</u>.   14. __unacceptable__
15. He claimed <u>to be the owner</u> of the stray cat.   15. __ownership__

Home Activity Your child spelled words with many syllables. Have your child draw lines to divide the list words into syllables.

Story Sequence B

Title	
Characters	**Setting**

Events
1. First

2. Next

3. Then

4. Last

Vocabulary • Prefixes and Suffixes

- A **prefix** is a word part added to the beginning of a word. A **suffix** is added to the end of a word. **Prefixes** and **suffixes** can help you figure out the meaning of a word you don't know.
- The **prefixes** *un-* and *dis-* mean "not" or "the opposite of." The **suffix** *-ful* means "full of."

Directions Read each pair of sentences. Circle the word that has the same meaning as the underlined words.

1. The girl pushed ahead of me in line. That is <u>not fair</u>.

   (unfair)   unhappy

2. Climbing this mountain is too hard. I am <u>not able</u> to do it.

   disease   (unable)

3. My father did not climb the ladder. He is <u>full of fear</u> high above the ground.

   under   (fearful)

4. He does not keep his word. That's why I <u>do not trust</u> him.

   (distrust)   untrue

5. That dog is mean. I <u>do not like</u> her.

   hateful   (dislike)

Directions Read each sentence. Circle the underlined word that best fits the sentence.

6. My room is in such (disorder)/unclear, I can't find anything.

7. A hammer is a very unused/(useful) tool for nailing things together.

8. My mother (disapproves)/unlike of my staying up late.

9. The strong man had a very unfair/(powerful) handshake.

10. Please (unzip)/disappear your jacket and hang it in the closet.

© Pearson Education, Inc., 3

Electronic Text

Directions Read the passage and answer the questions that follow.

You can find facts and opinions in books, in periodicals, and online. When you make a presentation or write a report, you restate facts and details you found in the reference sources.

There are two ways to restate information from a source. You can **quote** it, or you can **paraphrase** it. When you quote something, you copy exact words from a source. When you paraphrase, you explain the same idea in your own words.

Remember to **cite** your sources correctly. A writer often includes a **bibliography**— an alphabetical list of sources—at the end of a report. Sometimes a writer includes **footnotes.** A footnote is a citation that appears at the bottom of the page where the information is quoted or paraphrased.

This table shows you how to cite a source properly.

Type of Source	How To Cite	Example
Book	List the author, title, city where published, publisher's name, and copyright date.	Sachs, Hans. *A History of Carpenter Ants.* New York: Van Horn & Co., 2006.
Periodical	List the author, article title, periodical title, volume number, date and page numbers.	Klotz, J.H. "Trailing the Carpenter Ant." *American Entomologist,* vol. 42 (1996), pp. 33–39.
Web Site	Give the name of the Web site and the page, and copy the URL exactly as it is shown in the bar at the top of the screen.	Encyclopedia www.url.here

1. What does **quote** mean?

   to copy exact words from a source

2. What is the difference between a bibliography and a footnote?

   A bibliography lists all reference sources. A footnote only lists the source for one fact or detail.

3. What do you include in the citation of a Web site?

   include the name of the site and page, and copy the URL

 Home Activity Your child learned how to cite reference sources. Read an article together. Have your child quote something from the article. Then have your child paraphrase information from the article.

Multisyllabic Words

Proofread an Explanation Olivia wrote about how to bowl. Circle four spelling errors. Write the words correctly. Then add the missing comma.

Bowling is a remarkable sport. Almost (every body) likes it.

You should start with good equipment. Don't use a ball that is (unbareably) heavy⊙and don't settle for (unconfortable) shoes.

When it's your turn, swing the ball back gracefully as you walk toward the pins. Let go when you reach the line. Always aim (carefuly) at the pins.

Frequently Misspelled Words

everybody
everything

1. **everybody**   2. **unbearably**

3. **uncomfortable**   4. **carefully**

Correct the Words Write the correct spelling of each misspelled word.

5. unaceptable   5. **unacceptable**

6. oncomeing   6. **oncoming**

7. missbehaving   7. **misbehaving**

8. inpossibly   8. **impossibly**

9. reapeared   9. **reappeared**

10. leedership   10. **leadership**

Home Activity Your child is learning to spell words with many syllables. Have your child write a sentence using two or more of the list words.

Name _____

Two Bad Ants

Commas

Directions Read the selection. Then read each question that follows the selection. Decide which is the best answer to each question. Mark the space for the answer you have chosen.

Insect Communities

(1) Bees, wasps, termites and ants live in communities. (2) These insects work together to feed the community. (3) Other jobs in the community include builder soldier or, queen. (4) Communities are also called colonies. (5) They live in hives or nests. (6) Scientists study termite nests at the University of Kentucky in Lexington Kentucky.

1 What change, if any, should be made in sentence 1?

- ● Place a comma after *termites*
- ○ Change *Bees, wasps* to **Bees and wasps**
- ○ Place a comma after *and*
- ○ Make no change

2 Which change, if any, should be made in sentence 2?

- ○ Place a comma after *insects*
- ○ Place a comma after *work*
- ○ Place a comma after *together*
- ● Make no change

3 Which change, if any, should be made in sentence 3?

- ○ Change *builder soldier or, queen* to **builder, soldier or queen.**
- ○ Change *builder soldier or, queen* to **builder soldier, or queen.**
- ● Change *builder soldier or, queen* to **builder, soldier, or queen.**
- ○ Make no change

4 Which answer correctly uses commas to combine sentence 4 and sentence 5?

- ○ Communities are also called colonies, they live in hives or nests.
- ○ Communities are also called colonies and live in hives or, nests.
- ○ Communities, also called colonies, live in hives, or nests.
- ● Communities are also called colonies, and they live in hives or nests.

5 What change, if any, should be made in sentence 6?

- ○ Place a comma after *University of Kentucky*
- ● Place a comma after *Lexington*
- ○ Place a comma after *nests*
- ○ Make no change

© Pearson Education, Inc., 3

Home Activity Your child prepared for taking tests on commas. Have your child show you some sentences from a school paper or ad and explain why they need commas or not.

428 **Conventions** Commas

Related Words

Directions Choose the word that best matches each clue. Write the word on the line.

1. coverings for the body   cloth clothes   **clothes**

2. a person who plays sports   athlete athletics   **athlete**

3. a person's handwritten name   sign signature   **signature**

4. a tub for washing   bath bathe   **bath**

5. the world of living things and the outdoors   natural nature   **nature**

Directions Read each pair of related words. Underline the parts that are spelled the same but pronounced differently. Write a sentence using one of the words in each pair.

Sentences will vary.

6. f<u>ee</u>l   f<u>e</u>lt   **I felt tired so I went to bed.**

7. k<u>ee</u>p   kept   **I keep my coat in my locker.**

8. dec<u>i</u>de   dec<u>i</u>sion   **I made a decision about what to do tonight.**

9. m<u>ea</u>n   m<u>ea</u>nt   **I didn't mean to break the plate.**

10. def<u>i</u>ne   def<u>i</u>nition   **What is the definition of this word?**

11. volc<u>a</u>no   volc<u>a</u>nic   **I read about a volcano that erupted.**

12. pl<u>ea</u>se   pl<u>ea</u>sant   **Please pass the salt.**

13. r<u>e</u>l<u>a</u>te   r<u>e</u>l<u>a</u>tive   **Bill is my relative.**

14. s<u>i</u>gn   s<u>i</u>gnal   **I didn't see the stop sign.**

15. rep<u>ea</u>t   rep<u>e</u>tition   **Please repeat the question.**

Home Activity Your child read and wrote related words that have parts that are spelled the same but pronounced differently, as in *cloth* and *clothes*. Discuss the meanings of the related words on the page above. Then work together to write a story that uses some of the words.

Generalize

- When you make a general statement, you **generalize,** or tell how some things are mostly alike or all alike.
- You can use what you already know to help you make a generalization.
- When you generalize, support your generalization with facts and logic.

Directions Read the following passage. Think about generalizations you can make from what you have read.

Some cities, like New York, started small and grew larger. As more people and businesses moved in, New York became an important world center. Other cities did not do as well. Some cities in the West thrived during the Gold Rush years. But when the Gold Rush ended, people abandoned those cities. They are now ghost towns. Then there are cities that suffer tragedy and remake themselves. San Francisco and Chicago both had terrible fires years ago. But the people in those cities decided to rebuild. Today, these two cities are bigger and better than ever.

Directions: Fill in the graphic organizer with ideas from the passage that lead to the generalization. Then answer the questions.

Example 1. Some cities keep growing.

Example 2. Some cities become ghost towns.

Example 3. Some cities suffer tragedies and rebuild.

Generalization
Cities change over time.

4. How did you use ideas from the passage?
   Responses will vary. Possible response: I looked for ways cities are alike.

5. What things that you already knew helped you connect to the generalization?
   Responses will vary. Possible response: The town we live in has changed.

School + Home
Home Activity Your child read a passage and identified ideas that led to a provided generalization. Read an article about a city with your child and work together to use what you read to make a generalization about all or most cities.

Writing • Historical Fiction

Key Features of Historical Fiction

- set in the past
- events of the plot make sense
- characters, setting, or events may be based on historical fact

A Wonderful Flight

My name is Jean. I'm a servant in the castle of Chambord, France. The greatest person I've ever served was a man named Leonardo da Vinci (you may have heard of him) during the exciting days of the Renaissance period.

Da Vinci brought a flying machine he designed to the castle! Some of the servants got together and decided they wanted to take a ride. We sneaked up to the tower where da Vinci kept the flying machine. All the other servants were too scared to go flying, but I wasn't. I hopped into the machine, hung on tight, and jumped off the tower.

I flew down and soared over the castle wall. I flew round and round in a circle. Then the wind blew me right into the castle wall! Luckily I fell just a few feet. I crashed in the courtyard . . . right at the feet of Leonardo da Vinci himself! I looked up at him in fear. I was sure I'd be kicked out of the castle.

But Mr. da Vinci just grinned and said, "Isn't flying wonderful?"

1. Who is the main character? What type of job does he have?

The main character is Jean. He is a servant in a castle.

2. What is the climax of the story? Why is this moment exciting?

The climax is when Jean crashes at the feet of Leonardo da Vinci. This moment is exciting because the reader thinks that Leonardo da Vinci will be really mad.

Vocabulary

Directions: Match each word on the left with its meaning on the right. Draw a line from the word to its meaning.

1. aqueducts   squatted with bent knees

2. thermal   advice or counseling

3. pillar   channels for moving water

4. guidance   a vertical column

5. crouched   relating to heat or warmth

Check the Words You Know

___aqueducts
___content
___crouched
___guidance
___honor
___pillar
___thermal

Directions: Fill in the blank with the word from the box that fits the meaning of the sentence.

6. The people were __**content**__ to live on their island.

7. The __**thermal**__ currents in the ocean kept the weather fair and warm.

8. Stone __**aqueducts**__ carried fresh water to all parts of the island.

9. The people looked to their kind queen for __**guidance**__.

10. Once a year they held a huge feast to thank and __**honor**__ her.

Write a Description Write about your ideal place to live. Use as many vocabulary words from this week as you can. **Students should use vocabulary words to describe their ideal place to live.**

© Pearson Education, Inc., 3

Home Activity Your child identified and used new vocabulary words from *Atlantis: The Legend of a Lost City*. Read another myth or legend with your child. Then ask your child to talk about myths and legends using the vocabulary words on this page.

Name _____

Quotations and Parentheses

> **Quotation marks (" ")** show the exact words of a speaker in a conversation.
>
> - Use a comma to separate the speaker's exact words from the rest of the sentence.
> - Use a capital letter to begin the first words inside the quotation marks.
> - Put the punctuation mark that ends the quotation inside the quotation marks.
>   "I swim very well," said Penny.
>   She asked, "Would you like to learn to swim?"
>
> Quotation marks also indicate many kinds of titles, such as song, poem, story, and document titles.
>   We read "Atlantis."
>
> **Parentheses** show explanations or examples that are extra information.
>   That song (written in 1996) is my favorite.
>   Some singers (for example, Elton John) play the piano, too.

Directions Underline the part of each sentence that is a quotation.

1. "I want to learn about Atlantis," said Jeremy.

2. "I will teach you," replied Ms. Foster.

3. Ms. Foster said, "It is a very old story."

Directions Write the sentences. Add quotation marks and commas where they are needed.

4. I like to read about many things said Jeremy.

   "I like to read about many things," said Jeremy.

5. Jeremy read a story called The Legend of Kala.

   Jeremy read a story called "The Legend of Kala."

Home Activity Your child learned about quotations. Have your child read aloud a quotation in a book you are reading together and then point out each punctuation mark and explain the reason for it.

Related Words

Spelling Words				
cloth	clothes	nature	natural	able
ability	mean	meant	deal	dealt
please	pleasant	sign	signal	signature

Replacing Words Write list words to take the place of the underlined words.

1. I jumped out of the tub and put on my <u>shirt and shorts</u>.

1. __**clothes**__

2. It has been a <u>nice</u> day.

2. __**pleasant**__

3. Did you <u>write your name on</u> the card?

3. __**sign**__

4. Dogs have the <u>skill</u> to hear high-pitched sounds.

4. __**ability**__

5. Mom made a kerchief from a scrap of blue <u>fabric</u>.

5. __**cloth**__

6. Tom is never <u>cruel</u> to animals.

6. __**mean**__

7. We went to the mountains to enjoy <u>the environment</u>.

7. __**nature**__

8. Sara <u>gave</u> six cards to each player.

8. __**dealt**__

Missing Words Write the missing word.

9. She has a __**natural**__ talent for music.

10. His hand __**signal**__ warned me to stop.

11. A bat is the only mammal that is __**able**__ to fly.

12. That's not what I __**meant**__ .

13. I can do what I __**please**__ on Saturday morning.

14. Her __**signature**__ is on the credit card.

15. My big sister knows how to __**deal**__ with most emergencies.

School + Home **Home Activity** Your child spelled related words. Have your child pronounce each list word and use the word in a sentence.

© Pearson Education, Inc., 3

Scoring Rubric: Writing for Tests: Historical Fiction

	4	3	2	1
Focus/Ideas	Exciting story with interesting characters; historical time period and figures	Good story with developed characters; somewhat based on historical time period and figures	Story has some focus on characters; setting and characters are only loosely historical	Story has no focus on characters; not set in historical time period
Organization	Clear order of events	Can follow order of events	Unclear order of events	No order of events
Voice	Writer shows interest in the story and the characters	Writer shows some interest in the story and the characters	Writer shows little interest in the story or characters	Writer makes no effort to show interest in the story or characters
Word Choice	Strong use of specific adjectives to bring the story to life	Good try at using specific adjectives	Poor use of specific adjectives; descriptions are dull	No effort made to use specific adjectives
Sentences	Strong concluding statement	Adequate concluding statement	Weak concluding statement	No concluding statement
Conventions	Few, if any, errors; correct use of quotation marks and parentheses	Several small errors; use of quotation marks and parentheses	Many errors; weak use of quotation marks and parentheses	Many serious errors; incorrect or no use of quotation marks and parentheses

Vocabulary • Homographs

- **Homographs** are words that are spelled the same way but have different pronunciations and meanings.
- Use context clues, or the words around a homograph, to figure out which meaning and pronunciation to use.

Directions: Read the following passage. Then answer the questions below. Look for context clues that show the meanings and pronunciations of homographs as you read.

There are many myths and legends about ancient Greek gods. The stories are interesting because they are full of conflict. Many of the gods were not content with their lives. They caused trouble or fought with each other. When problems arose on Earth, the gods tried to solve them. But different gods offered alternate solutions, and they usually did not agree. Each god wanted to lead the others.

1. If you read this passage aloud, would you pronounce *conflict* with the accent on the first or second syllable?

   the first syllable

2. In this passage, does *content* mean "pleased with" or "what a speech or article is about"?

   "pleased with"

3. Is *lives* a noun or a verb? How do you know?

   a noun; The word *their* (an adjective) comes before *lives* (a noun).

4. Does *alternate* mean "take turns" or "different"?

   "different"

5. Does the word *lead* have a *long e* or a *short e* sound?

   a *long e* sound

Home Activity Your child used context clues to understand homographs. Write sentences with homographs such as *close* (to shut/near) or *dove* (a kind of bird/jumped into the water). Ask your child to use context clues to determine the meaning of each homograph and then read the sentence aloud.

Quote Sources/Paraphrase Sources

- There are two ways to repeat information from a reference source. You can **quote** it or you can **paraphrase** it.

- To quote means to copy exact words from a source. When you do this, enclose the words in quotation marks.

- To paraphrase means to explain the same idea in your own words. When you paraphrase, you do not use quotation marks. When you quote or paraphrase information, you must **cite** it correctly. This table shows you how.

Type of Source	How to Cite	Example
Book	List the author, title, city where published, publisher's name, and copyright date.	Breward, Christopher. *Oxford History of Fashion.* Oxford: Oxford University Press, 2003.
Periodical	List the author, article title, periodical title, volume number, date and page numbers.	Mack, Alexandra. "Hidden Gems." *Vogue,* Oct. 2007, pp. 258–272.
Web Site	Give the name of the page on the Web site, and copy the URL exactly as it is shown in the bar at the top of the screen.	Online Directory www.url.here

Directions Take this page to the library. Use its resources and the table above. Answer the questions on a separate sheet of paper. **Answers will vary according to sources. Make sure citations are correctly done.**

1. Look up a fact about glass in a book about glassmaking. Write a sentence quoting the information. Cite the source correctly.

2. The Italian island of Murano is famous for its glassblowers. Look up Murano online and write a sentence paraphrasing information you find about it. Cite the source correctly.

3. Find a magazine article about glass and write three or four sentences about glass. Quote and paraphrase information from the article. Cite the article correctly.

© Pearson Education, Inc., 3

Home Activity Your child quoted and paraphrased information from reference sources, and cited the sources correctly. Give your child a simple research project. Have him or her write a very short paper (no more than one page) summing up the information. Make sure your child quotes, paraphrases, and cites sources correctly.

Related Words

Proofread a Paragraph Circle four spelling errors and cross out the sentence that does not belong in the paragraph. Write the words correctly.

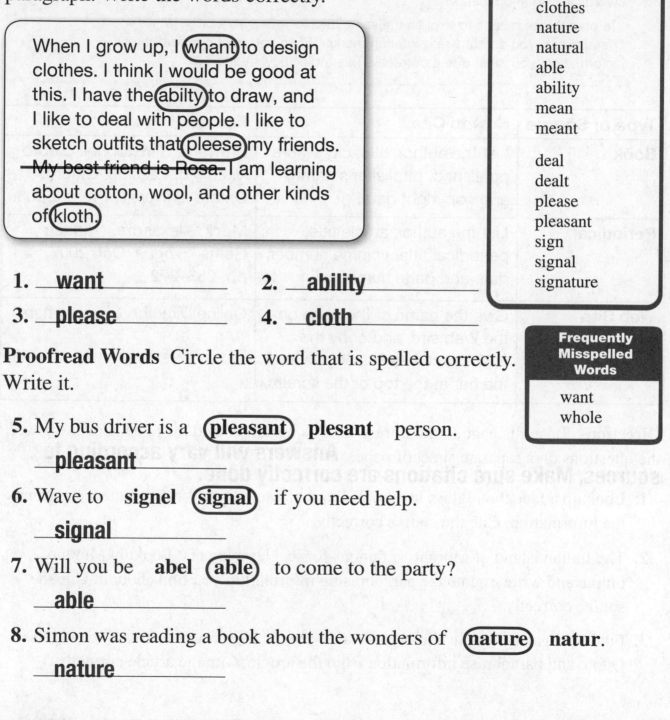

When I grow up, I (whant) to design clothes. I think I would be good at this. I have the (abilty) to draw, and I like to deal with people. I like to sketch outfits that (pleese) my friends. ~~My best friend is Rosa.~~ I am learning about cotton, wool, and other kinds of (kloth).

Spelling Words
cloth
clothes
nature
natural
able
ability
mean
meant
deal
dealt
please
pleasant
sign
signal
signature

Frequently Misspelled Words
want
whole

1. **want** 2. **ability**

3. **please** 4. **cloth**

Proofread Words Circle the word that is spelled correctly. Write it.

5. My bus driver is a (**pleasant**) plesant person.
   pleasant

6. Wave to signel (**signal**) if you need help.
   signal

7. Will you be abel (**able**) to come to the party?
   able

8. Simon was reading a book about the wonders of (**nature**) natur.
   nature

School + Home **Home Activity** Your child spelled related words. Have your child point out a pair of related list words and explain how the spellings differ.

Quotations and Parentheses

Directions Read the selection. Then read each question that follows the selection. Decide which is the best answer to each question. Mark the space for the answer you have chosen.

A Conversation at the Beach

(1) The seashore is great, Tim said.
(2) Look at the ocean, I responded.
(3) Tim said, There are cliffs, too!
(4) The water goes on forever, I replied.
(5) Do sharks live here? Tim asked.

1 In sentence 1, what words and punctuation marks should go inside quotation marks?

- ⬭ Tim said
- ⬭ The seashore
- ⬭ The seashore is great, Tim
- ⬛ The seashore is great,

2 In sentence 2, what words and punctuation marks should go inside quotation marks?

- ⬭ Look
- ⬛ Look at the ocean,
- ⬭ Look at the ocean, I
- ⬭ I responded

3 In sentence 3, what words and punctuation marks should go inside quotation marks?

- ⬭ Tim said,
- ⬭ Tim said, there
- ⬛ There are cliffs, too!
- ⬭ There are cliffs,

4 In sentence 4, what words and punctuation marks should go inside quotation marks?

- ⬛ The water goes on forever,
- ⬭ The water goes on forever
- ⬭ The water goes on
- ⬭ I replied

5 In sentence 5, what words and punctuation marks should go inside quotation marks?

- ⬭ Do sharks
- ⬛ Do sharks live here?
- ⬭ Tim asked.
- ⬭ live here? Tim asked

Home Activity Your child prepared for taking tests on quotations. Have your child identify words in quotation marks in a newspaper article and explain why they are punctuated in that way.

© Pearson Education, Inc., 3

Vowel Sounds in *moon* and *foot*

Spelling Words				
few	school	true	goose	fruit
cookie	cushion	noodle	bookmark	balloon
suit	chew	glue	Tuesday	bushel

Word Clues Read the two meaning clues. Write the list word that the clues tell about.

1. a group of fish
   place where students learn   **1.** __school__

2. a pillow
   to pad   **2.** __cushion__

3. a sticky paste
   to paste something   **3.** __glue__

4. a toy filled with air
   to get bigger   **4.** __balloon__

5. matched pieces of clothing
   to please or satisfy   **5.** __suit__

Meaning Connections Change the underlined word or words to a list word. Write the word.

6. I ate a chocolate chip <u>sweet treat</u>.   **6.** __cookie__

7. A <u>bird that honks</u> chased me.   **7.** __goose__

8. Darla put a <u>paper placeholder</u> in the book.   **8.** __bookmark__

9. On <u>the day after Monday</u>, it rained.   **9.** __Tuesday__

10. We bought <u>apples, grapes, and pears</u>.   **10.** __fruit__

11. I saw a <u>piece of pasta</u> in my soup.   **11.** __noodle__

12. I <u>chomp</u> on raw carrots for a snack.   **12.** __chew__

13. The farmer put corn in the <u>32-quart</u> basket. **13.** __bushel__

14. What she said was <u>not false</u>.   **14.** __true__

15. <u>Not many</u> people can be called heroes.   **15.** __Few__

© Pearson Education, Inc., 3

School + Home **Home Activity** Your child spelled words with the vowel sound in *moon* (spelled *oo, ew, ue, ui*) and in *foot* (spelled *oo, u*). Play Tic-Tac-Toe. One person chooses a word for the other person to spell. If the person spells the word correctly, he or she marks an X or an O on the grid.

Name _____

Capital Letters

Directions If a sentence has capitalization mistakes, write correctly the words that should have capital letters. If a sentence has no capitalization mistakes, write *C*.

1. In may of 2005, my family flew to Paris, France.
May

2. On tuesday I visited the Eiffel Tower. **Tuesday**

3. The Eiffel Tower was designed by Alexandre Gustave Eiffel.
C

4. The frame of the Statue of Liberty in new york was also designed by mr. Eiffel.
New York; Mr. Eiffel

5. Next september, mrs. Austin will take us to see the Statue of Liberty.
September; Mrs. Austin

Directions Write the sentences. Use capital letters correctly.

6. On independence day, Mom called philadelphia.
On Independence Day, Mom called Philadelphia.

7. On martin luther king, jr., day in january, we went to the Washington Monument.
On Martin Luther King, Jr., Day in January, we went to the Washington Monument.

8. mr. and mrs. pines drove to plymouth, massachusetts, for thanksgiving.
Mr. and Mrs. Pines drove to Plymouth, Massachusetts, for Thanksgiving.

9. Dad stopped at Mount Rushmore last memorial day.
Dad stopped at Mount Rushmore last Memorial Day.

10. On presidents' day in february, Sam visited the Lincoln Memorial.
On Presidents' Day in February, Sam visited the Lincoln Memorial.

© Pearson Education, Inc., 3

Schwa

Spelling Words				
above	another	upon	animal	paper
open	family	travel	afraid	nickel
sugar	circus	item	gallon	melon

Classifying Write the list word that belongs with each pair of words.

1. penny, dime, ___   1. __nickel__
2. pint, quart, ___   2. __gallon__
3. go, journey, ___   3. __travel__
4. movie, play, ___   4. __circus__
5. thing, object, ___   5. __item__
6. below, beside, ___   6. __above__
7. group, tribe, ___   7. __family__

Complete the Phrase Write the list word that completes each phrase.

8. not a plant but an ___ | a | n | i | m | a | l |
9. a pencil and some ___ | p | a | p | e | r |
10. not a berry but a ___ | m | e | l | o | n |
11. not closed but ___ | o | p | e | n |
12. not under but ___ | u | p | o | n |
13. as sweet as ___ | s | u | g | a | r |
14. ___ of the dark | a | f | r | a | i | d |
15. one thing and ___ | a | n | o | t | h | e | r |

© Pearson Education, Inc., 3

Riddle Write the letters from the boxes above to find the answer to the riddle.

What do you get when you ask a lemon for help?

__l__ __e__ __m__ __o__ __n__ __a__ __d__ __e__

Home Activity Your child learned to spell words with the schwa sound (an unstressed vowel sound such as the *a* in *about*). Take turns choosing and spelling a word. Then each of you say a word you associate with the chosen word: *family—Mom, Dad*.

442 Spelling

Abbreviations

Directions Write each sentence correctly. Use correct capitalization and periods for abbreviations.

1. On nice days, dr Chin and mr Lee meet at the park.

   On nice days, Dr. Chin and Mr. Lee meet at the park.

2. On Monday, dr Chin brought his son c j and his dog.

   On Monday, Dr. Chin brought his son C. J. and his dog.

3. Mr and mrs. Lau were at the park also.

   Mr. and Mrs. Lau were at the park also.

4. They had seen ms Parks and d w Cho there on Saturday.

   They had seen Ms. Parks and D. W. Cho there on Saturday.

5. People brought their birds and cages to l. k. Williams Park.

   People brought their birds and cages to L. K. Williams Park.

Directions Write each telephone message. Correct mistakes in initials and abbreviations.

6. j b Logan called: got your order   **J. B. Logan called: got your order**

7. mr Logan, 6 parakeets, jan 10   **Mr. Logan, 6 parakeets, Jan. 10**

8. Pick up fri, jan 12   **Pick up Fri., Jan. 12**

9. ms Ryan's parakeet, p j   **Ms. Ryan's parakeet, P. J.**

10. Got bird wed, dec 10   **Got bird Wed., Dec. 10**

Final Syllables

Spelling Words

question	creature	furniture	division	collision
action	direction	culture	vacation	mansion
fiction	feature	sculpture	vision	celebration

Crossword Puzzle Write the list word that each clue describes.

Across

1. north
5. a make-believe story
6. a statue
8. Aztec or Native American
9. a special trip
10. sight

Down

1. repeated subtraction
2. a big, big house
3. a party
4. a movement
5. chairs and sofas
7. an important part

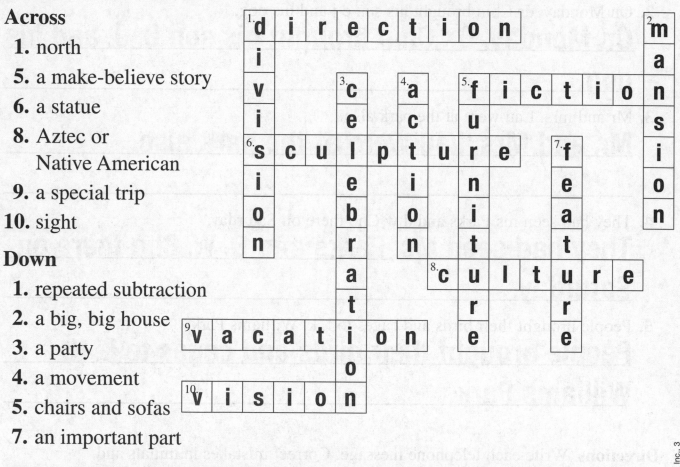

Alphabetizing Read the two guide words. Write the list word that would come between them in a dictionary.

13. pride ___**question**___ rate
14. cave ___**collision**___ comet
15. cracker ___**creature**___ crop

collision
question
creature

© Pearson Education, Inc., 3

Home Activity Your child spelled words that end with *-tion*, *-sion*, and *-ture*. Use newspapers or junk mail to look for words with the lesson endings. Circle the words and spell them together. Check to see if any circled words are on the spelling list.

Combining Sentences

Directions Combine each pair of sentences into a compound sentence. Use a comma and the conjunction in ( ).

1. Our class painted a mural. We worked very hard on it. (and)
   Our class painted a mural, and we worked very hard on it.

2. We had never painted a mural. It looks great. (but)
   We had never painted a mural, but it looks great.

3. Shall I tell you about the mural? Would you like to see it? (or)
   Shall I tell you about the mural, or would you like to see it?

Directions Combine each pair of sentences. Use the underlined words or a form of the underlined words only once in your new sentence.

4. <u>Lewis and Clark</u> sailed up the Missouri River. <u>Lewis and Clark</u> crossed the Rocky Mountains.
   Lewis and Clark sailed up the Missouri River and crossed the Rocky Mountains.

5. <u>The land</u> was a wilderness. <u>The land</u> had not been carefully explored.
   The land was a wilderness and had not been carefully explored.

6. Lewis <u>kept a journal of the trip</u>. Clark <u>kept a journal of the trip</u>.
   Lewis and Clark kept journals of the trip.

Multisyllabic Words

Spelling Words				
leadership	gracefully	refreshment	uncomfortable	overdoing
remarkable	carefully	unbearably	ownership	unacceptable
impossibly	reappeared	unprepared	oncoming	misbehaving

Word Building Read the word in dark type. Add the part or parts to the given word. Write the list word you make.

1. **grace** + suffix + suffix   __gracefully__

2. prefix + **appear** + ending   __reappeared__

3. **remark** + suffix   __remarkable__

4. prefix + **comfort** + suffix   __uncomfortable__

5. prefix + **accept** + suffix   __unacceptable__

6. **care** + suffix + suffix   __carefully__

7. prefix + **prepare** + ending   __unprepared__

8. prefix + **fresh** + suffix   __refreshment__

9. **lead** + suffix + suffix   __leadership__

10. **own** + suffix + suffix   __ownership__

Finish the Phrase Circle the list word that completes each phrase. Write it. Say the word. Write in the box the number of syllables you hear in the word.

11. (unprepared (unbearably)) hot   __unbearably__   **4**

12. ((overdoing) reappeared) it a bit   __overdoing__   **4**

13. ((oncoming) unprepared) traffic   __oncoming__   **3**

14. (leadership (misbehaving)) puppy   __misbehaving__   **4**

15. ((impossibly) carefully) difficult problem   __impossibly__   **4**

Total   **19**

© Pearson Education, Inc., 3

Syllable Addition Add the numbers in the boxes. If you get 19, you did a great job!

 Home Activity Your child is learning to spell words with many syllables. Together, say each word and clap the syllables. Let your child pick the three words he or she finds most difficult. Have your child write them and spell them to you.

Commas

Directions Fix the comma errors in the sentences in the letter. If a sentence does not have a comma error, write *C*.

1. Dear Thomas,

   C

2. I saw something wonderful and I had to tell you.

   I saw something wonderful, and I had to tell you.

3. I saw millions of yellow blue and orange butterflies. **I saw millions of yellow, blue, and orange butterflies.**

4. The palm, pine, and fruit trees were full of butterflies.

   C

5. Your friend
   Justin

   Your friend,

Directions Write each sentence. Add commas where they are needed.

6. We took a trip to the rain forest on June 23 2005.

   We took a trip to the rain forest on June 23, 2005.

7. We hiked climbed and rested in the forest.

   We hiked, climbed, and rested in the forest.

8. We saw incredible plants birds and insects.

   We saw incredible plants, birds, and insects.

9. On the ground were fire ants harvester ants and army ants. **On the ground were fire ants, harvester ants, and army ants.**

10. The ants looked dangerous but they left us alone.

    The ants looked dangerous, but they left us alone.

Related Words

Spelling Words				
cloth	clothes	nature	natural	able
ability	mean	meant	deal	dealt
please	pleasant	sign	signal	signature

Word Pairs Write the list words that complete each sentence.

1.–2. Here is a STOP _____**sign**_____, and there is a traffic _____**signal**_____.

3.–4. My new _____**clothes**_____ are made from colorful _____**cloth**_____.

5.–6. Plants in _____**nature**_____ are _____**natural**_____ things.

7.–8. After you _____**deal**_____ the cards, they have been _____**dealt**_____.

9.–10. If you _____**sign**_____ your name, you are using your _____**signature**_____.

Little Crosswords Read the word clue. Write a synonym for the word in the boxes going across. Write a related word in the boxes going down.

11.–12. skill

a					
a	**b**	**i**	**l**	**i**	**t**	**y**
l					
e					

13.–14. intended

	m			
m	**e**	**a**	**n**	**t**
	a			
	n			

15.–16. nice

	p					
	l					
p	**l**	**e**	**a**	**s**	**a**	**n**	**t**
	s					
	e					

© Pearson Education, Inc., 3

School + Home

Home Activity Your child is learning to spell related words. Choose two related words from the list. Say one word. Have your child say and spell the related word.

Quotations and Parentheses

Directions Write *C* if a sentence is correct. If it is not correct, make the corrections that are needed.

1. Maria said, "I can have an adventure." _____

2. "I will find the lost city of Atlantis!" she exclaimed. _____

3. "I will become a famous explorer," Maria said. **C**

4. "Can you drive a big boat?" Chris asked. _____

5. "No, but I would love to learn," Maria answered. **C**

Directions Write each sentence. Add a comma and quotation marks where they are needed.

6. Maria's mother asked What will you take on your journey?

Maria's mother asked, "What will you take on your journey?"

7. I will take maps, food, and books about Atlantis Maria answered.

"I will take maps, food, and books about Atlantis," Maria answered.

8. Maria's mother asked How long will you be gone?

Maria's mother asked, "How long will you be gone?"

9. Maria replied It will take a long time to find the island.

Maria replied, "It will take a long time to find the island."

10. I wish I could go with you! Maria's mother exclaimed.

"I wish I could go with you!" Maria's mother exclaimed.

KWL Chart

Directions Fill out this KWL chart to help you organize your ideas.

Topic _____

What I **K**now	What I **W**ant to Know	What I **L**earned
Answers should include details about each element of the research report.		

Controlling Question _____

Topic and Detail Sentences

> A topic sentence tells the main idea of a paragraph. Detail sentences give supporting facts, descriptions, and examples about the main idea.

Directions Decide how you will organize your paragraphs. Then write a topic sentence and supporting details for each paragraph.

Paragraph 1

Topic Sentence **Answers should be topic**
sentences and supporting details
Detail Sentences _____
on the research topic.
_____

_____

Paragraph 2

Topic Sentence _____

Detail Sentences _____

_____

_____

Paragraph 3

Topic Sentence _____

Detail Sentences _____

_____

_____

Paragraph 4

Topic Sentence _____

Detail Sentences _____

_____

_____

Combining Sentences

When you revise, you can combine two short simple sentences to make a compound or complex sentence. The two simple sentences must be related in some way.

- To make a compound sentence, join the sentences with a comma and a conjunction such as *and, but,* or *or.*
- To make a complex sentence, join the sentences with a word such as *when, because,* or *if.*

Directions Use the word in ( ) to combine each pair of sentences. Use a comma with exercises 1 and 2.

1. Washington, D.C., has many monuments. People like to visit them. (and)

   Washington, D.C., has many monuments, and people like to visit them.

2. Many of the monuments honor presidents. Some monuments honor soldiers or other heroes. (but) **Many of the monuments honor presidents, but some monuments honor soldiers or other heroes.**

3. People visit the Lincoln Memorial. They see a huge statue of Abraham Lincoln. (when)

   When people visit the Lincoln Memorial, they see a huge statue of Abraham Lincoln.

4. The Washington Monument is easy to see. It is the tallest monument. (because)

   The Washington Monument is easy to see because it is the tallest monument.

© Pearson Education, Inc., 3

Peer and Teacher Conferencing
Research Report

Directions Read your partner's report. Refer to the Revising Checklist as you write
your comments or questions. Offer compliments as well as revision suggestions. Then
take turns talking about each other's draft. Give your partner your notes. After you and
your teacher talk about your report, add your teacher's comments to the notes.

Revising Checklist

Focus/Ideas

☐ Is the research report focused?

☐ Are there enough facts, details, and explanations?

Organization

☐ Are the paragraphs organized?

☐ Does each paragraph have a central idea stated in a topic sentence?

☐ Does each paragraph have supporting sentences that tell facts, details, or explanations?

Voice

☐ Does the writer sound interested in the topic?

Word Choice

☐ Has the writer paraphrased the material?

Sentences

☐ Have some short, simple sentences been combined to make compound or complex
sentences?

Things I Thought Were Good _____

_____

Things I Thought Could Be Improved _____

_____

Teacher's Comments _____

_____